Student Solutions Manual

John Garlow
Tarrant County College

John Tobey   Jeffrey Slater

Beginning Algebra

Sixth Edition

PEARSON

Prentice
Hall

Upper Saddle River, NJ 07458

Editor-in-Chief: Chris Hoag
Executive Editor: Paul Murphy
Supplement Editor: Christina Simoneau
Executive Managing Editor: Kathleen Schiaparelli
Assistant Managing Editor: Becca Richter
Production Editor: Donna Crilly
Supplement Cover Manager: Paul Gourhan
Supplement Cover Designer: Joanne Alexandris
Manufacturing Buyer: Ilene Kahn

© 2006 Pearson Education, Inc.
Pearson Prentice Hall
Pearson Education, Inc.
Upper Saddle River, NJ 07458

Printed in the United States of America

10 9 8 7 6 5

ISBN 0-13-153060-7 Standalone
      0-13-185801-7 Student Study Pack Component

Pearson Education Ltd., *London*
Pearson Education Australia Pty. Ltd., *Sydney*
Pearson Education Singapore, Pte. Ltd.
Pearson Education North Asia Ltd., *Hong Kong*
Pearson Education Canada, Inc., *Toronto*
Pearson Educación de Mexico, S.A. de C.V.
Pearson Education—Japan, *Tokyo*
Pearson Education Malaysia, Pte. Ltd.

CONTENTS

Chapter 0

1. $\dfrac{12}{13}$: numerator = 12

3. When two or more numbers are multiplied, each number that is multiplied is called a factor. In 2×3, 2 and 3 are factors.

5. $2\dfrac{2}{3}$

7. $\dfrac{18}{24} = \dfrac{3 \times 6}{4 \times 6} = \dfrac{3}{4}$

9. $\dfrac{12}{36} = \dfrac{1 \times 12}{3 \times 12} = \dfrac{1}{3}$

11. $\dfrac{60}{12} = \dfrac{12 \times 5}{12 \times 1} = 5$

13. $\dfrac{17}{6} = 2\dfrac{5}{6}$

15. $\dfrac{111}{9} = 9\overline{)111}^{\,12} = 12\dfrac{3}{9} = 12\dfrac{1}{3}$

$$\underline{9}$$
$$21$$
$$\underline{18}$$
$$3$$

17. $\dfrac{38}{7} = 7\overline{)38}^{\,5} = 5\dfrac{3}{7}$

19. $3\dfrac{1}{5} = \dfrac{5 \times 3 + 1}{5} = \dfrac{16}{5}$

21. $6\dfrac{3}{5} = \dfrac{5 \times 6 + 3}{5} = \dfrac{33}{5}$

23. $\dfrac{72}{9} = \dfrac{8 \times 9}{1 \times 9} = \dfrac{8}{1} = 8$

25. $\dfrac{3}{11} \times \dfrac{4}{4} = \dfrac{12}{44}$

27. $\dfrac{3}{5} \times \dfrac{7}{7} = \dfrac{21}{35}$

29. $\dfrac{4}{13} = \dfrac{?}{39} \Rightarrow \dfrac{4 \times 3}{13 \times 3} = \dfrac{12}{39}$

31. $\dfrac{1560}{68} = 22\dfrac{64}{68} = 22\dfrac{16}{17}$

$$68\overline{)1560}^{\,22}$$
$$\underline{136}$$
$$200$$
$$\underline{136}$$
$$64$$

33. $\dfrac{13,200}{64,000} = \dfrac{400 \times 33}{400 \times 160} = \dfrac{33}{160}$

35. $\dfrac{1}{1+1+2} = \dfrac{1}{4}$

37. $\dfrac{1+1}{1+1+2} = \dfrac{2}{4} = \dfrac{1}{2}$

1

39. Aaron: $\dfrac{15}{25} = \dfrac{3}{5}$

    Paul: $\dfrac{12}{30} = \dfrac{2}{5}$

    Tom: $\dfrac{28}{35} = \dfrac{4}{5}$

0.2 Exercises

1. 8 is the LCD of $\dfrac{3}{4}$ and $\dfrac{5}{8}$ because 8 is exactly divisible by 4.

3. $\dfrac{7}{15}$ and $\dfrac{11}{21}$

   $15 = 3 \cdot 5$

   $21 = 3 \cdot 7$

   $LCD = 3 \cdot 5 \cdot 7 = 105$

5. $\dfrac{7}{10}$ and $\dfrac{1}{4}$: $10 = 2 \cdot 5$

   $4 = 2 \cdot 2$

   $LCD = 2 \cdot 2 \cdot 5 = 20$

7. $\dfrac{5}{18}$ and $\dfrac{7}{54}$: $18 = 2 \cdot 3 \cdot 3$

   $54 = \quad 2 \cdot 3 \cdot 3 \cdot 3$

   $LCD = 2 \cdot 3 \cdot 3 \cdot 3 = 54$

9. $\dfrac{1}{2}, \dfrac{1}{18}$ and $\dfrac{13}{30}$

   $2 = 2$

   $18 = 2 \cdot 3 \cdot 3$

   $30 = 2 \cdot 3 \cdot 5$

   $LCD = 2 \cdot 3 \cdot 3 \cdot 5 = 90$

11. $\dfrac{3}{8} + \dfrac{2}{8} = \dfrac{5}{8}$

13. $\dfrac{5}{14} - \dfrac{1}{14} = \dfrac{4}{14} = \dfrac{2}{7}$

15. $\dfrac{3}{8} + \dfrac{5}{6} = \dfrac{3 \cdot 3}{8 \cdot 3} + \dfrac{5 \cdot 4}{6 \cdot 4} = \dfrac{9}{24} + \dfrac{20}{24} = \dfrac{29}{24} = 1\dfrac{5}{24}$

17. $\dfrac{5}{7} - \dfrac{2}{9} = \dfrac{5 \cdot 9}{7 \cdot 9} - \dfrac{2 \cdot 7}{9 \cdot 7}$

    $= \dfrac{45}{63} - \dfrac{14}{63}$

    $= \dfrac{31}{63}$

19. $\dfrac{1}{3} + \dfrac{2}{5} = \dfrac{1 \cdot 5}{3 \cdot 5} + \dfrac{2 \cdot 3}{5 \cdot 3} = \dfrac{5}{15} + \dfrac{6}{15} = \dfrac{11}{15}$

21. $\dfrac{7}{18} + \dfrac{1}{12} = \dfrac{7 \cdot 2}{18 \cdot 2} + \dfrac{1 \cdot 3}{12 \cdot 3} = \dfrac{14}{36} + \dfrac{3}{36} = \dfrac{17}{36}$

23. $\dfrac{2}{3} + \dfrac{7}{12} + \dfrac{1}{4} = \dfrac{8}{12} + \dfrac{7}{12} + \dfrac{3}{12} = \dfrac{18}{12} = \dfrac{3}{2} = 1\dfrac{1}{2}$

25. $\dfrac{5}{36} + \dfrac{7}{9} - \dfrac{5}{12} = \dfrac{5}{36} + \dfrac{7 \cdot 4}{9 \cdot 4} - \dfrac{5 \cdot 3}{12 \cdot 3}$

    $= \dfrac{5}{36} + \dfrac{28}{36} - \dfrac{15}{36}$

    $= \dfrac{18}{36} = \dfrac{1}{2}$

27. $4\dfrac{1}{3} + 3\dfrac{2}{5} = \dfrac{13}{3} + \dfrac{17}{5} = \dfrac{65}{15} + \dfrac{51}{15} = \dfrac{116}{15} = 7\dfrac{11}{15}$

29. $1\dfrac{5}{24} + \dfrac{5}{18} = 1\dfrac{15}{72} + \dfrac{20}{72} = 1\dfrac{35}{72}$

31. $7\frac{1}{6} - 2\frac{1}{4} = 7\frac{2}{12} - 2\frac{3}{12} = 6\frac{14}{12} - 2\frac{3}{12} = 4\frac{11}{12}$

33. $8\frac{5}{7} - 2\frac{1}{4} = \frac{61}{7} - \frac{9}{4} = \frac{244}{28} - \frac{63}{28}$
$$= \frac{181}{28} = 6\frac{13}{28}$$

35. $2\frac{1}{8} + 3\frac{2}{3} = 2\frac{3}{24} + 3\frac{16}{24} = 5\frac{19}{24}$

37. $11\frac{1}{7} - 6\frac{5}{7} = \frac{78}{7} - \frac{47}{7} = \frac{31}{7} = 4\frac{3}{7}$

39. $2\frac{1}{8} + 6\frac{3}{4} = 2\frac{1}{8} + 6\frac{6}{8} = 8\frac{7}{8}$

41. $\frac{7}{9} + \frac{5}{6} = \frac{14}{18} + \frac{15}{18}$
$$= \frac{29}{18} = 1\frac{11}{18}$$

43. $2\frac{1}{7} + 3\frac{11}{14} = \frac{15}{7} + \frac{53}{14}$
$$= \frac{30}{14} + \frac{53}{14}$$
$$= \frac{83}{14} = 5\frac{13}{14}$$

45. $\frac{16}{21} - \frac{2}{7} = \frac{16}{21} - \frac{6}{21}$
$$= \frac{10}{21}$$

47. $5\frac{1}{5} - 2\frac{1}{2} = \frac{26}{5} - \frac{5}{2}$
$$= \frac{52}{10} - \frac{25}{10}$$
$$= \frac{27}{10} = 2\frac{7}{10}$$

49. $3\frac{1}{8} + 2\frac{2}{3} + 4\frac{1}{2} = \frac{25}{8} + \frac{8}{3} + \frac{9}{2} = \frac{75}{24} + \frac{64}{24} + \frac{108}{24}$
$$= \frac{247}{24} = 10\frac{7}{24} \text{ miles}$$

51. $8\frac{1}{2} - 2\frac{2}{3} - 1\frac{3}{4} = \frac{17}{2} - \frac{8}{3} - \frac{7}{4}$
$$= \frac{102}{12} - \frac{32}{12} - \frac{21}{12}$$
$$= \frac{49}{12} = 4\frac{1}{12} \text{ hours}$$

53. height $= 2 + \frac{1}{2} + 3\frac{1}{2} + \frac{1}{2} + 3\frac{1}{2} + \frac{1}{2} + 1\frac{1}{2}$
$$= 12 \text{ in.}$$

$A = 2 + \frac{1}{2} + 3\frac{1}{2} + \frac{1}{2} + 3\frac{1}{2} + \frac{1}{2} + 1\frac{1}{2} = 12 \text{ in.}$

$B = \frac{1}{2} + 4\frac{5}{8} + \frac{1}{2} + 4\frac{5}{8} + \frac{1}{2} + 4\frac{5}{8} + \frac{1}{2} = 15\frac{7}{8} \text{ in.}$

55. $2\frac{1}{2} - \frac{7}{8} = \frac{5}{2} - \frac{7}{8} = \frac{20}{8} - \frac{7}{8} = \frac{13}{8} = 1\frac{5}{8}$

$1\frac{5}{8}$ inches

Cumulative Review

57. $\frac{36}{44} = \frac{9 \cdot 4}{11 \cdot 4} = \frac{9}{11}$

0.3 Exercises

1. First change each mixed number to an improper fraction. Look for a common factor in the numerator and denominator to divide by ; if one is found, perform the division. Multiply the numerators. Multiply the denominators.

3. $\dfrac{36}{7} \times \dfrac{5}{9} = \dfrac{9 \cdot 4}{7} \times \dfrac{5}{9} = \dfrac{20}{7} = 2\dfrac{6}{7}$

5. $\dfrac{17}{18} \times \dfrac{3}{5} = \dfrac{17}{6 \cdot 3} \times \dfrac{3}{5} = \dfrac{17}{30}$

7. $\dfrac{4}{5} \times \dfrac{3}{10} = \dfrac{2 \cdot 2}{5} \times \dfrac{3}{2 \cdot 5} = \dfrac{6}{25}$

9. $\dfrac{24}{25} \times \dfrac{5}{2} = \dfrac{12 \cdot 2}{5 \cdot 5} \times \dfrac{5}{2} = \dfrac{12}{5} = 1\dfrac{7}{5}$

11. $9 \times \dfrac{2}{5} = \dfrac{9}{1} \times \dfrac{2}{5} = \dfrac{18}{5} = 3\dfrac{3}{5}$

13. $\dfrac{8}{5} \div \dfrac{8}{3} = \dfrac{8}{5} \times \dfrac{3}{8} = \dfrac{3}{5}$

15. $\dfrac{3}{7} \div 3 = \dfrac{3}{7} \div \dfrac{3}{1} = \dfrac{3}{7} \times \dfrac{1}{3} = \dfrac{1}{7}$

17. $10 \div \dfrac{5}{7} = \dfrac{10}{1} \times \dfrac{7}{5} = \dfrac{2 \cdot 5}{1} \times \dfrac{7}{5} = 14$

19. $\dfrac{\frac{7}{8}}{\frac{3}{4}} = \dfrac{7}{8} \times \dfrac{4}{3} = \dfrac{7}{2 \cdot 4} \times \dfrac{2 \cdot 2}{3} = \dfrac{14}{12} = \dfrac{7}{6} = 1\dfrac{1}{6}$

21. $\dfrac{\frac{5}{6}}{\frac{7}{9}} = \dfrac{5}{6} \times \dfrac{9}{7} = \dfrac{5}{2 \cdot 3} \times \dfrac{3 \cdot 3}{7} = \dfrac{15}{14} = 1\dfrac{1}{14}$

23. $1\dfrac{3}{7} \div 6\dfrac{1}{4} = \dfrac{10}{7} \div \dfrac{25}{4} = \dfrac{10}{7} \times \dfrac{4}{25} = \dfrac{2 \cdot 5}{7} \times \dfrac{4}{5 \cdot 5} = \dfrac{8}{35}$

25. $3\dfrac{1}{3} \div 2\dfrac{1}{2} = \dfrac{10}{3} \div \dfrac{5}{2}$
$= \dfrac{2 \cdot 5}{3} \times \dfrac{2}{5}$
$= \dfrac{4}{3} = 1\dfrac{1}{3}$

27. $\dfrac{\frac{7}{9}}{1\frac{1}{3}} = \dfrac{\frac{7}{9}}{\frac{4}{3}} = \dfrac{7}{9} \times \dfrac{3}{4} = \dfrac{7}{3 \cdot 3} \times \dfrac{3}{4} = \dfrac{7}{12}$

29. $\dfrac{\frac{2}{3}}{1\frac{1}{4}} = \dfrac{\frac{2}{3}}{\frac{5}{4}} = \dfrac{2}{3} \times \dfrac{4}{5} = \dfrac{8}{15}$

31. $\dfrac{6}{5} \times \dfrac{10}{12} = \dfrac{6}{5} \times \dfrac{2 \cdot 5}{2 \cdot 6} = 1$

33. $\dfrac{5}{14} \div \dfrac{2}{7} = \dfrac{5}{14} \times \dfrac{7}{2} = \dfrac{5}{2 \cdot 7} \times \dfrac{7}{2} = \dfrac{5}{4} = 1\dfrac{1}{4}$

35. $10\dfrac{3}{7} \times 5\dfrac{1}{4} = \dfrac{73}{7} \times \dfrac{21}{4} = \dfrac{73}{7} \times \dfrac{3 \cdot 7}{4} = \dfrac{219}{4} = 54\dfrac{3}{4}$

37. $2\dfrac{1}{8} \div \dfrac{1}{4} = \dfrac{17}{8} \div \dfrac{1}{4}$
$= \dfrac{17}{2 \cdot 4} \times \dfrac{4}{1}$
$= \dfrac{17}{2} = 8\dfrac{1}{2}$

39. $6 \times 4\dfrac{2}{3} = \dfrac{6}{1} \times \dfrac{14}{3} = \dfrac{2 \cdot 3}{1} \times \dfrac{14}{3} = 28$

41. $2\dfrac{1}{2} \times \dfrac{1}{10} \times \dfrac{3}{4} = \dfrac{5}{2} \times \dfrac{1}{5 \cdot 2} \times \dfrac{3}{4} = \dfrac{3}{16}$

4

43. $2\dfrac{3}{4} \times 26 = \dfrac{11}{4} \times \dfrac{26}{1} = \dfrac{11}{2 \cdot 2} \times \dfrac{2 \cdot 13}{1} = \dfrac{143}{2}$

$$= 71\dfrac{1}{2} \text{ yards}$$

45. $\dfrac{2}{3} \times 4\dfrac{1}{5} = \dfrac{2}{3} \times \dfrac{21}{5} = \dfrac{2}{1} \times \dfrac{7}{5} = \dfrac{14}{5} = 2\dfrac{4}{5} \text{ miles}$

Cumulative Review

47. $\dfrac{116}{124} = \dfrac{4 \times 29}{4 \times 31} = \dfrac{29}{31}$

0.4 Exercises

1. A decimal is another way of writing a fraction whose denominator is $10; 100; 1000; 10,000;$ and so on.

3. When dividing 7432.9 by 1000 we move the decimal point $\underline{3}$ places to the <u>left</u>.

5. $\dfrac{5}{8} = 8\overline{)5.000} = 0.625$

$$\begin{array}{r} 0.625 \\ 8\,\overline{)5.000} \\ \underline{48} \\ 20 \\ \underline{16} \\ 40 \\ \underline{40} \\ 0 \end{array}$$

7. $\dfrac{3}{15} = 15\overline{)3.0} = 0.2$

$$\begin{array}{r} 0.2 \\ 15\,\overline{)3.0} \\ \underline{3.0} \\ 0 \end{array}$$

9. $11\overline{)7.000} = 0.\overline{63}$

$$\begin{array}{r} 0.63 \\ 11\,\overline{)7.000} \\ \underline{66} \\ 40 \\ \underline{33} \\ 7 \end{array}$$

11. $0.8 = \dfrac{8}{10} = \dfrac{4}{5}$

13. $0.625 = \dfrac{625}{1000} = \dfrac{5}{8}$

15. $2.6 = \dfrac{26}{10} = \dfrac{13}{5} = 2\dfrac{3}{5}$

17. $\begin{array}{r} 1.71 \\ +0.38 \\ \hline 2.09 \end{array}$

19. $\begin{array}{r} 2.50 \\ 3.42 \\ +\quad 4.90 \\ \hline 10.82 \end{array}$

21. $\begin{array}{r} 46.030 \\ 215.100 \\ +\quad 0.078 \\ \hline 261.208 \end{array}$

23. $\begin{array}{r} 147.18 \\ -\ 15.39 \\ \hline 131.79 \end{array}$

25.
$$\begin{array}{r} 7.21 \\ \times\ 4.2 \\ \hline 1442 \\ 2884 \\ \hline 30.282 \end{array}$$

27.
$$\begin{array}{r} 4.23 \\ \times\ 0.025 \\ \hline 2115 \\ 846 \\ \hline 0.10575 \end{array}$$

29.
$$\begin{array}{r} 169,000 \\ \times\ 0.0013 \\ \hline 507000 \\ 169000 \\ \hline 219.7000 \end{array}$$
or 219.7

31.
$$\begin{array}{r} 2.64 \\ 3.02\overline{)7.9728} \\ \underline{604} \\ 1932 \\ \underline{1812} \\ 1208 \\ \underline{1208} \\ 0 \end{array}$$

33.
$$\begin{array}{r} 261.5 \\ 0.002\overline{)0.5230} \\ \underline{4} \\ 12 \\ \underline{12} \\ 3 \\ \underline{2} \\ 10 \\ \underline{10} \\ 0 \end{array}$$

35.
$$\begin{array}{r} 0.257 \\ 0.08\overline{)0.02056} \\ \underline{16} \\ 45 \\ \underline{40} \\ 56 \\ \underline{56} \end{array}$$

37. $3.45 \times 1000 = 3450$

39. $0.76 \div 100 = 0.0076$

41. $7.36 \times 10,000 = 73,600. = 73,600$

43. $73,892 \div 100,000 = 0.73892$

45.
$$\begin{array}{r} 23.75 \\ \times\ 0.06 \\ \hline 1.4250 \end{array}$$

47.
$$\begin{array}{r} 1.62 \\ 2.005 \\ +\ 8.1007 \\ \hline 11.7257 \end{array}$$

6

49.

$$
\begin{array}{r}
2.12 \\
0.027{\overline{\smash{\big)}\,0.05724}} \\
\underline{54} \\
32 \\
\underline{27} \\
54 \\
\underline{54} \\
0
\end{array}
$$

51. $0.7683 \times 1000 = 768.3$

53.

$$
\begin{array}{r}
2.54 \\
\times\ \ 9.5 \\
\hline
1270 \\
2286 \\
\hline
24.130 \\
\end{array}
$$

24.13 cm

55. $11.50 \times 18.5 = \$212.75$

57. $1.3 \times 5 = 6.5$ milligrams
no; there was 0.3 milligrams of
copper in excess of the standard
for 5 liters of water.

Cumulative Review

59. $3\dfrac{1}{2} \div 5\dfrac{1}{4} = \dfrac{7}{2} \div \dfrac{21}{4}$

$$= \dfrac{7}{2} \cdot \dfrac{4}{21} = \dfrac{1 \cdot 2}{1 \cdot 3} = \dfrac{2}{3}$$

61. $\dfrac{12}{25} + \dfrac{9}{20} = \dfrac{48}{100} + \dfrac{45}{100} = \dfrac{93}{100}$

How Am I Doing? Sections 0.1–0.4

1. $\dfrac{15}{55} = \dfrac{3 \cdot 5}{11 \cdot 5} = \dfrac{3}{11}$

2. $\dfrac{46}{115} = \dfrac{2 \cdot 23}{5 \cdot 23} = \dfrac{2}{5}$

3. $\dfrac{15}{4} = 4{\overline{\smash{\big)}\,15}} = 3\dfrac{3}{4}$ (with quotient 3 above)

4. $4\dfrac{5}{7} = \dfrac{4 \cdot 7 + 5}{7} = \dfrac{28 + 5}{7} = \dfrac{33}{7}$

5. $\dfrac{3}{7} = \dfrac{?}{14} \Rightarrow \dfrac{3 \cdot 2}{7 \cdot 2} = \dfrac{6}{14}$

6. $\dfrac{7}{4} = \dfrac{?}{20} \Rightarrow \dfrac{7 \cdot 5}{4 \cdot 5} = \dfrac{35}{20}$

7. $8 = 2 \cdot 2 \cdot 2$
$6 = 2 \cdot 3$
$15 = 3 \cdot 5$
$\text{LCD} = 2 \cdot 2 \cdot 2 \cdot 3 \cdot 5 = 120$

8. $\dfrac{3}{7} + \dfrac{2}{7} = \dfrac{5}{7}$

9. $\dfrac{5}{14} + \dfrac{2}{21} = \dfrac{5 \cdot 3}{14 \cdot 3} + \dfrac{2 \cdot 2}{21 \cdot 2} = \dfrac{15}{42} + \dfrac{4}{42} = \dfrac{19}{42}$

10. $2\dfrac{3}{4}+5\dfrac{2}{3}=\dfrac{11}{4}+\dfrac{17}{3}$

$\qquad = \dfrac{11\cdot 3}{4\cdot 3}+\dfrac{17\cdot 4}{3\cdot 4}$

$\qquad = \dfrac{33}{12}+\dfrac{68}{12}$

$\qquad = \dfrac{101}{12}=8\dfrac{5}{12}$

11. $\dfrac{17}{18}-\dfrac{5}{9}=\dfrac{17}{18}-\dfrac{5\cdot 2}{9\cdot 2}$

$\qquad = \dfrac{17}{18}-\dfrac{10}{18}$

$\qquad = \dfrac{7}{18}$

12. $\dfrac{6}{7}-\dfrac{2}{3}=\dfrac{6\cdot 3}{7\cdot 3}-\dfrac{2\cdot 7}{3\cdot 7}$

$\qquad = \dfrac{18}{21}-\dfrac{14}{21}$

$\qquad = \dfrac{4}{21}$

13. $3\dfrac{1}{5}-1\dfrac{3}{8}=\dfrac{16}{5}-\dfrac{11}{8}$

$\qquad = \dfrac{16\cdot 8}{5\cdot 8}-\dfrac{11\cdot 5}{8\cdot 5}$

$\qquad = \dfrac{128}{40}-\dfrac{55}{40}$

$\qquad = \dfrac{73}{40}=1\dfrac{33}{40}$

14. $\dfrac{25}{7}\times\dfrac{14}{45}=\dfrac{5\cdot 5}{7}\times\dfrac{2\cdot 7}{5\cdot 9}=\dfrac{10}{9}=1\dfrac{1}{9}$

15. $2\dfrac{4}{5}\times 3\dfrac{3}{4}=\dfrac{14}{5}\times\dfrac{15}{4}=\dfrac{2\cdot 7}{5}\times\dfrac{3\cdot 5}{2\cdot 2}$

$\qquad = \dfrac{21}{2}$

$\qquad = 10\dfrac{1}{2}$

16. $4\div\dfrac{8}{7}=\dfrac{4}{1}\times\dfrac{7}{2\cdot 4}=\dfrac{7}{2}=3\dfrac{1}{2}$

17. $2\dfrac{1}{3}\div 3\dfrac{1}{4}=\dfrac{7}{3}\div\dfrac{13}{4}=\dfrac{7}{3}\times\dfrac{4}{13}$

$\qquad = \dfrac{28}{39}$

18. $\dfrac{7}{8}=8\overline{)7.000}=0.875$

$\qquad \dfrac{64}{}$

$\qquad 60$

$\qquad \dfrac{56}{}$

$\qquad 40$

$\qquad \dfrac{40}{}$

The quotient is 0.875.

19. $\dfrac{5}{9}=9\overline{)5.000}=0.\overline{5}$

$\qquad \dfrac{45}{}$

$\qquad 50$

$\qquad \dfrac{45}{}$

$\qquad 50$

$\qquad \dfrac{45}{}$

$\qquad 5$

20. $\dfrac{3}{200}=200\overline{)3.000}=0.15$

$\qquad \dfrac{200}{}$

$\qquad 1000$

8

21.
$$
\begin{array}{r}
15.230 \\
3.600 \\
+\ \ \ 0.821 \\
\hline
19.651
\end{array}
$$

22.
$$
\begin{array}{r}
3.28 \\
\times\ \ 0.63 \\
\hline
984 \\
1968 \\
\hline
2.0664
\end{array}
$$

23. $\dfrac{3.015}{6.7} - 6.7\overline{)3.015} = 0.45$

$$
\begin{array}{r}
0.45 \\
6.7\overline{)3.015} \\
\underline{268}\ \ \ \\
335 \\
\underline{335}
\end{array}
$$

24.
$$
\begin{array}{r}
12.130 \\
-9.884 \\
\hline
2.246
\end{array}
$$

0.5 Exercises

1. Answers may vary.

   19% means 19 out of 100 parts or $\dfrac{19}{100}$

3. $0.28 = 28\%$

5. $0.568 = 56.8\%$

7. $0.076 = 7.6\%$

9. $2.39 = 239\%$

11. $3\% = 0.03$

13. $0.4\% = 0.004$

15. $250\% = 2.5$

17. $7.4\% = 0.074$

19. 0.8% of 65

   $0.008 \times 65 = 0.52$

21. 10% of 130

   $0.10 \times 130 = 13$

23. 112% of 65

   $1.12 \times 65 = 72.8$

25. 36 is what percent of 24?

   $\dfrac{36}{24} = 1.50 = 150\%$

27. What percent of 340 is 17?

   $\dfrac{17}{340} = \dfrac{1}{20} = 0.05 = 5\%$

29. 75 is what percent of 30?

   $\dfrac{75}{30} = 2.5 = 250\%$

31. $\dfrac{68}{80} = 0.85 = 85\%$

   His grade was 85%.

33. $0.15 \times 32.80 = 4.92$

   $32.80 + 4.92 = 37.72$

   \$4.92 tip, \$37.72 new total

35. $\dfrac{380}{1850} \approx 0.21 = 21\%$

   About 21% of the budget is for food.

37. $1.5\% \times 36,000 = 0.015 \times 36,000 = 540$ gifts

39. $0.08 \times 12.50 = 1$

    $12.50 + 1 = 13.50$

    $1 per hour raise

    $13.50 per hour new rate

41. a. $(0.038)(780,000) = 29,640$

       $29,640

    b. $29,640 + 12(450) = 35,040$

       $35,040

43. Discount: $33\% \times 45 = 0.33 \times 45 = 14.85$

    Nancy: $20\% \times (45 - 14.85) = 0.2 \times 30.13$

    $\qquad\qquad\qquad\qquad\qquad = \$6.03$

    Fred: $20\% \times 45 = 0.2 \times 45 = \$9.00$

    Increase: $\$9.00 - \$6.03 = \$2.97$

Cumulative Review

45.
45.50	1.50
1189.00	98.00
33.90	128.00
1268.40	56.89
	445.88
	730.27

    Balance $1268.40 - 730.27 = \$538.13$

47. Distance: $69,229.5 - 68,459.5 = 770$

    $\dfrac{770}{35} = 22$ miles per gallon

0.6 Exercises

1. $693 \times 307 \approx 700 \times 300 = 210,000$

3. $2862 \times 5986 \approx 3000 \times 6000$

   $\qquad\qquad\qquad \approx 18,000,000$

5. $14 + 73 + 80 + 21 + 56$

   $\approx 10 + 70 + 80 + 20 + 60$

   $= 240$

7. $41\overline{)829,346} \approx 40\overline{)800,000}^{\,20,000}$

   $\qquad\qquad \approx 20,000$

9. $\dfrac{2714}{31,500} \approx \dfrac{3000}{30,000} = 0.1$

11. 317% of $21,365.85 \approx 0.20 \times 20,000$

    $\qquad\qquad\qquad\qquad \approx \$4000.00$

13. $18.5 \times 22.50 \approx 20 \times 20$

    $\qquad\qquad\qquad \approx \$400$

15. $4 \times 22 \times 82 \approx 4 \times 20 \times 80 = \$6400$

17. $\dfrac{117.7}{3.8} \approx \dfrac{100}{4} = 25$ miles per gallon

19. $\dfrac{491,549.00}{279} \approx \dfrac{500,000}{300} = \$1666.67$

21. $26\% \times 217,970,000,000$

    $\approx 0.30 \times 200,000,000,000$

    $\approx \$60,000,000,000$

23. $14\% \times 38,945.89 \approx 0.10 \times 40,000$

    $\qquad\qquad\qquad\qquad \approx \$4000$

10

25. $\dfrac{3247.54}{26,533.67} \approx \dfrac{3000}{30,000} = 0.10 = 10\%$

27. $43 \times 3.24 \approx 40 \times 3 = 120$
$12 \times 120 \times 23\% \approx 10 \times 120 \times 0.2$
$\approx \$240$ saved

Cumulative Review

29. $0.6\% \times 350 = 0.006 \times 350 = 2.1$

31. Tip $= 15\% \times 5.85 = 0.88$
Total $= 5.85 + 0.88 = \$6.73$

0.7 Exercises

1. Area $= 12\dfrac{3}{4} \times 9\dfrac{1}{2} = \dfrac{51}{4} \times \dfrac{19}{2} = \dfrac{969}{8}$

   Square yards $= \dfrac{969}{8} \div 9 = 13.4583$

   Cost $= 20 \times 13.4583 \approx \$269.17$

3. a. Length $= 2 \times 15\dfrac{1}{2} + 2 \times 25\dfrac{2}{3}$

   $= 2 \times \dfrac{31}{2} + 2 \times \dfrac{77}{3}$

   $= 31 + \dfrac{154}{3}$

   $= \dfrac{93}{3} + \dfrac{154}{3}$

   $= \dfrac{247}{3} = 82\dfrac{1}{3}$ feet

   b. Cost $= 2.10 \times \dfrac{247}{3} = \$172.90$

   She should purchase the prepackaged
   90 feet. She would save $\$172.90 - 155.00$
   $= \$17.90$.

5.
Day	Jog	Walk	Rest	Walk
1	$1\dfrac{1}{5}$	$1\dfrac{3}{4}$	$2\dfrac{1}{2}$	1
3	$2\dfrac{2}{15}$	$3\dfrac{1}{9}$	$4\dfrac{4}{9}$	$1\dfrac{7}{9}$

Increase $1\dfrac{1}{3} \times 1\dfrac{1}{3} = \dfrac{16}{9}$

$\dfrac{16}{9} \times 1\dfrac{1}{5} = \dfrac{16}{9} \times \dfrac{6}{5} = \dfrac{96}{45} = 2\dfrac{2}{15}$

$\dfrac{16}{9} \times 1\dfrac{3}{4} = \dfrac{16}{9} \times \dfrac{7}{4} = \dfrac{28}{9} = 3\dfrac{1}{9}$

$\dfrac{16}{9} \times 2\dfrac{1}{2} = \dfrac{16}{9} \times \dfrac{5}{2} = \dfrac{40}{9} = 4\dfrac{4}{9}$

$\dfrac{16}{9} \times 1 = \dfrac{16}{9} = 1\dfrac{7}{9}$ miles

7. Betty will have a more demanding
schedule on day 3 because Melinda
increases each activity by $\dfrac{2}{3}$ by day 3
and Betty increases each activity by
$\dfrac{7}{9}$ by day 3.

9. Increase: $1\dfrac{1}{2} \times \dfrac{1}{3} = \dfrac{3}{2} \times \dfrac{1}{3} = \dfrac{1}{2}$

   Day 7: $1\dfrac{1}{2} + \left(6 \times \dfrac{1}{2}\right) = \dfrac{3}{2} + \dfrac{6}{2} = \dfrac{9}{2}$

   $= 4\dfrac{1}{2}$ miles

11. 1st increase:

$30\% \times 350 = 66,200 = 19,860$

1990 price:

$66,200 + 19,860 = 86,060$

2nd increase:

$15\% \times 86,060 = 12,909$

2000 price:

$86,060 + 12,909 = \$98,969.00$

13. a. Percent available $= 100 - 28 = 72\%$

$0.72 \times 50,000 = \$36,000$

b. $0.31 \times 36,000 = \$11,160$

15. Federal: $\dfrac{139}{1150} \approx 0.12 = 12\%$

State: $\dfrac{68}{1150} \approx 0.06 = 6\%$

Local: $\dfrac{5}{1150} \approx 0.004 = 0\%$

Total: $12\% + 6\% = 18\%$

17. $\dfrac{790.47}{1150} \approx 0.69 = 69\%$

Putting Your Skills to Work

1. $26.6 - 13.9 = 12.7$

12,700 square miles

2. $31.8 - 22.4 = 9.4$

9400 square miles

3.
$$
\begin{array}{r}
4.2 \\
7540{\overline{\smash{\big)}\,31,800.0}} \\
\underline{30,160} \\
16400 \\
\underline{15080} \\
1320
\end{array}
$$

About 4 times

4.
$$
\begin{array}{r}
319.4 \\
72{\overline{\smash{\big)}\,23000.0}} \\
\underline{216} \\
140 \\
\underline{72} \\
680 \\
\underline{648} \\
320 \\
\underline{288} \\
32
\end{array}
$$

About 319 times

Chapter 0 Review Problems

1. $\dfrac{36}{48} = \dfrac{12 \times 3}{12 \times 4} = \dfrac{3}{4}$

2. $\dfrac{15}{30} = \dfrac{5 \times 3}{5 \times 10} = \dfrac{3}{10}$

3. $\dfrac{36}{82} = \dfrac{18 \times 2}{41 \times 2} = \dfrac{18}{41}$

4. $\dfrac{18}{30} = \dfrac{6 \times 3}{6 \times 5} = \dfrac{3}{5}$

5. $4\dfrac{3}{5} = \dfrac{4 \cdot 5 + 3}{5} = \dfrac{20 + 3}{5} = \dfrac{23}{5}$

12

6. $\dfrac{34}{5} = 6\dfrac{4}{5}$

7. $\dfrac{39}{6} = 6\overline{)39} = 6\dfrac{3}{6} = 6\dfrac{1}{2}$
$\phantom{\dfrac{39}{6} = 6\overline{)}}\underline{36}$
$\phantom{\dfrac{39}{6} = 6\overline{)3}}3$

8. $\dfrac{5}{8} = \dfrac{?}{24} \Rightarrow \dfrac{5\cdot3}{8\cdot3} = \dfrac{15}{24}$

9. $\dfrac{1}{7} = \dfrac{?}{35} \Rightarrow \dfrac{1\cdot5}{7\cdot5} = \dfrac{5}{35}$

10. $\dfrac{5}{9} = \dfrac{?}{72} \Rightarrow \dfrac{5\cdot8}{9\cdot8} = \dfrac{40}{72}$

11. $\dfrac{2}{5} = \dfrac{?}{55} \Rightarrow \dfrac{2\times11}{5\times11} = \dfrac{22}{55}$

12. $\dfrac{3}{5} + \dfrac{1}{4} = \dfrac{3\times4}{5\times4} + \dfrac{1\times5}{4\times5} = \dfrac{12}{20} + \dfrac{5}{20} = \dfrac{17}{20}$

13. $\dfrac{7}{12} + \dfrac{5}{8} = \dfrac{7\times2}{12\times2} + \dfrac{5\times3}{8\times3} = \dfrac{14}{24} + \dfrac{15}{24} = \dfrac{29}{24} = 1\dfrac{5}{24}$

14. $\dfrac{7}{20} - \dfrac{1}{12} = \dfrac{21}{60} - \dfrac{5}{60} = \dfrac{16}{60} = \dfrac{4}{15}$

15. $\dfrac{7}{10} - \dfrac{4}{15} = \dfrac{7\cdot3}{10\cdot3} - \dfrac{4\cdot2}{5\cdot2} = \dfrac{21}{30} - \dfrac{8}{30} = \dfrac{13}{30}$

16. $3\dfrac{1}{6} + 2\dfrac{3}{5} = 3\dfrac{5}{30} + 2\dfrac{18}{30} = 5\dfrac{23}{30}$

17. $1\dfrac{1}{4} + 2\dfrac{7}{10} = \dfrac{5}{4} + \dfrac{27}{10} = \dfrac{25}{20} + \dfrac{54}{20} = \dfrac{79}{20} = 3\dfrac{19}{20}$

18. $6\dfrac{2}{9} - 3\dfrac{5}{12} = \dfrac{56}{9} - \dfrac{41}{12} = \dfrac{56\cdot4}{9\cdot4} - \dfrac{41\cdot3}{12\cdot3}$
$\phantom{6\dfrac{2}{9} - 3\dfrac{5}{12}} = \dfrac{224}{36} - \dfrac{123}{36} = \dfrac{101}{36}$
$\phantom{6\dfrac{2}{9} - 3\dfrac{5}{12}} = 2\dfrac{29}{36}$

19. $3\dfrac{1}{15} - 1\dfrac{3}{20} = \dfrac{46}{15} - \dfrac{23}{20} = \dfrac{184}{60} - \dfrac{69}{60}$
$\phantom{3\dfrac{1}{15} - 1\dfrac{3}{20}} = \dfrac{115}{60} = 1\dfrac{55}{60} = 1\dfrac{11}{12}$

20. $6 \times \dfrac{5}{11} = \dfrac{6}{1} \times \dfrac{5}{11} = \dfrac{30}{11}$ or $2\dfrac{8}{11}$

21. $2\dfrac{1}{3} \times 4\dfrac{1}{2} = \dfrac{7}{3} \times \dfrac{9}{2} = \dfrac{7}{3} \times \dfrac{3\cdot3}{2} = \dfrac{21}{2} = 10\dfrac{1}{2}$

22. $1\dfrac{1}{8} \times 2\dfrac{1}{9} = \dfrac{9}{8} \times \dfrac{19}{9} = \dfrac{1}{8} \times \dfrac{19}{1} = \dfrac{19}{8}$ or $2\dfrac{3}{8}$

23. $\dfrac{4}{7} \times 5 = \dfrac{4}{7} \times \dfrac{5}{1} = \dfrac{20}{7} = 2\dfrac{6}{7}$

24. $\dfrac{3}{8} \div 6 = \dfrac{3}{8} \times \dfrac{1}{2\cdot3} = \dfrac{1}{16}$

25. $\dfrac{\frac{8}{3}}{\frac{5}{9}} = \dfrac{8}{3} \times \dfrac{9}{5} = \dfrac{8}{3} \times \dfrac{3\cdot3}{5} = \dfrac{24}{5} = 4\dfrac{4}{5}$

26. $\dfrac{15}{16} + 6\dfrac{1}{4} = \dfrac{15}{16} + \dfrac{25}{4} = \dfrac{15}{16} \times \dfrac{4}{25} = \dfrac{3}{4} \times \dfrac{1}{5} = \dfrac{3}{20}$

27. $2\dfrac{6}{7} \div \dfrac{10}{21} = \dfrac{20}{7} \times \dfrac{21}{10} = \dfrac{2\cdot10}{7} \times \dfrac{3\cdot7}{10} = 6$

13

28.　　$\begin{array}{r} 1.634 \\ 3.007 \\ +\ 2.560 \\ \hline 7.201 \end{array}$

29.　　$\begin{array}{r} 24.831 \\ -\ 17.094 \\ \hline 7.737 \end{array}$

30.　　$\begin{array}{r} 47.251 \\ -\ 17.690 \\ \hline 29.561 \end{array}$

31.　　$\begin{array}{r} 1.900 \\ 2.530 \\ +\ 0.006 \\ \hline 4.436 \end{array}$

32.　　$\begin{array}{r} 5.35 \\ \times\ 0.007 \\ \hline 0.03745 \end{array}$

33.　$362.341 \times 1000 = 362,341$

34.　$2.6 \times 0.03 \times 1.02 = 0.07956$

35.　$1.08 \times 0.06 \times 160 = 10.368$

36.　$0.186 \div 100 = 0.00186$

37.　$71.32 \div 1000 = 0.07132$

38.　$0.523 \div 0.4 = 1.3075$

39.　$0.015 \overline{)1.350} \quad \begin{array}{c} 90 \\ \hline \\ \underline{135} \\ 00 \end{array}$

40.　$\dfrac{4.186}{2.3} = 2.3\overline{)4.186} = 1.82$
$$\begin{array}{r} 1.82 \\ \hline \underline{23} \\ 188 \\ \underline{184} \\ 46 \\ \underline{46} \end{array}$$

41.　$0.38\overline{)0.190}$
$$\begin{array}{r} 0.5 \\ \hline \underline{190} \end{array}$$

42.　$\dfrac{3}{8} = 8\overline{)3.000} = 0.375$
$$\begin{array}{r} 0.375 \\ \hline \underline{24} \\ 60 \\ \underline{56} \\ 40 \end{array}$$

43.　$0.36 = \dfrac{36}{100} = \dfrac{9}{25}$

44.　$1.4\% = 0.014$

45.　$36.1\% = 0.361$

46.　$0.02\% = 0.0002$

47.　$125.3\% = 1.253$

48.　85% of 600
　　　$(0.85)(600) = 510$

14

49. 7.2% of 55

$$0.072 \times 55 = 3.96$$

50. 48 is what percent of 75?

$$\frac{48}{75} = 0.64 = 64\%$$

51. What percent of 120 is 15?

$$\frac{15}{120} = 0.125 = 12.5\%$$

52. $\dfrac{750}{1250} = 0.6 = 60\%$

53. 80.7% of 20,229,000

$$0.807 \times 20,229,000 = 16,324,803$$

54. $\dfrac{720}{960} = 0.75 = 75\%$

55. $234,897 \times 1,936,112$

$$\approx 200,000 \times 2,000,000$$
$$= 400,000,000,000$$

56. $400 + 900 + 800 + 400 = 2500$

57. $634,318 - 284,000 \approx 600,000 - 300,000$

$$\approx 300,000$$

58. $7 + 4 + 8 = 19$

59. 18% of 56,297 $\approx 0.2 \times 60,000 = \$12,000$

60. $12,000 \div 400 = 30$

61. $7.85 \times 32.5 \approx 8 \times 30 = \$240$

62. $\dfrac{900}{3} = 300$

$300

63. Area $= 12\dfrac{1}{2} \times 9\dfrac{2}{3} = \dfrac{25}{2} \times \dfrac{29}{3}$

$$= 120\dfrac{5}{6} \text{ sq. feet}$$

$$= \dfrac{120\frac{5}{6}}{9} = 13\dfrac{23}{54} \text{ sq. yards}$$

Cost $= 26.00 \times 13\dfrac{23}{54} = 26 \times \dfrac{725}{54}$

$$= \$349.07$$

64. Increase $= 36,720 - 34,000 = 2720$

$$\dfrac{2720}{34,000} = 0.08 = 8\%$$

65. Maximum distance $= 7\dfrac{2}{3} \times 240$

$$= \dfrac{23}{3} \times 240$$

$$= 1840 \text{ miles}$$

Longest trip $= 80\% \times 1840 = .8 \times 1840$

$$= 1472 \text{ miles}$$

66. Maximum speed distance $=$

$$6\dfrac{1}{4} \times 240 = \dfrac{25}{4} \times 240 = 1500 \text{ miles}$$

15

67. Volume $= 4 \times 2\dfrac{1}{2} \times \dfrac{3}{4}$

$= \dfrac{4}{1} \times \dfrac{5}{2} \times \dfrac{3}{4}$

$= \dfrac{15}{2}$

$= 7\dfrac{1}{2}$ cubic inches

68. Outer volume $= 16 \times 12\dfrac{1}{2} \times 7\dfrac{1}{2}$

$= \dfrac{16}{1} \times \dfrac{25}{2} \times \dfrac{15}{2}$

$= 1500$ cubic inches

$\dfrac{1500}{\frac{15}{2}} = \dfrac{1500}{1} \times \dfrac{2}{15} = 200$ boxes

69. 8% of 5785

$0.08 \times 5785 = \$462.80$

70. $\dfrac{34.5}{0.75} = 46$ packages

71. Amount paid $= 225 \times 4 \times 12 = \$10,800$

Interest $= 10,800 - 9214.50 = \$1585.50$

72. Regular pay $= 6.40 \times 40 = 256$

O/T hours $= 52 - 40 = 12$

O/T pay rate $= 1.5 \times 6.40 = 9.60$

O/T pay $= 9.60 \times 12 = 115.20$

Total pay $= 256 + 115.20 = \$371.20$

How Am I Doing? Chapter 0 Test

1. $\dfrac{16}{18} = \dfrac{2 \times 8}{2 \times 9} = \dfrac{8}{9}$

2. $\dfrac{48}{36} = \dfrac{4 \cdot 12}{3 \cdot 12} = \dfrac{4}{3}$

3. $6\dfrac{3}{7} = \dfrac{7 \times 6 + 3}{7} = \dfrac{45}{7}$

4. $\dfrac{105}{9} = 9\overline{)105} = 11\dfrac{6}{9} = 11\dfrac{2}{3}$

   $\begin{array}{r} 11 \\ \underline{9} \\ 15 \\ \underline{9} \\ 6 \end{array}$

5. $\dfrac{2}{3} + \dfrac{5}{6} + \dfrac{3}{8} = \dfrac{2 \cdot 8}{3 \cdot 8} + \dfrac{5 \cdot 4}{6 \cdot 4} + \dfrac{3 \cdot 3}{8 \cdot 3}$

   $= \dfrac{16}{24} + \dfrac{20}{24} + \dfrac{9}{24}$

   $= \dfrac{45}{24} = \dfrac{15}{8}$

   $= 1\dfrac{7}{8}$

6. $1\dfrac{1}{8} + 3\dfrac{3}{4} = \dfrac{9}{8} + \dfrac{15}{4} = \dfrac{9 + 30}{8} = 4\dfrac{7}{8}$

7. $3\dfrac{2}{3} - 2\dfrac{5}{6} = 3\dfrac{4}{6} - 2\dfrac{5}{6} = 2\dfrac{10}{6} - 2\dfrac{5}{6} = \dfrac{5}{6}$

8. $\dfrac{5}{7} \times \dfrac{28}{15} = \dfrac{1}{1} \times \dfrac{4}{3} = \dfrac{4}{3}$ or $1\dfrac{1}{3}$

9. $\dfrac{5}{18} \times \dfrac{3}{4} = \dfrac{5 \times 3}{6 \times 3 \times 4} = \dfrac{5}{24}$

16

10. $\dfrac{7}{4} \div \dfrac{1}{2} = \dfrac{7}{4} \times \dfrac{2}{1} = \dfrac{7}{2} \times \dfrac{1}{1}$

    $= \dfrac{7}{2}$ or $3\dfrac{1}{2}$

11. $2\dfrac{1}{2} \times 3\dfrac{1}{4} = \dfrac{5}{2} \times \dfrac{13}{4} = \dfrac{65}{8} = 8\dfrac{1}{8}$

12. $5\dfrac{3}{8} \div 2\dfrac{3}{4} = \dfrac{43}{8} \div \dfrac{11}{4}$

    $= \dfrac{43}{2 \cdot 4} \times \dfrac{4}{11}$

    $= \dfrac{43}{22}$

    $= 1\dfrac{21}{22}$

13. $\quad\quad 1.60$
     $\quad\quad 3.24$
     $\quad\underline{\quad 9.80}$
     $\quad\quad 14.64$

14. $\quad 7.0046$
     $\underline{-\ 3.0149}$
     $\quad 3.9897$

15. $\quad\quad 32.8$
     $\underline{\times\ \ 0.04}$
     $\quad\quad 1.312$

16. $0.07385 \times 1000 = 73.85$

17. $0.056\overline{)12.880}$ with quotient 230

    $\quad\ \underline{112}$
    $\quad\ \ 168$
    $\quad\ \ \underline{168}$
    $\quad\quad\ \ 0$

18. $26,325.9 \div 100 = 263.259$

19. $0.073 = 7.3\%$

20. $196.5\% = 1.965$

21. What is 3.5% of 180?

    $0.035 \times 180 = 6.3$

22. $(0.02)(16.8) = 0.336$

23. 39 is what percent of 650?

    $\dfrac{39}{650} = 0.06 = 6\%$

24. $\dfrac{138}{460} = 0.3 = 30\%$

25. $4 \div \dfrac{2}{9} = \dfrac{4}{1} \times \dfrac{9}{2} = \dfrac{2}{1} \times \dfrac{9}{1} = 18$

    18 chips

26. $50000\overline{)5000000}$ with quotient 100

27. $285.36 + 311.85 + 113.6 \approx 300 + 300 + 100$

    ≈ 700

28. Commission: $(0.03)(870,000) = 26,100$

    Total income: $26,100 + 14,000 = 40,100$

    Percent: $\dfrac{26,100}{40,100} \approx 0.65 = 65\%$

29. $210 \div 3\dfrac{1}{2} = 210 \div \dfrac{7}{2} = 210 \times \dfrac{2}{7} = 60$ tiles

Chapter 1

1.1 Exercises

	Number	WN	RaN	IR	ReN
1.	23	x	x		x
3.	π				x
5.	$-6.666...$		x		x
7.	$-2.3434...$		x		x
9.	$\sqrt{2}$			x	x

11. $-20,000$

13. Lost $37\frac{1}{2} \Rightarrow -37\frac{1}{2}$

15. Rise 7^0 F $\Rightarrow +7$

17. Additive inverse of 8 is -8

19. Opposite of -2.73 is 2.73

21. $|-1.3| = 1.3$

23. $\left|\dfrac{5}{6}\right| = \dfrac{5}{6}$

25. $-6 + (-5) = -11$

27. $-17 + (-14) = -31$

29. $-\dfrac{5}{16} + \dfrac{9}{16} = \dfrac{4}{16} = \dfrac{1}{4}$

31. $\left(-\dfrac{2}{13}\right) + \left(-\dfrac{5}{13}\right) = -\dfrac{7}{13}$

33. $-\dfrac{2}{5} + \dfrac{3}{7} = \dfrac{1}{35}$

35. $(-1.5) + (-2.3) = -3.8$

37. $(+0.6) + (-0.2) = 0.4$

39. $-5.26 + (-8.9) = -14.16$

41. $-8 + 5 + (-3) = -3 + (-3) = -6$

43. $-3 + 5 + (-7) = 2 + (-7) = -5$

45. $-\dfrac{4}{5} + \dfrac{8}{15} = -\dfrac{12}{15} + \dfrac{8}{15} = -\dfrac{4}{15}$

47. $-7 + (-9) + 8 = -16 + 8 = -8$

49. $8 + (-11) = -3$

51. $-83 + 142 = 59$

53. $-\dfrac{4}{9} + \dfrac{5}{6} = -\dfrac{8}{18} + \dfrac{15}{18} = \dfrac{7}{18}$

55. $-\dfrac{1}{10} + \dfrac{1}{2} = -\dfrac{1}{10} + \dfrac{5}{10} = \dfrac{4}{10} = \dfrac{2}{5}$

57. $4.36 + (-3.6) = 0.76$

59. $4 + (-8) + 16 = -4 + 16 = 12$

19

61. $34 + (-18) + 11 + (-27)$
$= 16 + 11 + (-27)$
$= 27 + (-27)$
$= 0$

63. $17.85 + (-2.06) + 0.15 = 15.79 + 0.15$
$= 15.94$

65. Profit $= 214 - 47 = \$167$

67. $-2300 + (-1500) = -3800$
He owed $-\$3800$.

69. $9 + (-11) + 5 = -2 + 5 = 3$
3 yard gain

71. $8000 + (-3000) + (-1500) = 5000 + (-1500)$
$= 3500$

73. $30 + 14 + (-12) = 32$
$\$32,000,000$

75. $-13 + ? = 5$
$? = 18$

77. $10 + (-8) + 4 = 2 + 4 = 6$
They must make 6 yards.

Cumulative Review

79. $\dfrac{3}{7} + \dfrac{5}{21} = \dfrac{9}{21} + \dfrac{5}{21} = \dfrac{14}{21} = \dfrac{2}{3}$

81. $\dfrac{2}{15} - \dfrac{1}{20} = \dfrac{8}{60} - \dfrac{3}{60} = \dfrac{5}{60} = \dfrac{1}{12}$

83. $0.72 + 0.8 = 1.52$

85. $\begin{array}{r} 1.63 \\ \times \quad 0.7 \\ \hline 1.141 \end{array}$

1.2 Exercises

1. $-8 - (-3) = -8 + 3 = -5$

3. $18 - 35 = 18 + (-35) = -17$

5. $(+15) - (+20) = (+15) + (-20) = -5$

7. $(-14) - (-3) = (-14) + (3) = -11$

9. $(-52) - (-60) = (-52) + (+60) = 8$

11. $(0) - (-5) = (0) + (+5) = 5$

13. $(-18) - (-18) = (-18) + (+18) = 0$

15. $-11 - (-8) = -11 + 8 = -3$

17. $\dfrac{2}{5} - \dfrac{4}{5} = \dfrac{2}{5} + \left(-\dfrac{4}{5}\right) = -\dfrac{2}{5}$

19. $\left(+\dfrac{3}{4}\right) - \left(-\dfrac{3}{5}\right) = \left(+\dfrac{15}{20}\right) + \left(+\dfrac{12}{20}\right)$
$= \dfrac{27}{20} = 1\dfrac{7}{20}$

21. $\left(-\dfrac{3}{4}\right) - \left(+\dfrac{5}{6}\right) = \left(-\dfrac{9}{12}\right) + \left(-\dfrac{10}{12}\right)$
$= -\dfrac{19}{12} = -1\dfrac{7}{12}$

20

23. $(-0.6)-(+0.3)=(-0.6)+(-0.3)=-0.9$

25. $(+2.64)-(-1.83)=(+2.64)+(+1.83)$
$$=4.47$$

27. $\dfrac{3}{5}-4=\dfrac{3}{5}+\left(-\dfrac{20}{5}\right)=-\dfrac{17}{5}=-3\dfrac{2}{5}$

29. $-\dfrac{2}{6}+6=-\dfrac{2}{7}+\dfrac{42}{7}=\dfrac{40}{7}=5\dfrac{5}{7}$

31. $34-87=34+(-87)=-53$

33. $-25-48=-25+(-48)$

35. $2.3-(-4.8)=2.3+(+4.8)=7.1$

37. $8-\left(-\dfrac{3}{4}\right)=8+\dfrac{3}{4}=8\dfrac{3}{4}$

39. $\dfrac{5}{6}-7=\dfrac{5}{6}+\left(-\dfrac{42}{6}\right)=-\dfrac{37}{6}=-6\dfrac{1}{6}$

41. $-\dfrac{3}{10}-\dfrac{3}{4}=\left(-\dfrac{6}{20}\right)+\left(-\dfrac{15}{20}\right)$
$$=-\dfrac{21}{20}=-1\dfrac{1}{20}$$

43. $-135-(-126.5)=-135+(+126.5)=-8.5$

45. $\dfrac{1}{5}-6=\dfrac{1}{5}+\left(-\dfrac{30}{5}\right)=-\dfrac{29}{5}=-5\dfrac{4}{5}$

47. $5-(-3.162)=5+(+3.162)=8.162$

49. $-3-2.047=-3+(-2.047)=-5.047$

51. $-2-(-9)=-2+(+9)=7$

53. $-35-(13)=-35+(-13)=-48$

55. $7+(-6)-(+3)=7+(-6)+(-3)$
$$=1+(-3)=-2$$

57. $-10+6-(-15)=-10+6+(+15)$
$$=-4+(+15)=11$$

59. $7+(-42)-27=7+(-42)+(-27)$
$$=-35+(-27)=-62$$

61. $\quad 6.4-(-2.7)+5.3$
$$=-6.4+(2.7)+5.3$$
$$=-3.7+5.3$$
$$=1.6$$

63. $\quad 42-(-30)-65-(-11)+20$
$$=42+(+30)+(-65)+(+11)+20$$
$$=72+(-65)+(+11)+20$$
$$=7+(+11)+20$$
$$=18+20=38$$

65. $112-(-37)=112+(+37)=\$149$

67. $5895-(-156)=5895+156$
$$=6051$$
The difference is 6051 m

69. $\quad -37+16=-21$

71. $-3+(-6)+(-10)=-9+(-10)$
$$=-19$$

21

73. $\left(\dfrac{4}{5}\right)\left(8\dfrac{1}{3}\right) = \left(\dfrac{4}{5}\right)\left(\dfrac{25}{3}\right) = \dfrac{20}{3}$

    $= 6\dfrac{2}{3}$ miles

1.3 Exercises

1. To multiply two real numbers, multiply the absolute values. The sign of the result is positive if both numbers have the same sign, but negative if the two numbers have opposite signs.

3. $5(-4) = -20$

5. $0(-12) = 0$

7. $16 \times 1.5 = 24$

9. $(-1.32)(-0.2) = 0.264$

11. $(0.7)(-2.5) = -1.75$

13. $\dfrac{3}{8}(-4) = \dfrac{3}{8}\left(-\dfrac{4}{1}\right) = -\dfrac{3}{2} = -1\dfrac{1}{2}$

15. $\left(-\dfrac{3}{5}\right)\left(-\dfrac{15}{11}\right) = \dfrac{9}{11}$

17. $\left(\dfrac{12}{13}\right)\left(\dfrac{-5}{24}\right) = -\dfrac{5}{26}$

19. $(-36) \div (-9) = 4$

21. $-48 \div (-8) = \dfrac{-48}{-8} = 6$

23. $(-220) \div (-11) = 20$

25. $156 \div (-13) = -12$

27. $-9.1 \div 0.07 = -\dfrac{9.1}{0.07} = -130$

29. $0.54 \div (-0.9) = \dfrac{0.54}{-0.9} = -0.6$

31. $-6.3 \div 7 = \dfrac{-6.3}{7} = -0.9$

33. $\left(-\dfrac{1}{5}\right) \div \left(\dfrac{2}{3}\right) = \left(-\dfrac{1}{5}\right)\left(\dfrac{3}{2}\right) = -\dfrac{3}{10}$

35. $\left(-\dfrac{5}{7}\right) \div \left(-\dfrac{3}{28}\right) = \dfrac{5}{7} \cdot \left(-\dfrac{28}{3}\right) = -\dfrac{20}{3} = -6\dfrac{2}{3}$

37. $-\dfrac{7}{12} \div \left(-\dfrac{5}{6}\right) = \left(\dfrac{7}{12}\right)\left(\dfrac{6}{5}\right) = \dfrac{7}{10}$

39. $\dfrac{-6}{-\frac{3}{7}} = \left(-\dfrac{6}{1}\right)\left(-\dfrac{7}{3}\right) = 14$

41. $\dfrac{\frac{-2}{3}}{\frac{8}{15}} = \left(-\dfrac{2}{3}\right)\left(\dfrac{15}{8}\right) = -\dfrac{5}{4} = -1\dfrac{1}{4}$

43. $\dfrac{-\frac{7}{8}}{-\frac{14}{15}} = \left(-\dfrac{7}{8}\right)\left(\dfrac{15}{14}\right) = \dfrac{15}{16}$

45. $(-1)(-2)(-3)(4) = -(1)(2)(3)(4) = -24$

47. $-2(-2)(2)(-1)(-3) = 24$

22

49. $(-3)(-2)\left(\dfrac{1}{3}\right)(-4)(2)$

$$= -(3)(2)\left(\dfrac{1}{3}\right)(4)(2) = -16$$

51. $-3(-0.03)(0.001)(-2)$
$$= (0.09)(0.001)(-2)$$
$$= (0.00009)(-2)$$
$$= -0.00018$$

53. $\left(-\dfrac{4}{5}\right)\left(-\dfrac{6}{7}\right)\left(-\dfrac{1}{3}\right) = -\left(\dfrac{24}{35}\right)\left(\dfrac{1}{3}\right) = -\dfrac{8}{35}$

55. $\left(-\dfrac{3}{4}\right)\left(-\dfrac{7}{15}\right)\left(-\dfrac{8}{21}\right)\left(-\dfrac{5}{9}\right)$

$$= +\left(\dfrac{3}{4}\right)\left(\dfrac{7}{3\cdot5}\right)\left(\dfrac{4\cdot2}{3\cdot7}\right)\left(\dfrac{5}{9}\right) - \dfrac{2}{27}$$

57. $-36 \div (-4) = \dfrac{-36}{-4} = 9$

59. $5 + (-7) = -2$

61. $8 - (-9) = 8 + (9) = 17$

63. $6(-12) = -72$

65. $(-37) \div 37 = \dfrac{-37}{37} = -1$

67. $17.60 \div 4 = \dfrac{17.60}{4} = 4.40$

He gave $4.40 to each boy and to himself.

69. $\dfrac{15,768}{48} = \$328.50$

71. $5(4) = +20$, gained 20 yards

73. $-10(7) = -70$, lost 70 yards

75. Total $= -70 + 90 = 20$, gained 20 yards

77. Additional large-losses $= -15(3)$
$$= -45$$
Avoided medium-gains $= -(+15)(4)$
$$= -60$$
Fewer yards gained $= 45 + 60$
$$= 105 \text{ yards}$$
The Panthers would have gained 105 fewer yards.

Cumulative Review

79. $-\dfrac{3}{4} + \left(-\dfrac{2}{3}\right) + \left(-\dfrac{5}{12}\right)$

$$= -\dfrac{9}{12} + \left(-\dfrac{8}{12}\right) + \left(-\dfrac{5}{12}\right)$$

$$= -\dfrac{17}{12} + \left(-\dfrac{5}{12}\right)$$

$$= -\dfrac{22}{12} = -\dfrac{11}{6}$$

$$= -1\dfrac{5}{6}$$

81. $(-37) - (51) = (-37) + (-51) = -88$

1.4 Exercises

1. $4^4 = (4)(4)(4)(4) = 256$

3. A negative number to an odd power is negative.

5. $(-2)^4 = (-2)(-2)(-2)(-2) = 64$
   $-2^4 = -(2)(2)(2)(2) = -64$

7. $(5)(5)(5)(5)(5)(5)(5) = 5^7$

9. $(w)(w) = w^2$

11. $(p)(p)(p)(p) = p^4$

13. $(3q)(3q)(3q) = (3q)^3$ or $3^3 q^3$

15. $3^3 = 27$

17. $3^4 = 81$

19. $6^3 = 216$

21. $(-3)^3 = -27$

23. $(-4)^2 = 16$

25. $-5^2 = -(5)(5) = -25$

27. $\left(\dfrac{1}{4}\right)^2 = \dfrac{1}{16}$

29. $\left(\dfrac{2}{5}\right)^3 = \dfrac{8}{125}$

31. $(1.1)^2 = 1.21$

23. $(0.2)^4 = 0.0016$

35. $(-16)^2 = 256$

37. $-16^2 = -256$

39. $5^3 + 6^2 = 125 + 36 = 161$

41. $5^3 - 3^2 = 125 - 9 = 116$

43. $(-3)^3 - (8)^2 = -27 - 64 = -91$

45. $2^5 - (-3)^2 = 32 - 9 = 23$

47. $(-4)^3 (-3)^2 = (-64)(9) = -576$

49. $8^2 (-2)^3 = 64(-8) = -512$

51. $4^{12} = 16,777,216$

53. $-343 = (-7)(-7)(-7) = (-7)^3$
    The number is -7.

Cumulative Review

55. $(-11) + (-13) + 6 + (-9) + 8$
    $= -24 + 6 + (-9) + 8$
    $= -18 + (-9) + 8$
    $= -27 + 8$
    $= -19$

24

57. $-17 - (-9) = -17 + 9 = -8$

59. Interest for 1 year:

$6\%(1600) = 0.06(1600) = 96$

Interest for 9 months:

$\dfrac{9}{12}(96) = 72$

Total $= 1600 + 72 = \$1672$

1.5 Exercises

1. $3(4) + 6(5)$

3. $3(4) + 6(5) = 12 + 6(5) = 18(5) = 90$

    (b) $3(4) + 6(5) = 12 + 30 = 42$

5. $(2-5)^2 \div 3 \times 4 = (-3)^2 \div 3 \times 4$

    $= 9 \div 3 \times 4$

    $= 3 \times 4$

    $= 12$

7. $2(3 - 5 + 6) + 5 = 2(4) + 5$

    $= 8 + 5$

    $= 13$

9. $8 - 2^3 \cdot 5 + 3 = 8 - 8 \cdot 5 + 3$

    $= 8 - 40 + 3 = -29$

11. $4 + 42 \div 3 \cdot 2 - 8$

    $= 4 + 14 \cdot 2 - 8$

    $= 4 + 28 - 8$

    $= 32 - 8$

    $= 24$

13. $3 \cdot 5 + 7 \cdot 3 - 5 \cdot 3 = 15 + 21 - 15$

    $= 21$

15. $8 - 5(2)^3 \div (-8) = 8 - 5(8) \div (-8)$

    $= 8 - 40 \div (-8)$

    $= 8 + 5$

    $= 13$

17. $3(5-7)^2 - 6(3) = 3(-2)^2 - 6(3)$

    $= 3(4) - 6(3) = 12 - 18 = -6$

19. $5 \cdot 6 - (3 - 5)^2 + 8 \cdot 2 = 5 \cdot 6 - (-2)^2 + 8 \cdot 2$

    $= 5 \cdot 6 - 4 + 8 \cdot 2$

    $= 30 - 4 + 16 = 42$

21. $\dfrac{1}{2} \div \dfrac{2}{3} + 6 \cdot \dfrac{1}{4} = \dfrac{1}{2} \cdot \dfrac{3}{2} + \dfrac{6}{1} \cdot \dfrac{1}{4}$

    $= \dfrac{3}{4} + \dfrac{6}{4} = \dfrac{9}{4} = 2\dfrac{1}{4}$

23. $0.8 + 0.3(0.6 - 0.2)^2$

    $= 0.8 + 0.3(0.4)^2$

    $= 0.8 + 0.3(0.16)$

    $= 0.8 + 0.048 = 0.848$

25. $\dfrac{3}{4}\left(-\dfrac{2}{5}\right) - \left(-\dfrac{3}{5}\right) = -\dfrac{3}{10} + \dfrac{6}{10} = \dfrac{3}{10}$

27. $(3-7)^2 \div 8 + 3 = (-4)^2 \div 8 + 3$

    $= 16 \div 8 + 3$

    $= 2 + 3$

    $= 5$

29. $\left(\dfrac{3}{4}\right)^2(-16)+\dfrac{4}{5}\div\dfrac{-8}{25}$

$=\dfrac{9}{16}(-16)+\dfrac{4}{5}\div\dfrac{-8}{25}$

$=-9+\dfrac{4}{5}\div\dfrac{-8}{25}$

$=-9+\dfrac{4}{5}\left(\dfrac{25}{-8}\right)$

$=-9+\left(\dfrac{5}{-2}\right)$

$=-\dfrac{18}{2}+\left(-\dfrac{5}{2}\right)$

$=-\dfrac{23}{2}=-11\dfrac{1}{2}$

31. $-6.3-(-2.7)(1.1)+(3.3)^2$

$=-6.3+2.97+10.89=7.56$

33. $\left(\dfrac{1}{2}\right)^3+\left(\dfrac{1}{4}\right)-\left(\dfrac{1}{6}-\dfrac{1}{12}\right)-\dfrac{2}{3}\cdot\left(\dfrac{1}{4}\right)^2$

$=\left(\dfrac{1}{2}\right)^3+\dfrac{1}{4}-\left(\dfrac{1}{12}\right)-\dfrac{2}{3}\cdot\left(\dfrac{1}{4}\right)^2$

$=\dfrac{1}{8}+\dfrac{1}{4}-\dfrac{1}{12}-\dfrac{2}{3}\cdot\dfrac{1}{16}$

$=\dfrac{1}{8}+\dfrac{1}{4}-\dfrac{1}{12}-\dfrac{1}{24}$

$=\dfrac{6}{24}=\dfrac{1}{4}$

35. $3(-2)+9(-1)+5(0)+1(1)$

37. 1 above par

Cumulative Review

39. $(0.5)^3=0.125$

41. $-1^{20}=-1$

43. $15\div2\times(6)=45$ ounces

45. $0.324\div0.6$

$\dfrac{0.324}{0.6}=0.6\overline{)0.324}=0.54$

$$\begin{array}{r} 0.54 \\ 0.6\overline{)0.324} \\ \underline{30} \\ 24 \\ \underline{24} \end{array}$$

How Am I Doing? Sections 1.1-1.5

1. $3+(-12)=-9$

2. $-\dfrac{5}{6}+\left(-\dfrac{7}{8}\right)=-\dfrac{20}{24}+\left(-\dfrac{21}{24}\right)$

$=\dfrac{-41}{24}$

$=-1\dfrac{17}{24}$

3. $\begin{array}{r} 0.34 \\ +\ 0.90 \\ \hline 1.24 \end{array}$

4. $-14+3+(-2.5)+6.4$

$=-11+(-2.5)+6.4$

$=-13.5+6.4$

$=-7.1$

5. $-23-(-34)=-23+34=11$

6. $-\dfrac{4}{5}-\dfrac{1}{3}=-\dfrac{4}{5}+\left(-\dfrac{1}{3}\right)$

       $=-\dfrac{12}{15}+\left(-\dfrac{5}{15}\right)$

       $=-\dfrac{17}{15}$

       $=-1\dfrac{7}{15}$

7. $4.5-(-7.8)=4.5+7.8=12.3$

8. $-4-(-5)+9=-4+5+9=10$

9. $(-3)(-8)(2)(-2)=24(2)(-2)$

                   $=48(-2)$

                   $=-96$

10. $\left(-\dfrac{6}{11}\right)\left(-\dfrac{5}{3}\right)=\dfrac{10}{11}$

11. $-0.072\div0.08=\dfrac{-0.072}{0.08}=-0.9$

12. $\dfrac{5}{8}\div\left(-\dfrac{17}{16}\right)=\left(\dfrac{5}{8}\right)\cdot\left(-\dfrac{16}{17}\right)=-\dfrac{10}{17}$

13. $(0.7)^3=(0.7)(0.7)(0.7)$

             $=(0.49)(0.7)$

             $=0.343$

14. $(-4)^4=(-4)(-4)(-4)(-4)=256$

15. $0-2^8=-(2)(2)(2)(2)(2)(2)(2)(2)$

         $=-256$

16. $\left(\dfrac{2}{3}\right)^3=\left(\dfrac{2}{3}\right)\left(\dfrac{2}{3}\right)\left(\dfrac{2}{3}\right)=\dfrac{8}{27}$

17. $5^3+(-2)^4=125+16=141$

18. $12\div6(2)+3=2(2)+3=4+3=7$

19. $15+3-2+(-6)=18+(-2)+(-6)$

                      $=-16+(-6)$

                      $=10$

20. $(9-13)^2+15\div(-3)$

      $=(-4)^2+15\div(-3)$

      $=16+15\div(-3)$

      $=16+(-5)$

      $=11$

21. $-0.12\div0.6+(-3)(1.2)-(-0.5)$

      $=-0.2+(-3)(1.2)+0.5$

      $=-0.2+(-3.6)+0.5$

      $=-3.8+0.5$

      $=-3.3$

22. $\left(\dfrac{3}{4}\right)\left(-\dfrac{2}{5}\right)+\left(-\dfrac{1}{2}\right)\left(\dfrac{4}{5}\right)+\left(\dfrac{1}{2}\right)^2$

$=\left(\dfrac{3}{4}\right)\left(-\dfrac{2}{5}\right)+\left(-\dfrac{1}{2}\right)\left(\dfrac{4}{5}\right)+\dfrac{1}{4}$

$=-\dfrac{3}{10}+\left(-\dfrac{1}{2}\right)\left(\dfrac{4}{5}\right)+\dfrac{1}{4}$

$=-\dfrac{3}{10}+\left(-\dfrac{2}{5}\right)+\dfrac{1}{4}$

$=-\dfrac{6}{20}+\left(-\dfrac{8}{20}\right)+\dfrac{5}{20}$

$=-\dfrac{14}{20}+\dfrac{5}{20}$

$=-\dfrac{9}{20}$

1.6 Exercises

1. A var*iable* is a symbol used to represent an unknown number.

3. We are multiplying 4 by x by x. We know from the definition of exponents that x multiplied by x is x^2, this gives us an answer of $4x^2$.

5. Yes, $a(b-c)$ can be written as $a\left[b+(-c)\right]$.
$3(10-2)=(3\times10)-(3\times2)$
$3\times8=30-6$
$24=24$

7. $3(x-2y)=3(x)-3(2y)=3x-6y$

9. $-2(4a-3b)=-2(4a)-2(-3b)$
$=-8a+6b$

11. $3(3x+y)=3(3x)+3(y)=9x+3y$

13. $5(-2a-3b)=5(-2a)-5(3b)$
$=-10a-15b$

15. $-(x-3y)=(-1)(x)-(-1)(3y)$
$=-x+3y$

17. $-9(9x-5y+8)=-9(9x)-9(-5y)-9(8)$
$=-81x+45y-72$

19. $2(-5x+y-6)=2(-5x)+2(y)-2(6)$
$=-10x+2y-12$

21. $\dfrac{5}{6}\left(12x^2-24x+18\right)$

$=\left(\dfrac{5}{6}\right)\left(12x^2\right)+\left(\dfrac{5}{6}\right)(-24x)+\left(\dfrac{5}{6}\right)(18)$

$=10x^2-20x+15$

23. $\dfrac{x}{5}(x+10y-4)$

$=\dfrac{x}{5}(x)+\dfrac{x}{5}(10y)+\dfrac{x}{5}(-4)$

$=\dfrac{x^2}{5}+2xy-\dfrac{4x}{5}$

25. $5x(x+2y+z-1)$
$=5x(x)+5x(2y)+5x(z)+5x(-1)$
$=5x^2+10xy+5xz-5x$

27. $(2x-3)(-2)$
$=2x(-2)+(-3)(-2)$
$=-4x+6$

28

29. $(6x + y - 1)(3x) = 6x(3x) + y(3x) - 1(3x)$
$$= 18x^2 + 3xy - 3x$$

31. $(3x + 2y - 1)(-xy)$
$$= 3x(-xy) + 2y(-xy) - 1(-xy)$$
$$= -3x^2y - 2xy^2 + xy$$

33. $(2x + 3y - 2)(3xy)$
$$= (2x)(3xy) + 3y(3xy) - 2(3xy)$$
$$= 6x^2y + 9xy^2 - 6xy$$

35. $2.3(4.1x^2 - 2.3x + 0.4)$
$$= 2.3(4.1x^2) - 2.3(2.3x) + 2.3(0.4)$$
$$= 9.43x^2 - 5.29x + 0.92$$

37. $-0.3x(-1.2x^2 - 0.3x + 0.5)$
$$= -0.3x(-1.2x^2) + (-0.3x)(-0.3x)$$
$$+ (-0.3x)(0.5)$$
$$= 0.36x^3 + 0.09x^2 - 0.15x$$

39. $0.5x(0.6x + 0.8y - 5)$
$$= 0.5x(0.6x) + 0.5x(0.8y) + 0.5x(-5)$$
$$= 0.3x^2 + 0.4xy - 2.5x$$

41. $800(5x + 14y) = 800(5x) + 800(14y)$
$$= 4000x + 11,200y \text{ square feet}$$

43. $4y(2x - 5) = (8xy - 20y) \text{ dollars}$

45. $4x(3000 - 2y) = 4x(3000) + 4x(-2y)$
$$= 12,000x - 8xy \text{ square feet}$$

Cumulative Review

47. $(-2)^6 = (-2)(-2)(-2)(-2)(-2)(-2)$
$$= 64$$

49. $25 \div 5(2) + (-6) = 5(2) + (-6)$
$$= 10 + (-6)$$
$$= 4$$

51. $\dfrac{205}{365} \approx 0.56 = 56\%$

1.7 Exercises

1. A term is a number, a variable, or a product of numbers and variables.

3. The two terms $3x$ and $-8x$ are like terms because they both have the variable x with the exponent of one.

5. The only like terms are $7xy$ and $-14xy$ because the other two have different exponents even though they have the same variables.

7. $-14b^2 - 11b^2 = (-14 - 11)b^2 = -25b^2$

9. $10x^4 + 8x^4 + 7x^2 = (10 + 8)x^4 + 7x^2$
$$= 18x^4 + 7x^2$$

11. $3x + 2y - 8x - 7y$
$$= (3 - 8)x + (2 - 7)y$$
$$= -5x - 5y$$

13. $1.3x - 2.6y + 5.8x - 0.9y$
$= (1.3 + 5.8)x + (-2.6 - 0.9)y$
$= 7.1x - 3.5y$

15. $1.6x - 2.8y - 3.6x - 5.9y$
$= (1.6 - 3.6)x + (-2.8 - 5.9)y$
$= -2x - 8.7y$

17. $3p - 4q + 2p + 3 + 5q - 21$
$= (3 + 2)p + (-4 + 5)q + 3 - 21$
$= 5p + q - 18$

19. $2ab + 5bc - 6ac - 2ab$
$= (2 - 2)ab + 5bc - 6ac$
$= 5bc - 6ac$

21. $2x^2 - 3x - 5 - 7x + 8 - x^2$
$= (2 - 1)x^2 + (-3 - 7)x - 5 + 8$
$= x^2 - 10x + 3$

23. $2y^2 - 8y + 9 - 12y^2 - 8y + 3$
$= (2 - 12)y^2 + (-8 - 8)y + 9 + 3$
$= -10y^2 - 16y + 12$

25. $\dfrac{1}{3}x - \dfrac{2}{3}y - \dfrac{2}{5}x + \dfrac{4}{7}y$
$= \left(\dfrac{1}{3} - \dfrac{2}{5}\right)x + \left(-\dfrac{2}{3} + \dfrac{4}{7}\right)y$
$= \left(\dfrac{5}{15} - \dfrac{6}{15}\right)x + \left(-\dfrac{14}{21} + \dfrac{12}{21}\right)y$
$= -\dfrac{1}{15}x - \dfrac{2}{21}y$

27. $\dfrac{3}{4}a^2 - \dfrac{1}{3}b - \dfrac{1}{5}a^2 - \dfrac{1}{2}b$
$= \left(\dfrac{3}{4} - \dfrac{1}{5}\right)a^2 + \left(-\dfrac{1}{3} - \dfrac{1}{2}\right)b$
$= \left(\dfrac{15}{20} - \dfrac{4}{20}\right)a^2 + \left(-\dfrac{2}{6} - \dfrac{3}{6}\right)b$
$= -\dfrac{11}{20}a^2 - \dfrac{5}{6}b$

29. $ab - 7a - 9ab + 4a - 6b$
$= (1 - 9)ab + (-7 + 4)a - 6b$
$= -8ab - 3a - 6b$

31. $5(2a - b) - 3(5b - 6a)$
$= 10a - 5b - 15b + 18a$
$= 28a - 20b$

33. $-3b(5a - 3b) + 4(-3ab - 5b^2)$
$= -15ab + 9b^2 - 12ab - 20b^2$
$= -27ab - 11b^2$

35. $-3(x^2 + 3y) + 5(-6y - x^2)$
$= -3x^2 - 9y - 30y - 5x^2$
$= -8x^2 - 39y$

37. $4(2 - x) - 3(-5 - 12x)$
$= 8 - 4x + 15 + 36x$
$= 32x + 23$

39. $3a + 2b + 4a + 7b = 7a + 9b$

41. $2a + 7b + (5a + 3) = 7a + 7b + 3$ cm

43. $4[(9x - 2) - 3] = 4(9x - 5) = 36x - 20$ inches

Cumulative Review

45. $-\dfrac{1}{3}-\left(-\dfrac{1}{5}\right) = -\dfrac{5}{15}+\dfrac{3}{15} = -\dfrac{2}{15}$

47. $\dfrac{4}{5}+\left(-\dfrac{1}{25}\right)+\left(-\dfrac{3}{10}\right)$

$= \dfrac{40}{50}+\left(-\dfrac{2}{50}\right)+\left(-\dfrac{15}{50}\right) = \dfrac{23}{50}$

49. $\dfrac{1.9}{9.5} = 0.2$ liters per serving

1.8 Exercises

1. If $x = 3$, then $-2x+1$

$= -2(3)+1 = -6+1 = -5$

3. If $x = -9$, then $\dfrac{2}{3}x-5 = \dfrac{2}{3}(-9)-5$

$= -6-5 = -11$

5. If $x = \dfrac{1}{2}$, then $5x+10$

$= 5\left(\dfrac{1}{2}\right)+10 = \dfrac{5}{2}+10 = \dfrac{25}{2} = 12\dfrac{1}{2}$

7. If $x = 7$, then $2-4x = 2-4(7)$

$= 2-28 = -26$

9. If $x = 2.4$, then $3.5-2x$

$= 3.5-2(2.4) = 3.5-4.8 = -1.3$

11. If $x = -\dfrac{3}{4}$, then $9x+13$

$= 9\left(-\dfrac{3}{4}\right)+13 = -\dfrac{27}{4}+\dfrac{52}{4} = \dfrac{25}{4}$

13. If $x = -2$, then $x^2-3x = (-2)^2-3(-2)$

$= 4+6 = 10$

15. If $x = -1$, then $3x^2 = 3(-1)^2 = 3$

17. If $x = 2$, then $-3x^3 = -3(2)^3 = -3(8)$

$= -24$

19. If $x = -2$, then $-5x^2 = -5(-2)^2$

$= -5(4) = -20$

21. If $x = -3$, then $2x^2+3x = 2(-3)^2+3(-3)$

$= 2(9)-9 = 18-9 = 9$

23. If $x = 3$, then $(2x)^2+x$

$= \left[2(3)\right]^2+3$

$= \left[6\right]^2+3 = 36+3 = 39$

25. If $x = -2$, then $2-(-x)^2$

$= 2-\left[-(-2)\right]^2 = 2-(2)^2 = 2-4 = -2$

27. If $x = -3$, then

$7x+(2x)^2 = 7(-3)+\left[2(-3)\right]^2$

$= -21+(-6)^2 = -21+36 = 15$

29. If $x = -3$, $3x^2-5x = 3(-3)^2-5(-3)$

$= 3(9)+15 = 27+15 = 42$

31. If $x = 3$, then $x^2 - 7x + 3 = (3)^2 - 7(3) + 3$
$$= 9 - 21 + 3 = -9$$

33. If $x = -4$, then $\frac{1}{2}x^2 - 3x + 9$
$$= \frac{1}{2}(-4)^2 - 3(-4) + 9$$
$$= \frac{1}{2}(16) + 12 + 9$$
$$= 8 + 12 + 9 = 29$$

35. If $x = -3$ and $y = 4$, then $x^2 - 2y + 3y^2$
$$= (-3)^2 - 2(4) + 3(4)^2$$
$$= 9 - 8 + 3(16)$$
$$= 9 - 8 + 48 = 49$$

37. If $a = 5$, $b = 8$, and $c = -1$, then
$$a^3 + 2abc - 3c^2 = 5^3 + 2(5)(9)(-1) - 3(-1)^2$$
$$= 125 - 90 - 3(1)$$
$$= 125 - 90 - 3 = 32$$

39. If $a = -1$ and $b = -2$, then
$$\frac{a^2 + ab}{3b} = \frac{(-1)^2 + (-1)(-2)}{3(-2)}$$
$$= \frac{1 + 2}{-6} = -\frac{1}{2}$$

41. $A = ab$, $b = 22$, $a = 16$
$$A = (22)(16) = 352 \text{ square feet}$$

43. $A = s^2$
Increase $= A_{\text{new}} - A_{\text{old}}$
$$= (3.2)^2 - (3)^2$$
$$= 10.24 - 9$$
$$= 1.24 \text{ square centimeters}$$

45. $A = \frac{1}{2}a(b_1 + b_2)$, $a = 4$, $b_1 = 9$, $b_2 = 7$
$$A = \frac{1}{2}(4)(9 + 7) = \frac{4(16)}{2}$$
$$= 32 \text{ square inches}$$

47. $A = \frac{1}{2}ab$, $a = 400$, $b = 280$
$$A = \frac{1}{2}(400)(280) = 56,000 \text{ square feet}$$

49. $A = \pi r^2 = (3.14)(4)^2 = (3.14)(16)$
$$= 50.24 \text{ square cm}$$

4 cm

51. $C = \frac{5}{9}(F - 32)$
$$C = \frac{5}{9}(-109.3 - 32)$$
$$C = \frac{5}{9}(-141.3)$$
$$C = 5(-15.7)$$
$$C = -78.5°C$$

53. $A = \dfrac{1}{2}ab,\ a = 20,\ b = 12$

$A = \dfrac{1}{2}(20)(12) = 120$ square feet

55. $F = \dfrac{9}{5}C + 32$

$F = \dfrac{9}{5}(60) + 32 = 108 + 32 = 140$

$F = \dfrac{9}{5}(-50) + 32 = -90 + 32 = -58$

$140°$ F to $-58°$ F

57. $k = 1.61r$

$2.3 - 1.61r$

$r = 1.4$

1.4 miles

The air is thin and lacks the usual amount of oxygen at this elevation.

Cumulative Review

59. $(-2)^4 - 4 \div 2 - (-2) = 16 - 2 + 2$

$= 16$

61. $\dfrac{93}{15} = 6.2$ minutes/song

1.9 Exercises

1. $-3x - 2y = -(3x + 2y)$

3. To simplify expressions with grouping symbols, we use the *distributive* property.

5. $6x - 3(x - 2y) = 6x - 3x + 6y$

$= 3x + 6y$

7. $2(a + 3b) - 3(b - a)$

$= 2a + 6b - 3b + 3a$

$= 5a + 3b$

9. $-3(x + 3y) + 2(2x + y)$

$= -3x - 9y + 4x + 2y$

$= x - 7y$

11. $2x\left[4x^2 - 2(x - 3)\right]$

$= 2x\left[4x^2 - 2x + 6\right]$

$= 8x^3 - 4x^2 + 12x$

13. $2\left[5(x + y) - 2(3x - 4y)\right]$

$= 2\left[5x + 5y - 6x + 8y\right]$

$= 2(-x + 13y)$

$= -2x + 26y$

15. $2(x - 2y) - \left[3 - 2(x - y)\right]$

$= 2x - 4y - (3 - 2x + 2y)$

$= 2x - 4y - 3 + 2x - 2y$

$= 4x - 6y - 3$

17. $5\left[3a - 2a(3a + 6b) + 6a^2\right]$

$= 5\left[3a - 6a^2 - 12ab + 6a^2\right]$

$= 5\left[3a - 12ab\right]$

$= 15a - 60ab$

19. $6a\left(2a^2 - 3a - 4\right) - a(a - 2)$

$= 12a^3 - 18a^2 - 24a - a^2 + 2a$

$= 12a^3 - 19a^2 - 22a$

21. $3a^2 - 4\left[2b - 3b(b + 2)\right]$

$= 3a^2 - 4\left(2b - 3b^2 - 6b\right)$

$= 3a^2 - 4\left(-4b - 3b^2\right)$

$= 3a^2 + 16b + 12b^2$

23. $6b - \left\{5a - 2\left[a + (b - 2a)\right]\right\}$

$= 6b - \left\{5a - 2\left[a + b - 2a\right]\right\}$

$= 6b - \left\{5a - 2\left[-a + b\right]\right\}$

$= 6b - \left\{5a + 2a - 2b\right\}$

$= 6b - \left\{7a - 2b\right\}$

$= 6b - 7a + 2b$

$= -7a + 8b$

25. $3\left\{3b^2 + 2\left[5b - (2 - b)\right]\right\}$

$= 3\left\{3b^2 + 2\left[5b - 2 + b\right]\right\}$

$= 3\left\{3b^2 + 2\left[6b - 2\right]\right\}$

$= 3\left\{3b^2 + 12b - 4\right\}$

$= 9b^2 + 36b - 12$

27. $-4\left\{3a^2 - 2\left[4a^2 - (b + a^2)\right]\right\}$

$= -4\left[3a^2 - 2\left(4a^2 - b - a^2\right)\right]$

$= -4\left[3a^2 - 2\left(3a^2 - b\right)\right]$

$= -4\left(3a^2 - 6a^2 + 2b\right)$

$= -4\left(-3a^2 + 2b\right)$

$= 12a^2 - 8b$

29. Attempts $= (4)(6)(365) = 8760$

Successful $= 2.5\%(8760)$

$= (.025)(8760)$

$= 219$

Unsuccessful $= 8760 - 219 = 8541$

Cumulative Review

31. If $C = 36.4,$ then

$F = 1.8C + 32$

$= 1.8(36.4) + 32 = 65.52 + 32 = 97.52^0\,\text{F}$

33. $A = \dfrac{1}{2}a(b_1 + b_2),$

$a = 400,\ b_1 = 800,\ b_2 = 700$

$A = \dfrac{1}{2}(400)(800 + 700) = 200(1500)$

$= 300,000$ sq. ft.

Cost $= 55(300,000) = \$16,500,000$

35. If $k = 2.205p$

If $p = 120,\ k = 2.205(120) = 264.6$

If $p = 150,\ k = 2.205(150) = 330.75$

Great Danes weigh on average from 264.6 to 330.75 kg.

34

Putting Your Skills to Work

1. 66.8% of 31,723

$0.668 \times 31,723 = 21,190.964$

About 21,190,964 use e-mail.

2.   31,712
      $- \, 22,205$
         9,518

   About 9,518,000 more use computers.

3. $(0.77)x = 65,190,000$

$$x = \frac{65,190,000}{0.77}$$

$$x = 846,622,338 \text{ people}$$

4. 117.5% of 65,190,000

$(1.175)(65,190,000) = 76,598,250$

About 76,598,250 people.

5. $N = 65,190,000 + 4,500,000x$
   when $x = 6$
   $N = 65,190,000 + 4,500,000(6)$
   $N = 65,190,000 + 27,000,000$
   $N = 92,190,000 \text{ people}$

6. $N = 65,190,000 + 4,500,000x$
   when $x = 9$
   $N = 65,190,000 + 4,500,000(9)$
   $N = 65,190,000 + 40,500,000$
   $N = 105,190,000 \text{ people}$

Chapter 1 Review Problems

1. $(-6) + (-2) = -8$

2. $(-12) + (+7.8) = -4.2$

3. $(+5) + (-2) + (-12) = (+3) + (-12) = -9$

4. $(+3.7) + (-1.8) = 1.9$

5. $\left(+\frac{1}{2}\right) + \left(-\frac{5}{6}\right) = \left(+\frac{3}{6}\right) + \left(-\frac{5}{6}\right) = -\frac{2}{6} = -\frac{1}{3}$

6. $\left(-\frac{3}{11}\right) + \left(-\frac{1}{22}\right) = \left(-\frac{6}{22}\right) + \left(-\frac{1}{22}\right)$
   $= -\frac{7}{22}$

7. $\left(+\frac{3}{4}\right) + \left(-\frac{1}{12}\right) + \left(-\frac{1}{2}\right)$
   $= \left(+\frac{9}{12}\right) + \left(-\frac{1}{12}\right) + \left(-\frac{6}{12}\right) = \frac{2}{12} = \frac{1}{6}$

8. $\left(-\frac{4}{15}\right) + \left(+\frac{12}{5}\right) + \left(-\frac{2}{3}\right)$
   $= \left(-\frac{4}{15}\right) + \left(+\frac{36}{15}\right) + \left(-\frac{10}{15}\right) = \frac{22}{15}$

9. $(+5) - (-3) = (+5) + (+3) = 8$

10. $(-2) - (-15) = (-2) + (+15)$
    $= 13$

11. $(-30) - (+3) = (-30) + (-3)$
    $= -33$

12. $(+8) - (-1.2) = (+8) + (+1.2)$

    $= 9.2$

13. $\left(-\dfrac{7}{8}\right) + \left(-\dfrac{3}{4}\right) = \left(-\dfrac{7}{8}\right) + \left(-\dfrac{6}{8}\right)$

    $= -\dfrac{13}{8} = -1\dfrac{5}{8}$

14. $\left(-\dfrac{3}{14}\right) + \left(+\dfrac{5}{7}\right) = \left(-\dfrac{3}{14}\right) + \left(+\dfrac{10}{14}\right)$

    $= \dfrac{7}{14} = \dfrac{1}{2}$

15. $-20.8 - 1.9 = -20.8 + (-1.9) = -22.7$

16. $-151 - (-63) = -151 + 63 = -88$

17. $87 \div (-29) = -3$

18. $-5(-6) + 4(-3) = 30 + (-12) = 18$

19. $\dfrac{-24}{-\frac{3}{4}} = \left(\dfrac{-24}{1}\right)\left(-\dfrac{4}{3}\right) = 32$

20. $\left(-\dfrac{1}{2}\right) \div \dfrac{3}{4} = \left(-\dfrac{1}{2}\right)\left(\dfrac{2 \cdot 2}{3}\right) = -\dfrac{2}{3}$

21. $\left(\dfrac{5}{7}\right) \div \left(-\dfrac{5}{25}\right) = \dfrac{5}{7} \cdot \left(-\dfrac{25}{5}\right)$

    $= -\dfrac{25}{7}$ or $-3\dfrac{4}{7}$

22. $(-6)(3)(4) = (-18)(4)$

    $= -72$

23. $(-1)(-2)(-3)(-5) = (1)(2)(3)(5) = 30$

24. $(-5)\left(-\dfrac{1}{2}\right)(4)(-3) = \left(\dfrac{5}{2}\right)(-12)$

    $= -30$

25. $-5 + (-2) - (-3) = -5 + (-2) + (+3)$

    $= (-7) + (+3) = -4$

26. $6 - (-4) + (-2) + (8) = 6 + 4 + (-2) + (8)$

    $= 18 + (-2)$

    $= 16$

27. $(-16) + (-13) = -29$

28. $(-11) - (-12) = -11 + 12 = 1$

29. $-\dfrac{4}{3} + \dfrac{2}{3} + \dfrac{1}{6} = -\dfrac{2}{3} + \dfrac{1}{6} = -\dfrac{4}{6} + \dfrac{1}{6}$

    $= -\dfrac{3}{6} = -\dfrac{1}{2}$

30. $-\dfrac{6}{7} + \dfrac{1}{2} + \left(-\dfrac{3}{14}\right) = -\dfrac{12}{14} + \dfrac{7}{14} + \left(-\dfrac{3}{14}\right)$

    $= -\dfrac{5}{14} + \left(-\dfrac{3}{14}\right)$

    $= -\dfrac{8}{14}$

    $= -\dfrac{4}{7}$

31. $(-3)(-2)(-5) = -(3)(2)(5) = -30$

32. $-6 + (-2) - (-3) = -6 + (-2) + 3$

    $= -8 + 3$

    $= -5$

33. $3.5(-2.6) = -9.1$

34. $(-5.4) \div 4(-6) = 0.9$

35. $5 - (-3.5) + 1.6 = 5 + 3.5 + 1.6 = 10.1$

36. $-8 + 2 - (-4.8) = -6 + 4.8$
    $= -1.2$

37. $17 + 3.4 + (-16) + (-2.5) = 20.4 + (-18.5)$
    $= 1.9$

38. $37 + (-44) + 12.5 + (-6.8)$
    $= 49.5 + (-50.8)$
    $= -1.3$

39. $(-8)(3) = -24$;   24 yards lost

40. $-34 + 12 = -22$
    $-22° \text{F}$

41. $6895 - (-468) = 6895 + 468 = 7363$ feet

42. $+1\frac{1}{2} - 3\frac{1}{4} + 2 - 2\frac{1}{2} = 3\frac{1}{2} + \left(-5\frac{3}{4}\right)$
    $= -2\frac{1}{4}$
    $2\frac{1}{4}$ point loss

43. $(-3)^4 = (-3)(-3)(-3)(-3) = 81$

44. $(-2)^7 = -128$

45. $(-5)^4 = -625$

46. $\left(\frac{2}{3}\right)^3 = \frac{8}{27}$

47. $-9^2 = -81$

48. $(0.6)^2 = 0.36$

49. $\left(\frac{5}{6}\right)^2 = \left(\frac{5}{6}\right)\left(\frac{5}{6}\right) = \frac{25}{36}$

50. $\left(\frac{3}{4}\right)^3 = \left(\frac{3}{4}\right)\left(\frac{3}{4}\right)\left(\frac{3}{4}\right)$
    $= \frac{27}{64}$

51. $(5)(-4) + (3)(-2)^3$
    $= (5)(-4) + (3)(-8)$
    $= -20 + (-24)$
    $= -44$

52. $20 - (-10) - (-6) + (-5) - 1$
    $= 20 + 10 + 6 + (-5) - 1$
    $= 36 - 6$
    $= 30$

53. $(7-9)^3 + (-6)(-2) + (-3)$
    $= (-2)^3 + (-6)(-2) + (-3)$
    $= -8 + (-6)(-2) + (-3)$
    $= -8 + (12) + (-3) = 1$

54. $5(3x - 7y) = 5(3x) + 5(-7y) = 15x - 35y$

37

55. $2x(3x - 7y + 4)$

    $= 2x(3x) + 2x(-7y) + 2x(4)$

    $= 6x^2 - 14xy + 8x$

56. $-(7x^2 - 3x + 11)$

    $= -1(7x^2) + (-1)(-3x) + (-1)(11)$

    $= -7x^2 + 3x - 11$

57. $(2xy + x - y)(-3y)$

    $= (2xy)(-3y) + x(-3y) - y(-3y)$

    $= -6xy^2 - 3xy + 3y^2$

58. $3a^2b - 2bc + 6bc^2 - 8a^2b - 6bc^2 + 5bc$

    $= (3 - 8)a^2 + (-2 + 5)bc + (6 - 6)bc^2$

    $= -5a^2b + 3bc$

59. $9x + 11y - 12x - 15y = -3x - 4y$

60. $4x^2 - 13x + 7 - 9x^2 - 22x - 16$

    $= (4 - 9)x^2 + (-13 - 22)x + 7 - 16$

    $= -5x^2 - 35x - 9$

61. $-x + \dfrac{1}{2} + 14x^2 - 7x - 1 - 4x^2$

    $= (14 - 4)x^2 + (-7 - 1)x + \dfrac{1}{2} - 1$

    $= 10x^2 - 8x - \dfrac{1}{2}$

62. If $x = -7$, then $7x - 6 = 7(-7) - 6$

    $= -49 - 6 = -55$

63. If $x = 8$, then $7 - \dfrac{3}{4}x = 7 - \dfrac{3}{4}(8)$

    $= 7 - 6 = 1$

64. $x^2 + 3x - 4 = (-3)^2 + 3(-3) - 4$

    $= 9 - 9 - 4$

    $= -4$

65. If $x = 2$, then

    $-3x^2 - 4x + 5 = -3(2)^2 - 4(2) + 5$

    $= -3(4) - 4(2) + 5$

    $= -12 - 8 + 5 = -15$

66. $-3x^3 - 4x^2 + 2x + 6$

    $= -3(-2)^3 - 4(-2)^2 + 2(-2) + 6$

    $= -3(-8) - 4(4) - 4 + 6$

    $= 24 - 16 - 4 + 6$

    $= 30 - 20$

    $= 10$

67. If $v = 24$, $t = 2$, and $a = 32$, then

    $vt - \dfrac{1}{2}at^2 = 24(2) - \dfrac{1}{2}(32)(2)^2$

    $= 48 - 16(4) = 48 - 64 = -16$

68. $\dfrac{nRT}{V} = \dfrac{16(-2)(4)}{-20}$

    $= \dfrac{-32}{-5} = \dfrac{32}{5}$

69. If $p = 6000$, $r = 18\%$, and $t = \dfrac{3}{4}$, then

    $I = prt = 6000(0.18)\left(\dfrac{3}{4}\right) = \$810$

38

70. $F = \dfrac{9C+160}{5} = \dfrac{9(30)+160}{5}$

$= \dfrac{270+160}{5} = \dfrac{430}{5} = 86$

$86° F$

71. If $r = 15,\ A = \pi r^2 = 3.14(15)^2$

$= 3.14(225) = 706.5$ square meters

Cost $= (706.5$ sq m$)(\$3/$sq m$)$

$= \$2119.50$

72. $P = 180S - R - C$

$= 180(56) - 300 - 1200$

$= 10,080 - 300 - 1200$

$= 8580$

$\$8580$

73. $A = \dfrac{1}{2}a(b_1 + b_2),$

$a = 200,\ b_1 = 700,\ b_2 = 300$

$A = \dfrac{1}{2}(200)(700 + 300)$

$= 100(1000)$

$= 100,000$ square feet

Cost $= 2(100,000) = \$200,000$

74. $A = \dfrac{1}{2}ab,\ a = 3.8,\ b = 5.5$

$A = \dfrac{1}{2}(3.8)(5.5) = 10.45$ square feet

Cost $= 66(10.45) = \$689.70$

75. $5x - 7(x-6) = 5x - 7x + 42$

$= -2x + 42$

76. $3(x-2) - 4(5x+3)$

$= 3x - 6 - 20x - 12$

$= -17x - 18$

77. $2[3 - (4-5x)] = 2(3 - 4 + 5x)$

$= 2(-1 + 5x) = -2 + 10x$

78. $-3x[x + 3(x-7)] = -3x(x + 3x - 21)$

$= -3x(4x - 21)$

$= -12x^2 + 63x$

79. $2xy^3 - 6x^3y - 4x^2y^2 + 3(xy^3 - 2x^2y - 3x^2y^2)$

$= 2xy^3 - 6x^3y - 4x^2y^2 + 3xy^3 - 6x^2y - 9x^2y^2$

$= (2+3)xy^3 - 6x^3y + (-4-9)x^2y^2 - 6x^2y$

$- 5xy^3 - 6x^3y - 13x^2y^2 - 6x^2y$

80. $-5(x + 2y - 7) + 3x(2 - 5y)$

$= -5x - 10y + 35 + 6x - 15xy$

$= x - 10y + 35 - 15xy$

81. $2\{x - 3(y-2) + 4[x - 2(y+3)]\}$

$= 2[x - 3y + 6 + 4(x - 2y - 6)]$

$= 2(x - 3y + 6 + 4x - 8y - 24)$

$= 2(5x - 11y - 18)$

$= 10x - 22y - 36$

82. $-5\{2a - b[5a - b(3+2a)]\}$

$= -5[2a - b(5a - 3b - 2ab)]$

$= -5(2a - 5ab + 3b^2 + 2ab^2)$

$= -10a + 25ab - 15b^2 - 10ab^2$

83. $-3\left\{2x-\left[x-3y\left(x-2y\right)\right]\right\}$

$= -3\left[2x-\left(x-3xy+6y^2\right)\right]$

$= -3\left(2x-x+3xy-6y^2\right)$

$= -3\left(x+3xy-6y^2\right)$

$= -3x-9xy+18y^2$

84. $2\left\{3x+2\left[x+2y\left(x-4\right)\right]\right\}$

$= 2\left[3x+2\left(x+2xy-8y\right)\right]$

$= 2\left(3x+2x+4xy-16y\right)$

$= 2\left(5x+4xy-16y\right)$

$= 10x+8xy-32y$

85. $-6.3+4 = -2.3$

86. $4+\left(-8\right)+12 = -4+12 = 8$

87. $-\dfrac{2}{3}-\dfrac{4}{5} = -\dfrac{10}{15}+\left(-\dfrac{12}{15}\right)$

$= \dfrac{-22}{15}$

$= -1\dfrac{7}{15}$

88. $-\dfrac{7}{8}-\left(-\dfrac{3}{4}\right) = -\dfrac{7}{8}+\dfrac{6}{8} = -\dfrac{1}{8}$

89. $3-\left(-4\right)+\left(-8\right) = 3+4+\left(-8\right)$

$= 7+\left(-8\right)$

$= -1$

90. $-1.1-\left(-0.2\right)+0.4$

$= -1.1+0.2+0.4$

$= -0.9+0.4$

$= -0.5$

91. $\left(-\dfrac{3}{5}\right)\left(-2\dfrac{1}{2}\right) = \left(-\dfrac{3}{5}\right)\left(-\dfrac{5}{2}\right)$

$= \dfrac{3}{2} = 1\dfrac{1}{2}$

92. $\left(-4.2\right)\div\left(-0.7\right) = 6$

93. $-14.4\div\left(-0.06\right) = 240$

94. $\left(-8.2\right)\left(3.1\right) = -25.42$

95. $400+1000-800 = 1400-800 = 600$

Her score was $600.

96. $\left(-0.3\right)^4 = \left(-0.3\right)\left(-0.3\right)\left(-0.3\right)\left(-0.3\right)$

$= 0.0081$

97. $-0.5^4 = -\left(0.5\right)\left(0.5\right)\left(0.5\right)\left(0.5\right)$

$= -0.0625$

98. $9\left(5\right)-5\left(2\right)^3+5 = 9\left(5\right)-5\left(8\right)+5$

$= 45-5\left(8\right)+5$

$= 45-40+5$

$= 5+5$

$= 10$

99. $3.8x-0.2y-8.7x+4.3y$

$= \left(3.8-8.7\right)x+\left(-0.2+4.3\right)y$

$= -4.9x+4.1y$

100. If $p = -2$ and $q = 3$, then

$$\frac{2p+q}{3q} = \frac{2(-2)+3}{3(3)}$$

$$= \frac{-4+3}{9}$$

$$= -\frac{1}{9}$$

101. If $s = -3$ and $t = -2$, then

$$\frac{4s-7t}{s} = \frac{4(-3)-7(-2)}{-3}$$

$$= \frac{-12+14}{-3}$$

$$= -\frac{2}{3}$$

102. $F = \frac{9}{5}C + 32,\ C = 38.6$

$$F = \frac{9}{5}(38.6) + 32$$

$$F = 69.48 + 32$$

$$F = 101.48°$$

Your dog does not have a fever; in fact, its temperature is below normal.

103. $-7(x - 3y^2 + 4) + 3y(4 - 6y)$

$$= -7x + 21y^2 - 28 + 12y - 18y^2$$

$$= -7x + 3y^2 + 12y - 28$$

104. $-2\{6x - 3[7y - 2y(3 - x)]\}$

$$= -2\{6x - 3[7y - 6y + 2xy]\}$$

$$= -2\{6x - 3[y + 2xy]\}$$

$$= -2\{6x - 3y - 6xy\}$$

$$= -12x + 6y + 12xy$$

How Am I Doing? Chapter 1 Test

1. $-2.5 + 6.3 + (-4.1) = 3.8 + (-4.1) = -0.3$

2. $-5 - (-7) = -5 + 7 = 2$

3. $\left(-\frac{2}{3}\right)(7) = -\frac{14}{3} = -4\frac{2}{3}$

4. $(-5)(-2)(7)(-1) = -(10)(7)(1)$

$$= -(70)(1) = -70$$

5. $(-12) \div (-3) = 4$

6. $(-1.8) \div (0.6) = -3$

7. $(-4)^3 = (-4)(-4)(-4) = -64$

8. $(1.6)^2 = (1.6)(1.6) = 2.56$

9. $\left(\frac{2}{3}\right)^4 = \left(\frac{2}{3}\right)\left(\frac{2}{3}\right)\left(\frac{2}{3}\right)\left(\frac{2}{3}\right) = \frac{16}{81}$

10. $(0.2)^2 - (2.1)(-3) + 0.46$

$$= 0.04 - (2.1)(-3) + 0.46$$

$$= 0.04 - (-6.3) + 0.46$$

$$= 0.04 + 6.3 + 0.46$$

$$= 6.34 + 0.46$$

$$= 6.8$$

11. $3(4-6)^3 + 12 \div (-4) + 2$

$= 3(-2)^3 + 12 \div (-4) + 2$

$= 3(-8) + 12 \div (-4) + 2$

$= -24 - 3 + 2$

$= -25$

12. $-5x(x + 2y - 7)$

$= -5x(x) - 5x(2y) - 5x(-7)$

$= -5x^2 - 10xy + 35x$

13. $-2ab^2(-3a - 2b + 7ab)$

$= -2ab^2(-3a) - 2ab^2(-2b) - 2ab^2(7ab)$

$= 6a^2b^2 + 4ab^3 - 14a^2b^3$

14. $6ab - \frac{1}{2}a^2b + \frac{3}{2}ab + \frac{5}{2}a^2b$

$= \left(6 + \frac{3}{2}\right)ab + \left(-\frac{1}{2} + \frac{5}{2}\right)a^2b$

$= \left(\frac{12}{2} + \frac{3}{2}\right)ab + \frac{4}{2}a^2b$

$= \frac{15}{2}ab + 2a^2b$

15. $2.3x^2y - 8.1xy^2 + 3.4xy^2 - 4.1x^2y$

$= (2.4 - 4.1)x^2y + (-8.1 + 3.4)xy^2$

$= -1.8x^2y - 4.7xy^2$

16. $3(2-a) - 4(-6 - 2a) = 6 - 3a + 24 + 8a$

$= 5a + 30$

17. $5(3x - 2y) - (x + 6y)$

$= 15x - 10y - x - 6y$

$= (15 - 1)x + (-10 - 6)y$

$= 14x - 16y$

18. $x^3 - 3x^2y + 2y - 5$

$= 3^3 - 3(3)^2(-4) + 2(-4) - 5$

$= 27 - 3(9)(-4) - 8 - 5$

$= 27 + 108 - 8 - 5$

$= 122$

19. If $x = -3$, then $3x^2 - 7x - 11$

$= 3(-3)^2 - 7(-3) - 11$

$= 37$

20. $2a - 3b$

$= 2(-4) - 3(-3)$

$= -8 + 9$

$= 1$

21. (60 miles/hr)(1.61 km/mile)

$= 96.6$ kilometers per hour

22. $A = \frac{1}{2}a(b_1 + b_2),$

$a = 120, \ b_1 = 200, \ b_2 = 180$

$A = \frac{1}{2}(120)(200 + 180) = 60(380)$

$= 22{,}800$ square feet

23. $A = \frac{1}{2}ab, \ a = 6.8, \ b = 8.5$

$A = \frac{1}{2}(6.8)(8.5) = 28.9$ square feet

Cost $= 0.80(28.9) = \$23.12$

24. $A = 60 \times 10 = 600$ sq. ft.

600 sq. ft. $\times \dfrac{1 \text{ can}}{200 \text{ sq. ft.}} = 3$ cans

25. $3\left[x - 2y(x + 2y) - 3y^2\right]$

  $= 3\left[x - 2xy - 4y^2 - 3y^2\right]$

  $= 3\left[x - 2xy - 7y^2\right]$

  $= 3x - 6xy - 21y^2$

26. $-3\left\{a + b\left[3a - b(1 - a)\right]\right\}$

  $= -3\left[a + b(3a - b + ab)\right]$

  $= -3\left(a + 3ab - b^2 + ab^2\right)$

  $= -3a - 9ab + 3b^2 - 3ab^2$

Chapter 2

2.1 Exercises

1. When we use the <u>equals</u> sign, we indicate two expressions are <u>equal</u> in value.

3. The <u>solution</u> of an equation is a value of the variable that makes the equation true.

5. Answers may vary. A sample answer is to isolate the variable x.

7.
$$x + 11 = 15$$
$$x + 11 + (-11) = 15 + (-11)$$
$$x = 4$$

Check: $4 + 11 \overset{?}{=} 15$
$$15 = 15$$

9.
$$17 = x + 5$$
$$17 + (-5) = x + 5 + (-5)$$
$$12 = x$$

Check: $17 \overset{?}{=} 5 + 12$
$$17 = 17$$

11.
$$x - 3 = 14$$
$$x - 3 + 3 = 14 + 3$$
$$x = 17$$

Check: $17 - 3 \overset{?}{=} 14$
$$14 = 14$$

13.
$$0 = x + 5$$
$$0 + (-5) = x + 5 + (-5)$$
$$-5 = x$$

Check: $0 \overset{?}{=} -5 + 5$
$$0 = 0$$

15.
$$x - 6 = -19$$
$$x - 6 + 6 = -19 + 6$$
$$x = -13$$

Check: $-13 - 6 \overset{?}{=} -19$
$$-19 = -19$$

17.
$$-12 + x = 50$$
$$-12 + 12 + x = 50 + 12$$
$$x = 62$$

Check: $-12 + 62 \overset{?}{=} 50$
$$50 = 50$$

19.
$$3 + 5 = x - 7$$
$$8 = x - 7$$
$$8 + 7 = x - 7 + 7$$
$$15 = x$$

Check: $3 + 5 \overset{?}{=} 15 - 7$
$$8 = 8$$

21.
$$32 - 17 = x - 6$$
$$15 = x - 6$$
$$15 + 6 = x - 6 + 6$$
$$21 = x$$

Check: $32 - 17 \overset{?}{=} 21 - 6$
$$15 = 15$$

44

23. $4 + 8 + x = 6 + 6$

$12 + x = 12$

$12 + (-12) + x = 12 + (-12)$

$x = 0$

Check: $4 + 8 + 0 \overset{?}{=} 6 + 6$

$12 = 12$

25. $8 - 23 + 7 = 1 + x - 2$

$-8 = x - 1$

$-8 + 1 = x - 1 + 1$

$-7 = x$

Check: $8 - 23 + 7 \overset{?}{=} 1 + (-7) - 2$

$-8 = -8$

27. $-12 + x - 3 = 15 - 18 + 9$

$-15 + x = 6$

$-15 + 15 + x = 6 + 15$

$x = 21$

Check: $-12 + 21 - 3 \overset{?}{=} 15 - 18 + 9$

$6 = 6$

29. $-7 + x = 2, \quad x = 5$

$-7 + 5 \overset{?}{=} 2$

$-2 = 2$

$x = 5$ is not a solution.

31. $-18 - 2 \overset{?}{=} -3 - 7$

$-20 \neq -10$

$x = -3$ is not the solution.

$-18 - 2 = x - 7$

$-20 = x - 7$

$-20 + 7 = x - 7 + 7$

$-13 = x$

33. $x - 23 = -56, \quad x = -33$

$-33 - 23 \overset{?}{=} -56$

$-56 = -56$

$x = -33$ is a solution.

35. $15 - 3 + 20 = x - 3, \quad x = 35$

$15 - 3 + 20 \overset{?}{=} 35 - 3$

$32 = 32$

$x = 35$ is the solution.

37. $\qquad 2.5 + x = 0.7$

$2.5 + (-2.5) + x = 0.7 + (-2.5)$

$\qquad x = -1.8$

39. $\qquad 2.7 + x - 1.4 = 3.8$

$\qquad x + 1.3 = 3.8$

$x + 1.3 + (-1.3) = 3.8 + (-1.3)$

$\qquad x = 2.5$

41. $\qquad x - \dfrac{1}{4} = \dfrac{3}{4}$

$x - \dfrac{1}{4} + \dfrac{1}{4} = \dfrac{3}{4} + \dfrac{1}{4}$

$\qquad x = 1$

43.
$$\frac{2}{3} + x = \frac{1}{6} + \frac{1}{4}$$
$$\frac{8}{12} + x = \frac{2}{12} + \frac{3}{12}$$
$$\frac{8}{12} + x = \frac{5}{12}$$
$$\frac{8}{12} + \left(-\frac{8}{12}\right) + x = \frac{5}{12} + \left(-\frac{8}{12}\right)$$
$$x = -\frac{3}{12}$$
$$x = -\frac{1}{4}$$

45.
$$3 + x = -12 + 8$$
$$3 + x = -4$$
$$3 + (-3) + x = -4 + (-3)$$
$$x = -7$$

47.
$$5\frac{1}{6} + x = 8$$
$$\frac{31}{6} + x = \frac{48}{6}$$
$$\frac{31}{6} + \left(-\frac{31}{6}\right) + x = \frac{48}{6} + \left(-\frac{31}{6}\right)$$
$$x = \frac{17}{6} \text{ or } 2\frac{5}{6}$$

49.
$$\frac{5}{12} - \frac{5}{6} = x - \frac{3}{2}$$
$$\frac{5}{12} - \frac{10}{12} = x - \frac{18}{12}$$
$$-\frac{5}{12} = x - \frac{18}{12}$$
$$-\frac{5}{12} + \frac{18}{12} = x - \frac{18}{12} + \frac{18}{12}$$
$$\frac{13}{12} = x$$
$$1\frac{1}{12} = x$$

51.
$$1.6 + 4x - 3.2 = -2x + 5.6 + 5x$$
$$-1.6 + 4x = 3x + 5.6$$
$$-1.6 + 4x + (-3x) = -3x + (-3x) + 5.6$$
$$-1.6 + x = 5.6$$
$$-1.6 + 1.6 + x = 5.6 + 1.6$$
$$x = 7.2$$

53.
$$x + 0.7513 = 2.2419$$
$$x + 0.7513 + (-0.7513) = 2.2419 + (-0.7513)$$
$$x = 1.4906$$

Cumulative Review

55. $x + 3y - 5x - 7y + 2x$
$$= (1 - 5 + 2)x + (3 - 7)y$$
$$= -2x - 4y$$

57. percent $= \dfrac{8}{413} = 0.019 = 1.9\%$
yes, this was $1.9\% < 3\%$

59. Distance $= 90 - (-27) = 117$ feet

2.2 Exercises

1. Divide each side of $6x = -24$ by $\underline{6}$.

3. Multiply each side of $\frac{1}{7}x = -2$ by $\underline{7}$.

5. $\frac{1}{9}x = 4$

$$9\left(\frac{1}{9}x\right) = 9(4)$$

$$x = 36$$

Check: $\frac{1}{9}(36) \overset{?}{=} 4$

$$4 = 4$$

7. $\frac{1}{3}x = -9$

$$3\left(\frac{1}{3}x\right) = 3(-9)$$

$$x = -27$$

Check: $\frac{1}{3}(-27) \overset{?}{=} -9$

$$-9 = -9$$

9. $\frac{x}{5} = 16$

$$5\left(\frac{x}{5}\right) = 5(16)$$

$$x = 80$$

Check: $\frac{80}{5} \overset{?}{=} 16$

$$16 = 16$$

11. $-3 = \frac{x}{5}$

$$5(-3) = 5\left(\frac{x}{5}\right)$$

$$-15 = x$$

Check: $-3 \overset{?}{=} \frac{-15}{5}$

$$-3 = -3$$

13. $13x = 52$

$$\frac{13x}{13} = \frac{52}{13}$$

$$x = 4$$

Check: $13(4) \overset{?}{=} 52$

$$52 = 52$$

15. $56 = 7x$

$$\frac{56}{7} = \frac{7x}{7}$$

$$8 = x$$

Check: $56 \overset{?}{=} 7(8)$

$$56 = 56$$

17. $-16 = 6x$

$$\frac{-16}{6} = \frac{6x}{6}$$

$$-\frac{8}{3} = x$$

Check: $-16 \overset{?}{=} 6\left(-\frac{8}{3}\right)$

$$-16 = -16$$

19. $1.5x = 75$

$$\frac{1.5x}{1.5} = \frac{75}{1.5}$$

$x = 50$

Check: $1.5(50) \overset{?}{=} 75$

$75 = 75$

21. $-15 = -x$

$$\frac{-15}{-1} = \frac{-x}{-1}$$

$15 = x$

Check: $-15 \overset{?}{=} (-1)(15)$

$-15 = -15$

23. $-112 = 16x$

$$\frac{-112}{16} = \frac{16x}{16}$$

$-7 = x$

Check: $-112 \overset{?}{=} 16(7)$

$-112 = -112$

25. $0.4x = 0.08$

$$\frac{0.4x}{0.4} = \frac{0.08}{0.4}$$

$x = 0.2$ or $\dfrac{1}{5}$

Check: $(0.4)(0.2) \overset{?}{=} 0.08$

$0.08 = 0.08$

27. $-3.9x = -15.6$

$$\frac{-3.9x}{-3.9} = \frac{-15.6}{-3.9}$$

$x = 4$

Check: $-3.9(4) \overset{?}{=} -15.6$

$-15.6 = -15.6$

29. $-3x = 21, \quad x \overset{?}{=} 7$

$-3(7) \overset{?}{=} 21$

$-21 \neq 21$

$x = 7$ is not the solution.

$-3x = 21$

$$\frac{-3x}{-3} = \frac{21}{-3}$$

$x = -7$

31. $-11x = 66, \quad x \overset{?}{=} -6$

$-11(-6) \overset{?}{=} 66$

$66 = 66$

$x = -6$ is the solution.

33. $7y = -0.21$

$$\frac{7y}{7} = \frac{-0.21}{7}$$

$y = -0.03$

35. $-56 = -21t$

$$\frac{-56}{-21} = \frac{-21t}{-21}$$

$$\frac{8}{3} = t$$

Check: $-56 \overset{?}{=} -21\left(\dfrac{8}{3}\right)$

$-56 = -56$

37. $4.6y = -3.22$

$$\frac{4.6y}{4.6} = \frac{-3.22}{4.6}$$

$$y = -0.7$$

39. $4x + 3x = 21$

$$7x = 21$$

$$\frac{7x}{7} = \frac{21}{7}$$

$$x = 3$$

41. $2x - 7x = 20$

$$-5x = 20$$

$$\frac{-5x}{-5} = \frac{20}{-5}$$

$$x = -4$$

43. $-6x - 3x = -7$

$$-9x = -7$$

$$\frac{-9x}{-9} = \frac{-7}{-9}$$

$$x = \frac{7}{9}$$

45. $12 - 19 = -7x$

$$-7 = -7x$$

$$\frac{-7}{-7} = \frac{-7x}{-7}$$

$$1 = x$$

47. $6x = -18 + 36$

$$6x = 18$$

$$\frac{6x}{6} = \frac{18}{6}$$

$$x = 3$$

49. $\frac{2}{3}x = 18$

$$\frac{3}{2}\left(\frac{2}{3}x\right) = \frac{3}{2}(18)$$

$$x = 27$$

51. $3.6172x = -19.026472$

$$\frac{3.6172x}{3.6172} = \frac{-19.026472}{3.6172}$$

$$x = -5.26$$

53. To solve an equation, we are performing steps to get an equivalent equation that has the same solution. Now $a = b$ and $a(0) = b(0)$ are not equivalent equations because they do not have the same solution. So we must have the requirement that when we multiply both sides of the equation by c, it is essential that c is nonzero.

Cumulative Review

55. $(-6)(-8) + (-3)(2) = 48 - 6 = 42$

57. $5 + (2 - 6)^2 = 5 + (-4)^2$
$$= 5 + 16$$
$$= 21$$

59. $600 + 82 - 47 + 103 - 106$
$$= 785 - 153$$
$$= \$632$$

49

61. $100\% + 35\% = 135\%$

135% of 20

$1.35(20) = 27$

Expect 27 earthquakes

2.3 Exercises

1. $4x + 13 = 21$

$4x + 13 + (-13) = 21 + (-13)$

$4x = 8$

$\dfrac{4x}{4} = \dfrac{8}{4}$

$x = 2$

Check: $4(2) + 13 \overset{?}{=} 21$

$21 = 21$

3. $4x - 11 = 13$

$4x - 11 + 11 = 13 + 11$

$4x = 24$

$\dfrac{4x}{4} = -\dfrac{24}{4}$

$x = 6$

Check: $4(6) - 11 \overset{?}{=} 13$

$13 = 13$

5. $7x - 18 = -46$

$7x - 18 + 18 = -46 + 18$

$7x = -28$

$\dfrac{7x}{7} = -\dfrac{-28}{7}$

$x = -4$

Check: $7(-4) - 18 \overset{?}{=} -46$

$-28 - 18 \overset{?}{=} -46$

$-46 = -46$

7. $-4x + 17 = -35$

$-4x + 17 + (-17) = -35 + (-17)$

$-4x = -52$

$\dfrac{-4x}{-4} = \dfrac{-52}{-4}$

$x = 13$

Check: $-4(13) + 17 \overset{?}{=} -35$

$-52 + 17 \overset{?}{=} -35$

$-35 = -35$

9. $2x + 3.2 = 9.4$

$2x + 3.2 + (-3.2) = 9.4 + (-3.2)$

$2x = 6.2$

$\dfrac{2x}{2} = \dfrac{6.2}{2}$

$x = 3.1$

Check: $2(3.1) + 3.2 \overset{?}{=} 9.4$

$6.2 + 3.2 \overset{?}{=} 9.4$

$9.4 = 9.4$

11. $\dfrac{1}{5}x - 2 = 6$

$\dfrac{1}{5}x - 2 + 2 = 6 + 2$

$\dfrac{1}{5}x = 8$

$5\left(\dfrac{1}{5}x\right) = 5(8)$

$x = 40$

Check: $\dfrac{1}{5}(40) - 2 \overset{?}{=} 6$

$6 = 6$

13. $\frac{1}{3}x + 5 = -4$

$\frac{1}{3}x + 5 + (-5) = -4 + (-5)$

$\frac{1}{3}x = -9$

$3\left(\frac{1}{3}x\right) = 3(-9)$

$x = -27$

Check: $\frac{1}{3}(-27) + 5 \overset{?}{=} -4$

$-9 + 5 \overset{?}{=} -4$

$-4 = -4$

15. $8x = 48 + 2x$

$8x + (-2x) = 48 + 2x + (-2x)$

$6x = 48$

$\frac{6x}{6} = \frac{48}{6}$

$x = 8$

Check: $8(8) \overset{?}{=} 48 + 2(8)$

$64 \overset{?}{=} 48 + 16$

$64 = 64$

17. $-6x = -27 + 3x$

$-6x + (-3x) = -27 + 3x + (-3x)$

$-9x = -27$

$\frac{-9x}{-9} = \frac{-27}{-9}$

$x = 3$

Check: $-6(3) \overset{?}{=} -27 + 3(3)$

$-18 \overset{?}{=} -27 + 9$

$-18 = -18$

19. $63 - x = 8x$

$63 - x + x = 8x + x$

$63 = 9x$

$\frac{63}{9} = \frac{9x}{9}$

$7 = x$

Check: $63 - 7 \overset{?}{=} 8(7)$

$56 = 56$

21. $54 - 2x = -8x$

$54 - 2x + 2x = -8x + 2x$

$54 = -6x$

$\frac{54}{-6} = \frac{-6x}{-6}$

$-9 = x$

Check: $54 - 2(-9) \overset{?}{=} -8(-9)$

$54 + 18 \overset{?}{=} 72$

$72 = 72$

23. $2y + 3y = 12 - y$

$2(2) + 3(2) \overset{?}{=} 12 - 2$

$4 + 6 \overset{?}{=} 10$

$10 = 10$

$y = 2$ is the solution.

25. $7x + 6 - 3x = 2x - 5 + x$

$7(11) + 6 - 3(11) \overset{?}{=} 2(11) - 5 + 11$

$77 + 6 - 33 \overset{?}{=} 22 - 5 + 11$

$50 \neq 28$

$x = 11$ is not a solution.

$7x + 6 - 3x = 2x - 5 + x$

$4x + 6 = 3x - 5$

51

$$4x + (-3x) + 6 = 3x + (-3x) - 5$$
$$x + 6 = -5$$
$$x + 6 + (-6) = -5 + (-6)$$
$$x = -11$$

27.
$$14 - 2x = -5x + 11$$
$$14 - 2x + 5x = -5x + 5x + 11$$
$$14 + 3x = 11$$
$$3x + 14 + (-14) = 11 + (-14)$$
$$3x = -3$$
$$\frac{3x}{3} = \frac{-3}{3}$$
$$x = -1$$

29.
$$x - 6 = 8 - x$$
$$x + x - 6 = 8 - x + x$$
$$2x - 6 = 8$$
$$2x - 6 + 6 = 8 + 6$$
$$2x = 14$$
$$\frac{2x}{2} = \frac{14}{2}$$
$$x = 7$$

31.
$$0.8y - 0.4 = 0.9 - 0.5y$$
$$0.8y + 0.5y - 0.4 = 0.9 - 0.5y + 0.5y$$
$$1.3y - 0.4 = 0.9$$
$$1.3y - 0.4 + 0.4 = 0.9 + 0.4$$
$$1.3y = 1.3$$
$$\frac{1.3y}{1.3} = \frac{1.3}{1.3}$$
$$y = 1$$

33.
$$5x - 9 = 3x + 23$$
$$5x + (-3x) - 9 = 3x + (-3x) + 23$$
$$2x - 9 = 23$$
$$2x - 9 + 9 = 23 + 9$$
$$2x = 32$$
$$\frac{2x}{2} = \frac{32}{2}$$
$$x = 16$$

35.
$$-3 + 10y + 6 = 15 + 12y - 18$$

Left
$$10y + 3 = 12y - 3$$
$$10y + (-12y) + 3 = 12y + (-12y) - 3$$
$$-2y + 3 = -3$$
$$-2y + 3 + (-3) = -3 + (-3)$$
$$-2y = -6$$
$$\frac{-2y}{-2} = \frac{-6}{-2}$$
$$y = 3$$

Right
$$10y + 3 = 12y - 3$$
$$10y + (-10y) + 3 = 12y + (-10y) - 3$$
$$3 = 2y - 3$$
$$3 + 3 = 2y - 3 + 3$$
$$6 = 2y$$
$$\frac{6}{2} = \frac{2y}{2}$$
$$3 = y$$

Neither approach is better.

37. $5(x+3) = 35$

$$5x + 15 = 35$$
$$5x + 15 - 15 = 35 - 15$$
$$5x = 20$$
$$\frac{5x}{5} = \frac{20}{5}$$
$$x = 4$$

Check: $5(4+3) \overset{?}{=} 35$
$$5(7) \overset{?}{=} 35$$
$$35 = 35$$

39. $6(3x+2) - 8 = -2$
$$18x + 12 - 8 = -2$$
$$18x + 4 = -2$$
$$18x = -6$$
$$x = -\frac{1}{3}$$

Check: $6\left[3\left(-\frac{1}{3}\right)+2\right]-8 \overset{?}{=} -2$
$$6(-1+2)-8 \overset{?}{=} -2$$
$$-2 = -2$$

41. $7x - 3(5-x) = 10$
$$7x - 15 + 3x = 10$$
$$10x - 15 = 10$$
$$10x = 25$$
$$x = 2.5$$

Check: $7(2.5) - 3\left[5-(2.5)\right] \overset{?}{=} 10$
$$17.5 - 3(2.5) \overset{?}{=} 10$$
$$17.5 - 7.5 = 10$$
$$10 = 10$$

43. $0.5x - 0.3(2-x) = 4.6$
$$0.5x - 0.6 - 0.3x = 4.6$$
$$0.8x - 0.6 = 4.6$$
$$0.8x - 0.6 + 0.6 = 4.6 + 0.6$$
$$0.8x = 5.2$$
$$\frac{0.8x}{0.8} = \frac{5.2}{0.8}$$
$$x = 6.5 \text{ or } 6\frac{1}{2}$$

Check: $0.5(6.5) - 0.3(2-6.5) \overset{?}{=} 4.6$
$$0.5(6.5) - 0.3(-4.5) \overset{?}{=} 4.6$$
$$3.25 + 1.35 \overset{?}{=} 4.6$$
$$4.6 = 4.6$$

45.   44. $5(x-3) + 5 = 3(x+2) - 4$
$$5x - 15 + 5 = 3x + 6 - 4$$
$$5x - 10 = 3x + 2$$
$$5x - 3x - 10 = 3x - 3x + 2$$
$$2x - 10 = 2$$
$$2x - 10 + 10 = 2 + 10$$
$$2x = 12$$
$$x = 6$$

Check: $5(6-3)+5 \overset{?}{=} 3(6+2)-4$

$\qquad 5(3)+5 \overset{?}{=} 3(8)-4$

$\qquad\qquad 15+5 \overset{?}{=} 24-4$

$20 = 20$

47. $\quad -2(x+3)+4 = 3(x+4)+2$

$\qquad -2x-6+4 = 3x+12+2$

$\qquad -2x-2 = 3x+14$

$\qquad -2x+(-3x)-2 = 3x+(-3x)+14$

$\qquad\qquad -5x-2 = 14$

$\qquad -5x-2+2 = 14+2$

$\qquad\qquad -5x = 16$

$\qquad\qquad \dfrac{-5x}{-5} = \dfrac{16}{-5}$

$\qquad\qquad x = -3.2 \text{ or } -3\dfrac{1}{5}$

Check: $-2\big[(-3.2)+3\big]+4 \overset{?}{=} 3\big[(-3.2)+4\big]+2$

$\qquad -2(-0.2)+4 \overset{?}{=} 3(0.8)+2$

$\qquad\qquad 0.4+4 \overset{?}{=} 2.4+2$

$4.4 = 4.4$

49. $\quad -3(y-3y)+4 = -4(3y-y)+6+13y$

$\qquad -3(-2y)+4 = -4(2y)+6+13y$

$\qquad\qquad 6y+4 = -8y+6+13y$

$\qquad\qquad 6y+4 = 5y+6$

$\qquad 6y-5y+4 = 5y-5y+6$

$\qquad\qquad y+4 = 6$

$\qquad y+4-4 = 6-4$

$\qquad\qquad y = 2$

Check: $-3\big[2-3(2)\big]+4$

$\qquad \overset{?}{=} -4\big[3(2)-2\big]+6+13(2)$

$\qquad -3(2-6)+4 \overset{?}{=} -4(6-2)+6+26$

$\qquad -3(-4)+4 \overset{?}{=} -4(4)+32$

$\qquad\qquad 12+4 \overset{?}{=} -16+32$

$\qquad 16 = 16$

51. $\qquad 5.7x+3 = 4.2x-3$

$\qquad 5.7x-4.2x+3 = 4.2x-4.2x-3$

$\qquad\qquad 1.5x+3 = -3$

$\qquad\qquad 1.5x+3-3 = -3-3$

$\qquad\qquad 1.5x = -6$

$\qquad\qquad \dfrac{1.5x}{1.5} = \dfrac{-6}{1.5}$

$\qquad\qquad x = -4$

53. $\quad 5z+7-2z = 32-2z$

$\qquad 3z+7 = 32-2z$

$\qquad 3z+2z+7 = 32-2z+2z$

$\qquad\qquad 5z = 25$

$\qquad\qquad \dfrac{5z}{5} = \dfrac{25}{5}$

$\qquad\qquad z = 5$

55. $\qquad -0.3a+1.4 = -1.2-0.7a$

$\qquad -0.3a+0.7a+1.4 = -1.2-0.7a+0.7a$

$\qquad\qquad 0.4a+1.4 = -1.2$

$\qquad 0.4a+1.4+(-1.4) = -1.2+(-1.4)$

$\qquad\qquad 0.4a = -2.6$

$\qquad\qquad \dfrac{0.4a}{0.4} = \dfrac{-2.6}{0.4}$

$\qquad\qquad a = -6.5$

54

57.
$$6x + 8 - 3x = 11 - 12x - 13$$
$$3x + 8 = -12x - 2$$
$$3x + 12x + 8 = -12x + 12x - 2$$
$$15x + 8 = -2$$
$$15x + 8 - 8 = -2 - 8$$
$$15x = -10$$
$$\frac{15x}{15} = \frac{-10}{15}$$
$$x = -\frac{2}{3}$$

59.
$$-3.5x + 1.3 = -2.7x + 1.5$$
$$-3.5x + 3.5x + 1.3 = -2.7x + 3.5x + 1.5$$
$$1.3 = 0.8x + 1.5$$
$$1.3 - 1.5 = 0.8x + 1.5 - 1.5$$
$$-0.2 = 0.8x$$
$$\frac{-0.2}{0.8} = \frac{0.8x}{0.8}$$
$$-0.25 = x$$

61.
$$5(4 + x) = 3(3x - 1) - 9$$
$$20 + 5x = 9x - 3 - 9$$
$$20 + 5x = 9x - 12$$
$$20 + 5x - 5x = 9x - 5x - 12$$
$$20 = 4x - 12$$
$$20 + 12 = 4x - 12 + 12$$
$$32 = 4x$$
$$\frac{32}{4} = \frac{4x}{4}$$
$$8 = x$$

63.
$$4x + 3.2 - 1.9x = 0.3x - 4.9$$
$$2.1x + 3.2 = 0.3x - 4.9$$
$$2.1x + (-0.3x) + 3.2 = 0.3x + (-0.3x) - 4.9$$
$$1.8x + 3.2 = -4.9$$
$$1.8x + 3.2 + (-3.2) = -4.9 + (-3.2)$$
$$1.8x = -8.1$$
$$\frac{1.8x}{1.8} = \frac{-8.1}{1.8}$$
$$x = -4.5$$

65.
$$3(x + 4) - 5(3x - 2) = 8$$
$$3x + 12 - 15x + 10 = 8$$
$$-12x + 22 = 8$$
$$-12x + 22 - 22 = 8 - 22$$
$$-12x = -14$$
$$\frac{-12x}{-12} = \frac{-14}{-12}$$
$$x = \frac{7}{6}$$

67.
$$1.63x - 9.23 = 5.71x + 8.04$$
$$1.63x - 1.63x - 9.23 = 5.71x - 1.63x + 8.04$$
$$-9.23 = 4.08x + 8.04$$
$$-9.23 - 8.04 = 4.08x + 8.04 - 8.04$$
$$-17.27 = 4.08x$$
$$\frac{-17.27}{4.08} = \frac{4.08x}{4.08}$$
$$-4.23 = x$$

Cumulative Review

69.
$$2x(3x - y) + 4(2x^2 - 3xy)$$
$$= 6x^2 - 2xy + 8x^2 - 12xy$$
$$= (6 + 8)x^2 + (-2 - 12)xy$$
$$= 14x^2 - 14xy$$

71.
$$4 \times 52\frac{1}{8} = 4 \times \frac{417}{8} = 208\frac{1}{2}$$

$$3.2\left(81\frac{7}{8}\right) = \left(3\frac{1}{5}\right)\left(81\frac{7}{8}\right) = \left(\frac{16}{5}\right)\left(\frac{655}{8}\right)$$
$$= 262$$

$$5.2\left(71\frac{7}{8}\right) = \left(5\frac{1}{5}\right)\left(71\frac{7}{8}\right) = \left(\frac{26}{5}\right)\left(\frac{575}{8}\right)$$
$$= 373\frac{3}{4}$$

$$\text{Total} = 208\frac{1}{2} + 262 + 373\frac{3}{4} = \$844.25$$

2.4 Exercises

1.
$$\frac{1}{2}x + \frac{2}{3} = \frac{1}{6}$$

$$6\left(\frac{1}{2}x\right) + 6\left(\frac{2}{3}\right) = 6\left(\frac{1}{6}\right)$$
$$3x + 4 = 1$$
$$3x + 4 + (-4) = 1 + (-4)$$
$$3x = -3$$
$$\frac{3x}{3} = \frac{-3}{3}$$
$$x = -1$$

Check: $\frac{1}{2}(-1) + \frac{2}{3} \overset{?}{=} \frac{1}{6}$

$$-\frac{1}{2} + \frac{2}{3} \overset{?}{=} \frac{1}{6}$$
$$-\frac{3}{6} + \frac{4}{6} \overset{?}{=} \frac{1}{6}$$
$$\frac{1}{6} = \frac{1}{6}$$

3.
$$\frac{2}{3}x = \frac{1}{15}x + \frac{3}{5}$$

$$15\left(\frac{2}{3}x\right) = 15\left(\frac{1}{15}x\right) + 15\left(\frac{3}{5}\right)$$
$$10x = x + 9$$
$$10x + (-x) = x + (-x) + 9$$
$$9x = 9$$
$$\frac{9x}{9} = \frac{9}{9}$$
$$x = 1$$

Check: $\frac{2}{3}(1) \overset{?}{=} \frac{1}{15}(1) + \frac{3}{5}$

$$\frac{2}{3} \overset{?}{=} \frac{1}{15} + \frac{9}{15}$$
$$\frac{2}{3} \overset{?}{=} \frac{10}{15}$$
$$\frac{2}{3} = \frac{2}{3}$$

5.
$$\frac{x}{2} + \frac{x}{5} = \frac{7}{10}$$

$$10\left(\frac{x}{2}\right) + 10\left(\frac{x}{5}\right) = 10\left(\frac{7}{10}\right)$$
$$5x + 2x = 7$$
$$7x = 7$$
$$\frac{7x}{7} = \frac{7}{7}$$
$$x = 1$$

Check: $\dfrac{1}{2} + \dfrac{1}{5} \overset{?}{=} \dfrac{7}{10}$

$\dfrac{5}{10} + \dfrac{2}{10} \overset{?}{=} \dfrac{7}{10}$

$\dfrac{7}{10} = \dfrac{7}{10}$

7. $\qquad 20 - \dfrac{1}{3}x = \dfrac{1}{2}x$

$6(20) - 6\left(\dfrac{1}{3}x\right) = 6\left(\dfrac{1}{2}x\right)$

$120 - 2x = 3x$

$120 = 5x$

$24 = x$

Check: $20 - \dfrac{1}{3}(24) \overset{?}{=} \dfrac{1}{2}(24)$

$20 - 8 \overset{?}{=} 12$

$12 = 12$

9. $\qquad 2 + \dfrac{y}{2} = \dfrac{3y}{4} - 3$

$4(2) + 4\left(\dfrac{y}{2}\right) = 4\left(\dfrac{3y}{4}\right) - 4(3)$

$8 + 2y = 3y - 12$

$8 = y - 12$

$20 = y$

Check: $2 + \left(\dfrac{20}{2}\right) \overset{?}{=} \dfrac{3(20)}{4} - 3$

$2 + 10 \overset{?}{=} 15 - 3$

$12 = 12$

11. $\qquad \dfrac{x-3}{5} = 1 - \dfrac{x}{3}$

$15\left(\dfrac{x-3}{5}\right) = 15(1) - 15\left(\dfrac{x}{3}\right)$

$3(x-3) = 15 - 5x$

$3x - 9 = 15 - 5x$

$3x + 5x - 9 = 15 - 5x + 5x$

$8x - 9 = 15$

$8x - 9 + 9 = 15 + 9$

$8x = 24$

$\dfrac{8x}{8} = \dfrac{24}{8}$

$x = 3$

Check: $\dfrac{3-3}{5} \overset{?}{=} 1 - \dfrac{3}{3}$

$0 = 0$

13. $\qquad \dfrac{x+3}{4} = \dfrac{x}{2} + \dfrac{1}{6}$

$12\left(\dfrac{x+3}{4}\right) = 12\left(\dfrac{x}{2}\right) + 12\left(\dfrac{1}{6}\right)$

$3(x+3) = 6x + 2$

$3x + 9 = 6x + 2$

$3x + (-6x) + 9 = 6x + (-6x) + 2$

$-3x + 9 = 2$

$-3x + 9 + (-9) = 2 + (-9)$

$-3x = -7$

$\dfrac{-3x}{-3} = \dfrac{-7}{-3}$

$x = \dfrac{7}{3} \text{ or } 2\dfrac{1}{3}$

Check: $\dfrac{\frac{7}{3}+3}{4} \overset{?}{=} \dfrac{\frac{7}{3}}{2}+\dfrac{1}{6}$

$\dfrac{\frac{7}{3}+\frac{9}{3}}{4} \overset{?}{=} \dfrac{7}{3}\cdot\dfrac{1}{2}+\dfrac{1}{6}$

$\dfrac{16}{3}\cdot\dfrac{1}{4} \overset{?}{=} \dfrac{7}{6}+\dfrac{1}{6}$

$\dfrac{4}{3} \overset{?}{=} \dfrac{8}{6}$

$\dfrac{4}{3}=\dfrac{4}{3}$

15. $\qquad 0.6x+5.9=3.8$

$10(0.6x)+10(5.9)=10(3.8)$

$6x+59=38$

$6x+59-59=38-59$

$6x=-21$

$\dfrac{6x}{6}=\dfrac{-21}{6}$

$x=-\dfrac{7}{2}=-3.5$

Check: $0.6(-3.5)+5.9 \overset{?}{=} 3.8$

$-2.1+5.9 \overset{?}{=} 3.8$

$3.8=3.8$

17. $\dfrac{1}{2}(y-2)+2=\dfrac{3}{8}(3y-4), \quad y\overset{?}{=}4$

$\dfrac{1}{2}(4-2)+2\overset{?}{=}\dfrac{3}{8}(3\cdot4-4)$

$1+2\overset{?}{=}\dfrac{3}{8}(8)$

$3=3$

$y=4$ is a solution.

19. $\qquad \dfrac{1}{2}\left(y-\dfrac{1}{5}\right)=\dfrac{1}{5}(y+2), \quad y\overset{?}{=}\dfrac{5}{8}$

$\dfrac{1}{2}\left(\dfrac{5}{8}-\dfrac{1}{5}\right)\overset{?}{=}\dfrac{1}{5}\left(\dfrac{5}{8}+2\right)$

$\dfrac{1}{2}\left(\dfrac{17}{40}\right)\overset{?}{=}\dfrac{1}{5}\left(\dfrac{21}{8}\right)$

$\dfrac{17}{80}\neq\dfrac{42}{80}$

$y=\dfrac{5}{8}$ is not a solution.

21. $\qquad \dfrac{3}{4}(3x+1)=2(3-2x)+1$

$4\left(\dfrac{3}{4}\right)(3x+1)=4(2)(3-2x)+4(1)$

$3(3x+1)=8(3-2x)+4$

$9x+3=24-16x+4$

$9x+3=-16x+28$

$9x+16x+3=-16x+16x+28$

$25x+3=28$

$25x+3-3=28-3$

$25x=25$

$\dfrac{25x}{25}=\dfrac{25}{25}$

$x=1$

23.　　$2(x-2) = \dfrac{2}{5}(3x+1)+2$

$$5(2)(x-2) = 5\left(\dfrac{2}{5}\right)(3x+1)+5(2)$$

$$10(x-2) = 2(3x+1)+10$$

$$10x-20 = 6x+2+10$$

$$10x-20 = 6x+12$$

$$10x-6x-20 = 6x-6x+12$$

$$4x-20 = 12$$

$$4x-20+20 = 12+20$$

$$4x = 32$$

$$\dfrac{4x}{4} = \dfrac{32}{4}$$

$$x = 8$$

25.　　$0.3x - 0.2(3-5x) = -0.5(x-6)$

$$10(0.3x)-10(0.2)(3-5x) = 10(-0.5)(x-6)$$

$$3x-2(3-5x) = -5(x-6)$$

$$3x-6+10x = -5x+30$$

$$13x-6 = -5x+30$$

$$13x+5x-6 = -5x+5x+30$$

$$18x-6 = 30$$

$$18x-6+6 = 30+6$$

$$18x = 36$$

$$\dfrac{18x}{18} = \dfrac{36}{18}$$

$$x = 2$$

27. $-5(0.2x+0.1)-0.6 = 1.9$

$$-x-0.5-0.6 = 1.9$$

$$-x-1.1 = 1.9$$

$$-x = 3$$

$$x = -3$$

29.　　$\dfrac{1}{3}(y+2) = 3y-5(y-2)$

$$3\left(\dfrac{1}{3}\right)(y+2) = 3(3y)-3(5)(y-2)$$

$$y+2 = 9y-15y+30$$

$$y+2 = -6y+30$$

$$7y = 28$$

$$y = 4$$

31.　　　　$\dfrac{1+2x}{5} + \dfrac{4-x}{3} = \dfrac{1}{15}$

$$15\left(\dfrac{1+2x}{5}\right)+15\left(\dfrac{4-x}{3}\right) = 15\left(\dfrac{1}{15}\right)$$

$$3+6x+20 \quad 5x = 1$$

$$x+23 = 1$$

$$x = -22$$

33.　　$\dfrac{1}{5}(x+3) = 2x-3(2-x)-3$

$$5\left(\dfrac{1}{5}\right)(x+3) = 5(2x)-5(3)(2-x)-5(3)$$

$$x+3 = 10x-30+15x-15$$

$$x+3 = 25x-45$$

$$x-x+3 = 25x-x-45$$

$$3 = 24x-45$$

$$3+45 = 24x-45+45$$

$$48 = 24x$$

$$\dfrac{48}{24} = \dfrac{24x}{24}$$

$$2 = x$$

35. $\dfrac{1}{3}(x-2)=3x-2(x-1)+\dfrac{16}{3}$

$$3\left(\dfrac{1}{3}\right)(x-2)=3(3x)-3(2)(x-1)+3\left(\dfrac{16}{3}\right)$$

$$x-2=9x-6x+6+16$$

$$x-2=3x+22$$

$$-2x=24$$

$$x=-12$$

37. $\dfrac{4}{5}x-\dfrac{2}{3}=\dfrac{3x+1}{2}$

$$30\left(\dfrac{4}{5}x\right)-30\left(\dfrac{2}{3}\right)=30\left(\dfrac{3x+1}{2}\right)$$

$$24x-20=15(3x+1)$$

$$24x-20=45x+15$$

$$24x+(-45x)-20=45x+(-30x)+15$$

$$-21x-20=15$$

$$-21x-20+20=15+20$$

$$-21x=35$$

$$\dfrac{-21x}{-21}=\dfrac{35}{-21}$$

$$x=-\dfrac{5}{3}\text{ or }-1\dfrac{2}{3}$$

39. $0.2(x+3)=4(0.5x-0.03)$

$$0.2x+0.6=2xx-0.12$$

$$0.2x+(-0.2x)+0.6=2x+(-0.2x)-0.12$$

$$0.6=1.8x-0.12+0.12$$

$$0.72=1.8x$$

$$\dfrac{0.72}{1.8}=\dfrac{1.8x}{1.8}$$

$$0.4=x$$

41. $-1+5(x-2)=12x+3-7x$

$$-1+5x-10=5x+3$$

$$5x-11=5x+3$$

$$5x-5x-11=5x-5x+3$$

$$-11=3,\quad\text{No solution}$$

43. $9(x+3)-6=24-2x-3+11x$

$$9x+27-6=9x+21$$

$$9x+21=9x+21$$

$$9x-9x+21=9x-9x+21$$

$$21=21$$

Infinite number of solutions

45. $7x+6=2(3x-1)+8$

$$7x+6=6x-2+8$$

$$7x+6=6x+6$$

$$7x+(-6x)+6=6x+(-6x)+6$$

$$x+6=6$$

$$x+6+(-6)=6+(-6)$$

$$x=0$$

47. $3(4x+1)-2x=2(5x-3)$

$$12x+3-2x=10x-6$$

$$10x+3=10x-6$$

$$10x+(-10x)+3=10x+(-10x)-6$$

$$3=-6$$

No solution

Cumulative Review

How Am I Doing? Sections 2.1-2.4

49. $\dfrac{3}{7} + 1\dfrac{5}{10} = \dfrac{3}{7} + \dfrac{15}{10}$

$\qquad = \dfrac{30}{70} + \dfrac{105}{70}$

$\qquad = \dfrac{135}{70} = 1\dfrac{65}{70} = 1\dfrac{13}{14}$

1. $\quad 5 - 8 + x = -12$

$\qquad -3 + x = -12$

$\qquad -3 + 3 + x = -12 + 3$

$\qquad\qquad x = -9$

2. $\qquad\qquad 3.6 + x = -7.x$

$\qquad 3.6 + (-3.6) + x = -7.3 + (-3.6)$

$\qquad\qquad\qquad x - -10.9$

51. $100\% + 20\% = 120\%$

120% of $40 = 1.20(40) = 48$

$100\% + 450\% = 550\%$

550% of $48 = 5.50(48) = 264$

264 pairs were thriving in 2000.

3. $\quad -45 = -5x$

$\qquad \dfrac{-45}{-5} = \dfrac{-5x}{-5}$

$\qquad\quad 9 = x$

53. Population in 1985

$40 + 20\%(40) = 48$

Population in 2000

$48 + 450\%(48) = 264$ pairs

4. $12x - 6x = -48$

$\qquad 6x = -48$

$\qquad \dfrac{6x}{6} = \dfrac{-48}{6}$

$\qquad x = -8$

55. $A = \pi r^2,\ r = 6$

$A \approx 3.14(6)^2 = 113.04$ square inches

Cost $= 2(113.04) = \$226.08$

5. $\qquad\qquad -1.2x + 3.5 = 2.7$

$\qquad -1.2x + 3.5 + (-3.5) = 2.7 + (-3.5)$

$\qquad\qquad\qquad -1.2x = -0.8$

$\qquad\qquad\qquad \dfrac{-1.2x}{-1.2} = \dfrac{-0.8}{-1.2}$

$\qquad\qquad\qquad\qquad x = \dfrac{2}{3}$

6.
$$9x - 3 = -17x + 4$$
$$9x + 17x - 3 = -17x + 17x + 4$$
$$26x - 3 = 4$$
$$26x = 7$$
$$\frac{26x}{26} = \frac{7}{26}$$
$$x = \frac{7}{26}$$

7.
$$14x + 2(7x - 2) = 20$$
$$14x + 14 - 4x = 20$$
$$10x + 14 = 20$$
$$10x + 14 + (-14) = 20 + (-14)$$
$$10x = 6$$
$$\frac{10x}{10} = \frac{6}{10}$$
$$x = \frac{3}{5}$$

8.
$$0.5(1.2x - 3.4) = -1.4x + 5.8$$
$$0.6x - 1.7 = -1.4x + 5.8$$
$$0.6x + 1.4x - 1.7 = -1.4x + 1.4x + 5.8$$
$$2x - 1.7 = 5.8$$
$$2x - 1.7 + 1.7 = 5.8 + 1.7$$
$$2x = 7.5$$
$$\frac{2x}{2} = \frac{7.5}{2}$$
$$x = 3.75$$

9.
$$3(x + 6) = -2(4x - 1) + x$$
$$3x + 18 = -8x + 2 + x$$
$$3x + 18 = -7x + 2$$
$$3x + 7x + 18 = -7x + 7x + 2$$
$$10x + 18 = 2$$
$$10x + 18 + (-18) = 2 + (-18)$$
$$10x = -16$$
$$\frac{10x}{10} = -\frac{16}{10}$$
$$x = -\frac{8}{5} \text{ or } -1\frac{3}{5}$$

10.
$$\frac{x}{5} + \frac{x}{4} = \frac{2}{5}$$
$$20\left(\frac{x}{5}\right) + 20\left(\frac{x}{4}\right) = 20\left(\frac{2}{5}\right)$$
$$4x + 5x = 8$$
$$9x = 8$$
$$\frac{9x}{9} = \frac{8}{9}$$
$$x = \frac{8}{9}$$

11. $\dfrac{1}{4}(x+3) = 4x - 2(x-3)$

$$4\left(\dfrac{1}{4}\right)(x+3) = 4(4x) - 4(2)(x-3)$$

$$x + 3 = 16x - 8x + 24$$

$$x + 3 = 8x + 24$$

$$x + (-x) + 3 = 8x + (-x) + 24$$

$$3 = 7x + 24$$

$$3 + (-24) = 7x + 24 + (-24)$$

$$-21 = 7x$$

$$\dfrac{-21}{7} = \dfrac{7x}{7}$$

$$-3 = x$$

12. $\dfrac{1}{2}(x-1) + 2 = 3(2x-1)$

$$2\left(\dfrac{1}{2}\right)(x-1) + 2(2) = 2(3)(2x-1)$$

$$x - 1 + 4 = 12x - 6$$

$$x + 3 = 12x - 6$$

$$x + (-x) + 3 = 12x + (-x) - 6$$

$$3 = 11x - 6$$

$$3 + 6 = 11x - 6 + 6$$

$$9 = 11x$$

$$\dfrac{9}{11} = \dfrac{11x}{11}$$

$$\dfrac{9}{11} = x$$

13. $\dfrac{1}{7}(7x-14) - 2 = \dfrac{1}{3}(x-2)$

$$21\left(\dfrac{1}{7}\right)(7x-14) - 21(2) = 21\left(\dfrac{1}{3}\right)(x-2)$$

$$3(7x-14) - 42 = 7(x-2)$$

$$21x - 42 - 42 = 7x - 14$$

$$21x - 84 = 7x - 14$$

$$21x + (-7x) - 84 = 7x + (-7x) - 14$$

$$14x - 84 = -14$$

$$14x - 84 + 84 = -14 + 84$$

$$14x = 70$$

$$\dfrac{14x}{14} = \dfrac{70}{14}$$

$$x = 5$$

14. $0.2(x-3) = 4(0.2x - 0.1)$

$$0.2x - 0.6 = 0.8x - 0.4$$

$$0.2x + (-0.2x) - 0.6 = 0.8x + (-0.2x) - 0.4$$

$$-0.6 = 0.6x - 0.4$$

$$-0.6 + 0.4 = 0.6x - 0.4 + 0.4$$

$$-0.2 = 0.6x$$

$$\dfrac{-0.2}{0.6} = \dfrac{0.6x}{0.6}$$

$$-\dfrac{1}{3} = x$$

2.5 Exercises

1. Multiply each term by 5. Then add
   −160 to each side. Then divide each side
   by 9. We would obtain $\dfrac{5F-160}{9} = C$.

3. (a) $A = \dfrac{1}{2}bh$

   $$\dfrac{2A}{h} = \dfrac{2\left(\dfrac{1}{2}bh\right)}{h} = b$$

   $A = 60 \text{ m}^2, \quad h = 12 \text{ m}$

   $$b = \dfrac{2(60)}{12} = 10$$

   $\text{base } = 10 \text{ m}$

   (b) $A = \dfrac{1}{2}bh$

   $$\dfrac{2A}{b} = \dfrac{2\left(\dfrac{1}{2}bh\right)}{b}$$

   $$\dfrac{2A}{b} = h$$

   $A = 88 \; m^2, \; b = 11 \; m$

   $$h = \dfrac{2(88)}{11} = 16$$

   $\text{height} = 16 \; m$

5. $4x + 3y = 18$

   $4x + (-4x) + 3y = 18 + (-4x)$

   $3y = 18 - 4x$

   $\dfrac{3y}{3} = \dfrac{18-4x}{3}$

   $y = \dfrac{18-4x}{3}$ or $y = 6 - \dfrac{4}{3}x$

7. $A = \dfrac{1}{2}bh$

   $2A = bh$

   $\dfrac{2A}{h} = b$

9. $I = Ptr$

   $\dfrac{I}{rt} = P$

11. $y = mx + b$

    $y - b = mx$

    $\dfrac{y-b}{x} = m$

13. $8x - 12y = 24$

    $8x + (-8x) - 12y = 24 + (-8x)$

    $-12y = 24 - 8x$

    $\dfrac{-12y}{-12} = \dfrac{24-8x}{12}$

    $y = -\dfrac{8}{12}x + \dfrac{24}{12}$

    $y = -\dfrac{2}{3}x + 2$

15.
$$y = -\frac{2}{3}x + 4$$
$$3y = 3\left(-\frac{2}{3}x\right) + 3(4)$$
$$3y = -2x + 12$$
$$3y + (-12) = -2x + 12 + (-12)$$
$$3y - 12 = -2x$$
$$\frac{3y - 12}{-2} = \frac{-2x}{-2}$$
$$-\frac{3}{2}y + 6 = x$$

17. $ax + by = c$
$$by = c - ax$$
$$y = \frac{c - ax}{b}$$

19. $A = \pi r^2$
$$\frac{A}{\pi} = r^2$$

21. $S = \frac{1}{2}gt^2$
$$2S = 2gt^2$$
$$\frac{2S}{t^2} = g$$

23. $A = P(1 + rt)$
$$A = P + Ptr$$
$$A - P = Ptr$$
$$\frac{A - P}{Pr} = t$$

25.
$$S = 2\pi rh + 2\pi r^2$$
$$S - 2\pi r^2 = 2\pi rh + 2\pi r^2 - 2\pi r^2$$
$$S - 2\pi r^2 = 2\pi rh$$
$$\frac{S - 2\pi r^2}{2\pi r} = \frac{2\pi rh}{2\pi r}$$
$$\frac{S - 2\pi r^2}{2\pi r} = h$$

27. $V = \pi r^2 h$
$$\frac{V}{\pi r^2} = \frac{\pi r^2 h}{\pi r^2}$$
$$\frac{V}{\pi r^2} = h$$

29. $V = LWH$
$$\frac{V}{WH} = L$$

31. $V = \frac{1}{3}\pi r^2 h$
$$3V = \pi r^2 h$$
$$\frac{3V}{\pi h} = r^2$$

33. $P = 2L + 2W$
$$P - 2L = 2W$$
$$\frac{P - 2L}{2} = W$$

35. $c^2 = a^2 + b^2$
$$c^2 - b^2 = a^2$$

65

37.
$$F = \frac{9}{5}C + 32$$

$$F - 32 = \frac{9}{5}C$$

$$\frac{5}{9}(F - 32) = C$$

39. $P = \dfrac{E^2}{R}$

$$RP = R\left(\frac{E^2}{R}\right)$$

$$RP = E^2$$

$$\frac{RP}{P} = \frac{E^2}{P}$$

$$R = \frac{E^2}{P}$$

41. $A = \dfrac{\pi r^2 S}{360}$

(a) $360A = \pi r^2 S$

$$\frac{360A}{\pi r^2} = r^2$$

43. $W = \dfrac{P - 2L}{2}$, $P = 5.8$, $L = 2.1$

$$W = \frac{5.8 - 2(2.1)}{2} = 0.8 \text{ miles}$$

45. $L = \dfrac{V}{WH}$, $V = 5940$, $W = 22$, $H = 9$

$$L = \frac{5940}{(22)(9)} = 30 \text{ feet}$$

47. (a) $V = 1100x + 7050$

$$V - 7050 = 1100x$$

$$\frac{V - 7050}{1100} = x$$

(b) $V = 25,750$

$$x = \frac{25,750 - 7050}{1100} = 17 \text{ years}$$

$$\text{Year} = 1985 + 17 = 2002$$

49. $A = \dfrac{1}{2}ab$

If $b \to 2b$, $A = \dfrac{1}{2}a(2b) = ab$

A doubles

51. $A = \pi r^2$

If $r \Rightarrow 2r$, $A \Rightarrow \pi(2r)^2 = 4\pi r^2$

A is quadrupled if r doubles.

Cumulative Review

53. 12% of $260 = 0.12(260) = 31.2$

55. 40% of what is 500?

$$0.40x = 500$$

$$\frac{0.40x}{0.40} = \frac{500}{0.40}$$

$$x = 1250 \text{ feet of fencing}$$

57. $\left(3\dfrac{1}{4}\right)(12,000) = \dfrac{13}{4}(12,000)$

$$= 39,000 \text{ square feet}$$

2.6 Exercises

1. $5 > -6$ is equivalent to $-6 < 5$.
   Both statements imply that 5 is to the right of -6 on the number line.

3. $9 > -3$

5. $-4 < -2$

7. $\dfrac{3}{5} ? \dfrac{4}{7}$

   $\dfrac{21}{35} ? \dfrac{20}{35}$

   $\dfrac{3}{5} > \dfrac{4}{7}$

9. $4 < -2$

11. $-\dfrac{13}{3} < -4$

13. $-\dfrac{5}{8} < -\dfrac{3}{5}$

15. $\dfrac{123}{4986} = 0.024669$

    0.0247 is greater

17. $x > 7$

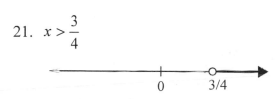

19. $x \geq -6$

21. $x > \dfrac{3}{4}$

23. $x \leq -5.3$

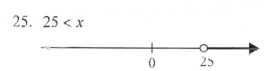

25. $25 < x$

27. $x \geq -\dfrac{2}{3}$

29. $x < -20$

31. $x > 2.8$

33. $W > 175$

35. $h \geq 37$

37. $h \geq 48$

39. $x \leq 2,\ x > -3,\ x < \dfrac{5}{2},\ x \geq -\dfrac{5}{2}$

    $-\dfrac{5}{2} \leq x \leq 2$

67

Cumulative Review

41. 16% of $38 = 0.16(38) = 6.08$

43. $\dfrac{16}{800} = 0.02 = 2\%$

45. Increase $= 10 - 8 = 2$

Percent Increase $= \dfrac{2}{8} = 0.25 = 25\%$

$100\% + 25\% = 125\%$

New price $= 125\%$ of 12

$\qquad = 1.25(12)$

$\qquad = \$15$

2.7 Exercises

1. $x + 7 \le 4$

$\quad x \le -3$

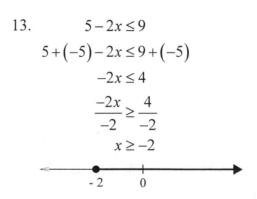

3. $5x \le 25$

$\quad x \le 5$

5. $-2x < 18$

$\quad x > -9$

7. $\dfrac{1}{2}x \ge 4$

$\quad x \ge 8$

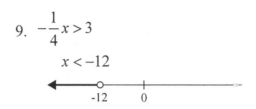

9. $-\dfrac{1}{4}x > 3$

$\quad x < -12$

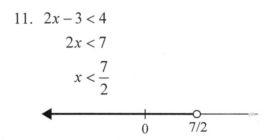

11. $2x - 3 < 4$

$\quad 2x < 7$

$\quad x < \dfrac{7}{2}$

13. $\qquad 5 - 2x \le 9$

$5 + (-5) - 2x \le 9 + (-5)$

$\qquad -2x \le 4$

$\qquad \dfrac{-2x}{-2} \ge \dfrac{4}{-2}$

$\qquad x \ge -2$

15. $$-4 + 5x < -3x + 8$$
$$-4 + 5x + 3x < -3x + 3x + 8$$
$$-4 + 8x < 8$$
$$-4 + 4 + 8x < 8 + 4$$
$$8x < 12$$
$$\frac{8x}{8} < \frac{12}{8}$$
$$x < \frac{3}{2}$$

Adding any number to both sides of an inequality does not reverse the direction.

23. $$3x + 8 < 7x - 4$$
$$3x + (-7x) + 8 < 7x + (-7x) - 4$$
$$-4x + 8 < -4$$
$$-4x + 8 + (-8) < -4 + (-8)$$
$$-4x < -12$$
$$\frac{-4x}{-4} > \frac{12}{-4}$$
$$x > 3$$

17. $$\frac{5x}{6} - 5 > \frac{x}{6} - 9$$
$$5x - 30 > x - 54$$
$$4x > -24$$
$$x > -6$$

25. $$6x - 2 \geq 4x + 6$$
$$2x \geq 8$$
$$x > 4$$

27. $$0.3(x - 1) < 0.1x - 0.5$$
$$0.3x - 0.3 < 0.1x - 0.5$$
$$3x - 3 < x - 5$$
$$2x < -2$$
$$x < -1$$

19. $$2(3x + 4) > 3(x + 3)$$
$$6x + 8 > 3x + 9$$
$$3x + 8 > 9$$
$$3x > 1$$
$$x > \frac{1}{3}$$

29. $$3 + 5(2 - x) \geq -3(x + 5)$$
$$3 + 10 - 5x \geq -3x - 15$$
$$13 - 5x \geq -3x - 15$$
$$-2x + 13 \geq -15$$
$$-2x \geq -28$$
$$x \leq 14$$

21. $$5 > 3$$
$$5 + (-2) > 3 + (-2)$$
$$3 > 1$$

69

31.
$$\frac{x+6}{7} - \frac{6}{14} > \frac{x+3}{2}$$

$$14\left(\frac{x+6}{7}\right) - 14\left(\frac{6}{14}\right) > 14\left(\frac{x+3}{2}\right)$$

$$2(x+6) - 6 > 7(x+3)$$

$$2x + 12 - 6 > 7x + 21$$

$$2x + 6 > 7x + 21$$

$$-5x > 15$$

$$x < -\frac{15}{5}$$

$$x < -3$$

33.
$$\frac{1}{6} - \frac{1}{2}(3x+2) < \frac{1}{3}\left(x - \frac{1}{2}\right)$$

$$1 - 3(3x+2) < 2\left(x - \frac{1}{2}\right)$$

$$1 - 9x - 6 < 2x - 1$$

$$-9x - 5 < 2x - 1$$

$$-11x < 4$$

$$x > -\frac{4}{11}$$

35.
$$\frac{75 + 83 + 86 + x}{4} \geq 80$$

$$\frac{244 + x}{4} \geq 80$$

$$244 + x \geq 320$$

$$x \geq 76$$

Must get a 76 or higher.

37. $268 + 4x \geq 300$

$$4x \geq 32$$

$$x \geq 8$$

8 days or more.

Cumulative Review

39. Width $= 36 + 8 = 44$

Length $= 78 + 8 = 86$

$P = 2L + 2W = 2(86) + 2(44) = 260$ feet

41. $A = \pi r^2$, $r = \frac{9}{2} = 4.5$

$A \approx 3.14(4.5)^2 \approx 63.6$ square inches

Putting Your Skills to Work

1. $28.3 - 19.9 = 8.4$ gallons per hour

2. $30(8.4) = 252$ gallons

3. $y = 0.8x - 3.7$, $x = 45$

$y = 0.8(45) - 3.7$

$y = 36 - 3.7$

$y = 32.3$ gallon per hour

4. $y = 0.8x - 3.7,\ y = 40.3$

$$40.3 = 0.8x - 3.7$$
$$40.3 + 3.7 = 0.8x - 3.7 + 3.7$$
$$44 = 0.8x$$
$$\frac{44}{0.8} = \frac{0.8x}{0.8}$$
$$55 = x$$

It travels 55 miles per hour.

5. $y = 0.5x - 0.1$

$$y + 0.1 = 0.5x - 0.1 + 0.1$$
$$y + 0.1 = 0.5x$$
$$\frac{y + 0.1}{0.5} = \frac{0.5x}{0.5}$$
$$\frac{y + 0.1}{0.5} = x \text{ or } x = 2y + 0.2$$

6. $x = 2y + 0.2,\ y = 17.4$

$$x = 2(17.4) + 0.2$$
$$x = 34.8 + 0.2$$
$$x = 35 \text{ miles per hour}$$

Chapter 2 Review Problems

1. $5x = -35$

$$\frac{5x}{5} = \frac{-35}{5}$$
$$x = -7$$

2. $x - 19 = -22$

$$x - 19 + 19 = -22 + 19$$
$$x = -3$$

3. $6 - 18x = 4 - 17x$

$$6 - 18x + 18x = 4 - 17x + 18x$$
$$6 - 4 + x$$
$$6 - 4 = 4 - 4 + x$$
$$2 = x$$

4. $18 - 10x = 63 + 5x$

$$18 - 10x + 10x = 63 + 5x + 10x$$
$$18 = 63 + 15x$$
$$18 - 63 = 63 - 63 + 15x$$
$$-45 = 15x$$
$$\frac{-45}{15} = \frac{15x}{15}$$
$$-3 = x$$

5. $6x - 2(x + 3) = 5$

$6x - 2x - 6 = 5$

$4x - 6 = 5$

$4x - 6 + 6 = 5 + 6$

$4x = 11$

$\dfrac{4x}{4} = \dfrac{11}{4}$

$x = \dfrac{11}{4} = 2.75$

6. $1 - 2(6 - x) = 3x + 2$

$1 - 12 + 2x = 3x + 2$

$2x - 11 = 3x + 2$

$2x - 11 + 11 = 3x + 2 + 11$

$2x = 3x + 13$

$-3x + 2x = -3x + 3x + 13$

7. $\quad x - (0.5x + 2.6) = 17.6$

$x - 0.5x - 2.6 = 17.6$

$0.5x - 2.6 = 17.6$

$10(0.5x) - 10(2.6) = 10(17.6)$

$5x - 26 = 176$

$5x - 26 + 26 = 176 + 26$

$5x = 202$

$\dfrac{5x}{5} = \dfrac{202}{5}$

$x = 40.4$

8. $\quad -0.2(x + 1) = 0.3(x + 11)$

$10\big[-0.2(x + 1)\big] = 10\big[0.3(x + 11)\big]$

$-2(x + 1) = 3(x + 11)$

$-2x - 2 = 3x + 33$

$-2x - 2 - 33 = 3x + 33 - 33$

$-2x - 35 = 3x$

$2x - 2x - 35 = 2x + 3x$

$-35 = 5x$

$\dfrac{-35}{5} = \dfrac{5x}{5}$

$-7 = x$

9. $\quad 3(x - 2) = -4(5 + x)$

$3x - 6 = -20 - 4x$

$3x + 4x - 6 = -20 - 4x + 4x$

$7x - 6 = -20$

$7x - 6 + 6 = -20 + 6$

$7x = -14$

$\dfrac{7x}{7} = \dfrac{-14}{7}$

$x = -2$

10. $\quad \dfrac{2}{3}x = -18$

$\dfrac{3}{2}\left(\dfrac{2}{3}x\right) = \dfrac{3}{2}(-18)$

$x = -27$

11. $\quad \dfrac{3}{4}x = 15$

$\dfrac{4}{3}\left(\dfrac{3}{4}x\right) = \dfrac{4}{3}(15)$

$x = 20$

12.
$$4(2x+3) = 5(x-3)$$
$$8x+12 = 5x-15$$
$$8x+(-5x)+12 = 5x+(-5x)-15$$
$$3x+12 = -15$$
$$3x+12+(-12) = -15+(-12)$$
$$3x = -27$$
$$\frac{3x}{3} = \frac{-27}{3}$$
$$x = -9$$

13.
$$3(x-3) = 13x+21$$
$$3x-9 = 13x+21$$
$$3x+(-3x)-9 = 13x+(-3x)+21$$
$$-9 = 10x+21$$
$$-21-9 = 10x+21+(-21)$$
$$-30 = 10x$$
$$\frac{-30}{10} = \frac{10x}{10}$$
$$-3 = x$$

14.
$$0.9x+1.0 = 0.3x+0.4$$
$$0.9x+(-0.3x)+1.0 = 0.3x+(-0.3x)+0.4$$
$$0.6x+1.0 = 0.4$$
$$0.6x+1.0+(-1.0) = 0.4+(-1.0)$$
$$0.6x = -0.6$$
$$\frac{0.6x}{0.6} = \frac{-0.6}{0.6}$$
$$x = -1$$

15.
$$2.4-0.3x = 0.4(x-1)$$
$$2.4-0.3x = 0.4x-0.4$$
$$2.4-0.3x+0.3x = 0.4x+0.3x-0.4$$
$$2.4 = 0.7x-0.4$$
$$2.4+0.4 = 0.7x-0.4+0.4$$
$$2.8 = 0.7x$$
$$\frac{2.8}{0.7} = \frac{0.7x}{0.7}$$
$$4 = x$$

16.
$$12-x+2 = 3x-10+4x$$
$$-x+14 = 7x-10$$
$$-x+14+10 = 7x-10+10$$
$$-x+24 = 7x$$
$$x-x+24 = x+7x$$
$$24 = 8x$$
$$\frac{24}{8} = \frac{8x}{8}$$
$$3 = x$$

17.
$$36 = 9x-(3x-18)$$
$$36 = 9x-3x+18$$
$$36 = 6x+18$$
$$36+(-18) = 6x+18+(-18)$$
$$18 = 6x$$
$$\frac{18}{6} = \frac{6x}{6}$$
$$3 = x$$

18. $12 - 5x = -7x - 2$
$12 - 5x + 7x = -7x + 7x - 2$
$12 + 2x = -2$
$12 - 12 + 2x = -2 - 12$
$2x = -14$
$\dfrac{2x}{2} = \dfrac{-14}{2}$
$x = -7$

19. $2(3 - x) = 1 - (x - 2)$
$6 - 2x = 1 - x + 2$
$6 - 2x + x = 3 - x + x$
$6 - x = 3$
$6 + (-6) - x = 3 + (-6)$
$-x = -3$
$\dfrac{-x}{-1} = \dfrac{-3}{-1}$
$x = 3$

20. $4(x + 5) - 7 = 2(x + 3)$
$4x + 2x - 7 = 2x + 6$
$4x + 13 = 2x + 6$
$4x + 13 - 13 = 2x + 6 - 13$
$4x = 2x - 7$
$-2x + 4x = -2x + 2x - 7$
$2x = -7$
$\dfrac{2x}{2} = \dfrac{-7}{2}$
$x = -\dfrac{7}{2}$ or $-3\dfrac{1}{2}$

21. $0.9y + 3 = 0.4y + 1.5$
$10(0.9y) + 10(3) = 10(0.4y) + 10(1.5)$
$9y + 30 = 4y + 15$
$9y + (-4y) + 30 = 4y + (-4y) + 15$
$5y + 30 = 15$
$54y + 30 + (-30) = 15 + (-30)$
$5y = -15$
$\dfrac{5y}{5} = \dfrac{-15}{5}$
$y = -3$

22. $7y - 3.4 = 1.3$
$7y - 3.4 + 3.4 = 1.3 + 3.4$
$7y = 14.7$
$\dfrac{7y}{7} = \dfrac{14.7}{7}$
$y = 2.1$

23. $3 = 2x + 5 - 3(x - 1)$
$3 = 2x + 5 - 3x + 3$
$3 = -x + 8$
$3 + (-8) = -x + 8 + (-8)$
$-5 = -x$
$\dfrac{-5}{-1} = \dfrac{-x}{-1}$
$5 = x$

74

24. $2(5x-1)-7 = 3(x-1)+5-4x$

$10x-2-7 = 3x-3+5-4x$

$10x-9 = -x+2$

$10x+x-9 = -x+x+2$

$11x-9 = 2$

$11x-9+9 = 2+9$

$11x = 11$

$\dfrac{11x}{11} = \dfrac{11}{11}$

$x = 1$

25. $\dfrac{3}{4}x-3 = \dfrac{1}{2}x+2$

$4\left(\dfrac{3}{4}x-3\right) - 4\left(\dfrac{1}{2}x+2\right)$

$3x-12 = 2x+8$

$3x-12+12 = 2x+8+12$

$3x = 2x+20$

$-2x+3x = -2x+2x+20$

$x = 20$

26. $1 = \dfrac{5x}{6}+\dfrac{2x}{3}$

$6 = 5x+4x$

$6 = 9x$

$\dfrac{2}{3} = x$

27. $\dfrac{7x}{5} = 5+\dfrac{2x}{5}$

$5\left(\dfrac{7x}{5}\right) = 5(5)+5\left(+\dfrac{2x}{5}\right)$

$7x = 25+2x$

$7x-2x = 25+2x-2x$

$5x = 25$

$\dfrac{5x}{5} = \dfrac{25}{5}$

$x = 5$

28. $\dfrac{7x-3}{2}-4 = \dfrac{5x+1}{3}$

$6\left(\dfrac{7x-3}{2}\right)-6(4) = 6\left(\dfrac{5x+1}{3}\right)$

$3(7x-3)-24 = 2(5x+1)$

$21x-9-24 = 10x+2$

$21x-33 = 10x+2$

$21x+(-10x)-33 = 10x+(-10x)+2$

$11x-33 = 2$

$11x-33+33 = 2+33$

$11x = 35$

$\dfrac{11x}{11} = \dfrac{35}{11}$

$x = \dfrac{35}{11}$

29. $\dfrac{3x-2}{2} + \dfrac{x}{4} = 2 + x$

$4\left(\dfrac{3x-2}{2} + \dfrac{x}{4}\right) = 4(2+x)$

$2(3x-2) + x = 8 + 4x$

$6x - 4 + x = 8 + 4x$

$7x - 4 = 4x + 8$

$7x - 4 + 4 = 4x + 8 + 4$

$7x = 4x + 12$

$-4x + 7x = -4x + 4x + 12$

$3x = 12$

$\dfrac{3x}{3} = \dfrac{12}{3}$

$x = 4$

30. $\dfrac{-3}{2}(x+5) = 1 - x$

$2\left(\dfrac{-3}{2}\right)(x+5) = 2(1-x)$

$-3x - 15 = 2 - 2x$

$-3x + 3x - 15 = 2 - 2x + 3x$

$-15 = 2 + x$

$-15 + (-2) = 2 + (-2) + x$

$-17 = x$

31. $\dfrac{-4}{3}(2x+1) = -x - 2$

$3\left[\dfrac{-4}{3}(2x+1)\right] = 3(-x-2)$

$-4(2x+1) = -3x - 6$

$-8x - 4 = -3x - 6$

$-8x - 4 + 4 = -3x - 6 + 4$

$-8x = -3x - 2$

$3x - 8x = 3x - 3x - 2$

$-5x = -2$

32. $\dfrac{1}{3}(x-2) = \dfrac{x}{4} + 2$

$12\left(\dfrac{1}{3}\right)(x-2) = 12\left(\dfrac{x}{4}\right) + 12(2)$

$4(x-2) = 3x + 24$

$4x - 8 = 3x + 24$

$4x + (-3x) - 8 = 3x + (-3x) + 24$

$x - 8 = 24$

$x - 8 + 8 = 24 + 8$

$x = 32$

76

33.
$$\frac{1}{5}(x-3) = 20 - \frac{x}{2}$$
$$10\left[\frac{1}{5}(x-3)\right] = 10\left(2 - \frac{x}{2}\right)$$
$$2(x-3) = 20 - 5x$$
$$2x - 6 = 20 - 5x$$
$$2x + 5x - 6 = 20 - 5x + 5x$$
$$7x - 6 = 20$$
$$7x - 6 + 6 = 20 + 6$$
$$7x = 26$$
$$\frac{7x}{7} = \frac{26}{7}$$
$$x = \frac{26}{7}$$

35.
$$2x - \frac{3}{4} + \frac{7}{2}x = \frac{1}{2}x + \frac{1}{4}$$
$$4(2x) - 4\left(\frac{3}{4}\right) + 4\left(\frac{7}{2}x\right) = 4\left(\frac{1}{2}x\right) + 4\left(\frac{1}{4}\right)$$
$$8x - 3 + 14x = 2x + 1$$
$$22x - 3 = 2x + 1$$
$$22x + (-2x) - 3 = 2x + (-2x) + 1$$
$$20x - 3 = 1$$
$$20x - 3 + 3 = 1 + 3$$
$$20x = 4$$
$$\frac{20x}{20} = \frac{4}{20}$$
$$x = \frac{1}{5}$$

34.
$$\frac{4}{5} + \frac{1}{2}x = \frac{1}{5}x + \frac{1}{2}$$
$$10\left(\frac{4}{5}\right) + 10\left(\frac{1}{2}x\right) = 10\left(\frac{1}{5}x\right) + 10\left(\frac{1}{2}\right)$$
$$8 + 5x = 2x + 5$$
$$5x + (-2x) + 8 = 2x + (-2x) + 5$$
$$3x + 8 = 5$$
$$3x + 8 + (-8) = 5 + (-8)$$
$$3x = -3$$
$$\frac{3x}{3} = \frac{-3}{3}$$
$$x = -1$$

36.
$$\frac{3}{2}x - \frac{5}{6} + x = \frac{1}{2}x + \frac{2}{3}$$
$$6\left(\frac{3}{2}x\right) - 6\left(\frac{5}{6}\right) + 6x = 6\left(\frac{1}{2}x\right) + 6\left(\frac{2}{3}\right)$$
$$9x - 5 + 6x = 3x + 4$$
$$15x - 5 = 3x + 4$$
$$15x + (-3x) - 5 = 3x + (-3x) + 4$$
$$12x - 5 = 4$$
$$12x - 5 + 5 = 4 + 5$$
$$12x = 9$$
$$\frac{12x}{12} = \frac{9}{12}$$
$$x = \frac{3}{4}$$

37.
$$-\frac{8}{3}x - 8 + 2x - 5 = -\frac{5}{3}$$
$$-\frac{8}{3}x - 13 + 2x = -\frac{5}{3}$$
$$3\left(-\frac{8}{3}x - 13 + 2x\right) = 3\left(-\frac{5}{3}\right)$$
$$-8x - 39 + 6x = -5$$
$$-2x - 39 + 6x = -5$$
$$-2x - 39 + 39 = -5 + 39$$
$$-2x = 34$$
$$\frac{-2x}{-2} = \frac{34}{-2}$$
$$x = -17$$

38.
$$3.5(2x + 3) = 2.4x - 1$$
$$7x + 10.5 = 2.4x - 1$$
$$7x + (-2.4x) + 10.5 = 2.4x + (-2.4x) - 1$$
$$4.6x + 10.5 = -1$$
$$4.6x + 10.5 + (-10.5) = -1 + (-10.5)$$
$$4.6x = -11.5$$
$$\frac{4.6x}{4.6} = \frac{-11.5}{4.6}$$
$$x = -2.5$$

39.
$$\frac{7}{12}(x - 3) = -\frac{1}{3}x + 1$$
$$12\left(\frac{7}{12}\right)(x - 3) = -12\left(\frac{1}{3}x\right) + 12(1)$$
$$7x - 21 = -4x + 12$$
$$7x + 4x - 21 = -4x + 4x + 12$$
$$11x - 21 = 12$$
$$11x - 21 + 21 = 12 + 21$$
$$11x = 33$$
$$\frac{11x}{11} = \frac{33}{11}$$
$$x = 3$$

40.
$$\frac{1}{6} + \frac{1}{3}(x - 3) = \frac{1}{2}(x + 9)$$
$$6\left(\frac{1}{6}\right) + 6\left(\frac{1}{3}\right)(x - 3) = 6\left(\frac{1}{2}\right)(x + 9)$$
$$1 + 2(x - 3) = 3(x + 9)$$
$$1 + 2x - 6 = 3x + 27$$
$$2x - 5 = 3x + 27$$
$$2x - 2x - 5 = 3x - 2x + 27$$
$$-5 = x + 27$$
$$-5 - 27 = x + 27 - 27$$
$$-32 = x$$

41.
$$\frac{1}{7}(x+5)-\frac{6}{14}=\frac{1}{2}(x+3)$$
$$14\left(\frac{1}{7}\right)(x+5)-14\left(\frac{6}{14}\right)=14\left(\frac{1}{2}\right)(x+3)$$
$$2x+10-6=7x+21$$
$$2x+4=7x+21$$
$$2x+(-2x)+4=7x+(-2x)+21$$
$$4=5x+21$$
$$4+(-21)=5x+21+(-21)$$
$$-17=5x$$
$$\frac{-17}{5}=\frac{5x}{5}$$
$$-\frac{17}{5}=x$$

43.
$$-\frac{2}{5}(3x+1)=\frac{1}{3}(2-x)$$
$$15\left(-\frac{2}{5}\right)(3x+1)=15\left(\frac{1}{3}\right)(2-x)$$
$$-6(3x+1)=5(2-x)$$
$$-18x-6=10-5x$$
$$-18x+5x-6=10-5x+5x$$
$$13x-6=10$$
$$-13x-6+6=10+6$$
$$-13x=16$$
$$\frac{-13x}{-13}=\frac{16}{-13}$$
$$x=-\frac{16}{13}\text{ or }-1\frac{3}{13}$$

42.
$$\frac{1}{6}(8x+3)=\frac{1}{2}(2x+7)$$
$$6\left[\frac{1}{6}(8x+3)\right]=6\left[\frac{1}{2}(2x+7)\right]$$
$$8x+3=3(2x+7)$$
$$8x+3=3(2x+7)$$

$$8x+3-3=6x+21-3$$
$$8x=6x+18$$
$$-6x+8x=-6x+6x+18$$
$$2x=18$$
$$\frac{2x}{2}=\frac{18}{2}$$
$$x=9$$

44.
$$\frac{7}{9}x+\frac{2}{3}=2+\frac{1}{3}x$$
$$9\left(\frac{7}{9}x+\frac{2}{3}\right)=9\left(2+\frac{1}{3}x\right)$$
$$7x+6=18+3x$$
$$7x+6-6=18-6+3x$$
$$7x=12+3x$$
$$7x-3x=12+3x-3x$$
$$4x=12$$
$$\frac{4x}{4}=\frac{12}{4}$$
$$x=3$$

45.
$$3x-y=10$$
$$3x+(-3x)-y=-3x+10$$
$$-y=-3x+10$$
$$\frac{-y}{-1}=\frac{-3x+10}{-1}$$
$$y=3x-10$$

46. $5x + 2y + 7 = 0$

$$5x + 2y = -7$$

$$2y = -5x - 7$$

$$y = \frac{-5x - 7}{2}$$

47. $A = P(1 + rt)$

$$A = P + \Pr t$$

$$A + (-P) = P + (-P) + \Pr t$$

$$A - P = \Pr t$$

$$\frac{A - P}{Pt} = \frac{\Pr t}{Pt}$$

$$\frac{A - P}{Pt} = r$$

48. $A = 4\pi r^2 + 2\pi rh$

$$A - 4\pi r^2 = 2\pi rh$$

$$\frac{A - 4\pi r^2}{2\pi r} = h$$

49. $H = \frac{1}{3}(a + 2p + 3)$

$$3H = 3\left(\frac{1}{3}\right)(a + 2p + 3)$$

$$3H = a + 2p + 3$$

$$3H + (-a) + (-3) = a + (-a) + 2p + 3 + (-3)$$

$$3H - a - 3 = 2p$$

$$\frac{3H - a - 3}{2} = \frac{2p}{2}$$

$$\frac{3H - a - 3}{2} = p$$

50. $ax + by = c$

$$ax - ax + by = c - ax$$

$$by = c - ax$$

$$\frac{by}{b} = \frac{c - ax}{b}$$

$$y = \frac{c - ax}{b}$$

51. a. $C = \dfrac{WRT}{1000}$

$$1000C = WRT$$

$$\frac{1000C}{WR} = T$$

  b. $T = \dfrac{1000(0.36)}{(30)(0.002)} = 6000$

52. a. $5x - 3y = 12$

$$5x + (-5x) - 3y = -5x + 12$$

$$-3y = -5x + 12$$

$$\frac{-3y}{-3} = \frac{-5x + 12}{-3}$$

$$y = \frac{5}{3}x - 4$$

  b. $x = 9$

$$y = \frac{5}{3}(9) - 4 = 15 - 4 = 11$$

80

53. a. $V = lwh$

$$\frac{V}{lw} = \frac{lwh}{lw}$$

$$\frac{V}{lw} = h$$

   b. $V = 48,\ l = 2,\ w = 4$

$$h = \frac{48}{2(4)} = 6$$

54. $7 - 2x \geq 4x - 5$

$$-6x \geq -12$$

$$x \leq 2$$

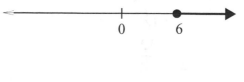

55. $2 - 3x \leq -5 + 4x$

$$2 + 2 - 3x \leq -2 - 5 + 4x$$

$$-3x \leq -7 + 4x$$

$$-3x - 4x \leq -7 + 4x - 4x$$

$$-7x \leq -7$$

$$\frac{-7x}{-7} \geq \frac{-7}{-7}$$

$$x \geq 1$$

56. $2x - 3 + x > 5(x + 1)$

$$3x - 3 > 5x + 5$$

$$-2x > 8$$

$$x < -4$$

57. $-x + 4 < 3x + 16$

$$-x + 4 - 4 < 3x + 16 - 4$$

$$-x < 3x + 12$$

$$-3x - x < -3x + 3x + 12$$

$$-4x < 12$$

$$\frac{-4x}{4} > \frac{12}{-4}$$

$$x > -3$$

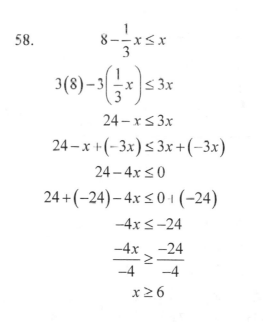

58. $8 - \frac{1}{3}x \leq x$

$$3(8) - 3\left(\frac{1}{3}x\right) \leq 3x$$

$$24 - x \leq 3x$$

$$24 - x + (-3x) \leq 3x + (-3x)$$

$$24 - 4x \leq 0$$

$$24 + (-24) - 4x \leq 0 + (-24)$$

$$-4x \leq -24$$

$$\frac{-4x}{-4} \geq \frac{-24}{-4}$$

$$x \geq 6$$

59. $7 - \dfrac{3}{5}x > 4$

$5(7) - 5\left(\dfrac{3}{5}x\right) > 5(4)$

$35 - 3x > 20$

$35 + (-35) - 3x > 20 + (-35)$

$-3x > -15$

$\dfrac{-3x}{-3} < \dfrac{-15}{-3}$

$x < 5$

60. $-4x - 14 < 4 - 2(3x - 1)$

$-4x - 14 < 4 - 6x + 2$

$-4x - 14 < 6 - 6x$

$2x < 20$

$x < 10$

61. $3(x - 2) + 8 < 7x + 14$

$3x - 6 + 8 < 7x + 14$

$3x + 2 < 7x + 14$

$3x - 2 + 2 < 7x + 14 - 2$

$3x < 7x + 12$

$-7x + 3x < -7x + 7x + 12$

$-4x < 12$

$\dfrac{-4x}{-4} > \dfrac{12}{-4}$

$x > -3$

62. $\dfrac{1}{2}(2x + 3) > 10$

$2x + 3 > 20$

$2x > 17$

$x > \dfrac{17}{2}$

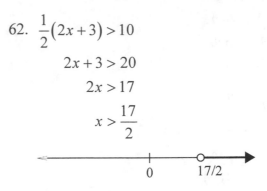

63. $5(1 - x) < 3(x - 1) - 2(3 - x)$

$5 - 5x < 3x - 3 - 6 + 2x$

$5 - 5x < 5x - 9$

$5 + 9 - 5x < 5x - 9 + 9$

$14 - 5x < 5x$

$14 - 5x + 5x < 5x + 5x$

$14 < 10x$

$\dfrac{14}{10} < \dfrac{10x}{10}$

$\dfrac{7}{5} < x \text{ or } x > \dfrac{7}{5}$

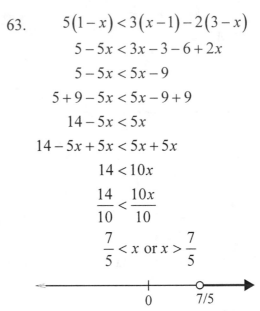

64. $15h \leq 480$

$\dfrac{15h}{15} \leq \dfrac{480}{15}$

$h \leq 32 \text{ hours}$

65. $85n \leq 1445$

$n \leq \dfrac{1445}{85}$

$n \leq 17$

66.

$$8(3x+5)-10=9(x-2)+13$$
$$24x+40-10=9x-18+13$$
$$24x+30=9x-5$$
$$24x+(-9x)+30=9x+(-9x)-5$$
$$15x+30=-5$$
$$15x+30+(-30)=-5+(-30)$$
$$15x=-35$$
$$\frac{15x}{15}=\frac{-35}{15}$$
$$x=\frac{-7}{3}\ \text{or}\ -2\frac{1}{3}$$

67.

$$8-3x+5=13+4x+2$$
$$-3x+13=4x+15$$
$$-3x+13-13=4x+15-13$$
$$-3x=4x+2$$
$$-4x-3x=-4x+4x+2$$
$$-7x=2$$
$$\frac{-7x}{-7}=\frac{2}{-7}$$
$$x=-\frac{2}{7}$$

68.

$$-2(x-3)=-4x+3(3x+2)$$
$$-2x+6=-4x+9x+6$$
$$-2x+6=5x+6$$
$$-2x+6-6=5x+6-6$$
$$-2x=5x$$
$$2x-2x=2x+5x$$
$$0=7x$$
$$\frac{0}{7}=\frac{7x}{7}$$
$$0=x$$

69.

$$\frac{1}{2}+\frac{5}{4}x=\frac{2}{5}x-\frac{1}{10}+4$$
$$20\left(\frac{1}{2}\right)+20\left(\frac{5}{4}x\right)=20\left(\frac{2}{5}x\right)-20\left(\frac{1}{10}\right)+20(4)$$
$$10+25x=8x-2+80$$
$$10+25x=8x+78$$
$$10+25x+(-8x)=8x+(-8x)+78$$
$$10+17x=78$$
$$10+(-10)+17x=78+(-10)$$
$$17x=68$$
$$\frac{17x}{17}=\frac{68}{17}$$
$$x=4$$

70.

$$\frac{1}{6}x-\frac{2}{3}=\frac{1}{3}(x-4)$$
$$6\left(\frac{1}{6}x\right)-6\left(\frac{2}{3}\right)=6\left(\frac{1}{3}\right)(x-4)$$
$$x-4=2x-8$$
$$x+(-x)-4=2x+(-x)-8$$
$$-4=x-8$$
$$-4+8=x-8+8$$
$$4=x$$

71.

$$\frac{1}{2}(x-3)=\frac{1}{4}(3x-1)$$
$$4\left[\frac{1}{2}(x-3)\right]=4\left[\frac{1}{4}(3x-1)\right]$$
$$2(x-3)=3x-1$$
$$2x-6=3x-1$$
$$2x-6+1=3x-1+1$$
$$2x-5=3x$$
$$-2x+2x-5=-2x+3x$$
$$-5=x$$

72.
$$H + 2d = 6c - 3d$$
$$H + 2d + 3d = 6c - 3d + 3d$$
$$H + 5d = 6c$$
$$H - H + 5d = 6c - H$$
$$5d = 6c - H$$
$$\frac{5d}{5} = \frac{6c - H}{5}$$
$$d = \frac{6c - H}{5}$$

73.
$$H = \frac{3c + 2b}{4}$$
$$4H = 4\left(\frac{3c + 2b}{4}\right)$$
$$4H = 3c + 2b$$
$$4H - 3c = 3c - 3c + 2b$$
$$4H - 3c = 2b$$
$$\frac{4H - 3c}{2} = \frac{2b}{2}$$
$$\frac{4H - 3c}{2} = b$$

74.
$$5 - \frac{1}{2}x > 4$$
$$2\left(5 - \frac{1}{2}x\right) > 2(4)$$
$$10 - x > 8$$
$$-10 + 10 - x > -10 + 8$$
$$-x > -2$$
$$\frac{-x}{-1} < \frac{-2}{-1}$$
$$x < 2$$

75.
$$2(x - 1) \geq 3(2 + x)$$
$$2x - 2 \geq 6 + 3x$$
$$-x \geq 8$$
$$x \leq -8$$

76.
$$\frac{1}{3}(x + 2) \leq \frac{1}{2}(3x - 5)$$
$$6\left[\frac{1}{3}(x + 2)\right] \leq 6\left[\frac{1}{2}(3x - 5)\right]$$
$$2(x + 2) \leq 3(3x - 5)$$
$$2x + 4 \leq 9x - 15$$
$$2x + 4 + 15 \leq 9x - 15 + 15$$
$$2x + 19 \leq 9x$$
$$-2x + 2x + 19 \leq -2x + 9x$$
$$19 \leq 7x$$
$$\frac{19}{7} \leq \frac{7x}{7}$$
$$\frac{19}{7} \leq x \text{ or } x \geq \frac{19}{7}$$

77.
$$4(2 - x) - (-5x + 1) \geq -8$$
$$8 - 4x + 5x - 1 \geq -8$$
$$x + 7 \geq -8$$
$$x \geq -15$$

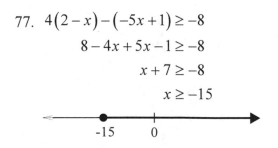

How Am I Doing? Chapter 2 Test

1. $3x + 5.6 = 11.6$

$3x + 5.6 - 5.6 = 11.6 - 5.6$

$3x = 6$

$\dfrac{3x}{3} = \dfrac{6}{3}$

$x = 2$

2. $9x - 8 = -6x - 3$

$9x + 6x - 8 = -6x + 6x - 3$

$15x - 8 = -3$

$15x - 8 + 8 = -3 + 8$

$15x = 5$

$\dfrac{15x}{15} = \dfrac{5}{15}$

$x = \dfrac{1}{3}$

3. $2(2y - 3) = 4(2y + 2)$

$4y - 6 = 8y + 8$

$4y - 6 + 6 = 8y + 8 + 6$

$4y = 8y + 14$

$-8y + 4y = -8y + 8y + 14$

$-4y = 14$

$\dfrac{-4y}{-4} = \dfrac{14}{-4}$

$y = -\dfrac{7}{2}$

4. $\dfrac{1}{7}y + 3 = \dfrac{1}{2}y$

$14\left(\dfrac{1}{7}y\right) + 14(3) = 14\left(\dfrac{1}{2}y\right)$

$2y + 42 = 7y$

$2y - 2y + 42 = 7y - 2y$

$42 = 5y$

$\dfrac{42}{5} = \dfrac{5y}{5}$

$8\dfrac{2}{5} = y$

5. $4(7 - 4x) = 3(6 - 2x)$

$28 - 16x = 18 - 6x$

$28 - 16x + 6x = 18 - 6x + 6x$

$28 - 10x = 18$

$28 + (-28) - 10x = 18 + (-28)$

$-10x = -10$

$\dfrac{-10x}{-10} = \dfrac{-10}{-10}$

$x = 1$

6. $0.8x + 0.18 - 0.4x = 0.3(x + 0.2)$

$100(0.8x + 0.18 - 0.4x) = 100\left[0.3(x + 0.2)\right]$

$80x + 18 - 40x = 30(x + 0.2)$

$40x + 18 = 30x + 6$

$40x + 18 - 18 = 30x + 6 - 18$

$40x = 30x - 12$

$-30x + 40x = -30x + 30x - 12$

$10x = -12$

$\dfrac{10x}{10} = \dfrac{-12}{10}$

$x = -\dfrac{6}{5}$ or -1.2

85

7.
$$\frac{2y}{3}+\frac{1}{5}-\frac{3y}{5}+\frac{1}{3}=1$$

$$15\left(\frac{2y}{3}\right)+15\left(\frac{1}{5}\right)-15\left(\frac{3y}{5}\right)+15\left(\frac{1}{3}\right)=15(1)$$

$$10y+3-9y+5=15$$
$$y+8=15$$
$$y+8-8=15-8$$
$$y=7$$

8.
$$3-2y=2(3y-2)-5y$$
$$3-2y=6y-4-5y$$
$$3-2y=y-4$$
$$3-2y+2y=y+2y-4$$
$$3=3y-4$$
$$3+3=3y-4+4$$
$$7=3y$$
$$\frac{7}{3}=\frac{3y}{3}$$
$$\frac{7}{3}=y$$

9. $5(20-x)+10x=165$
$$100-5x+10x=165$$
$$100+5x=165$$
$$-100+100+5x=-100+165$$
$$5x=65$$
$$\frac{5x}{5}=\frac{65}{5}$$
$$x=13$$

10. $5(x+40)-6x=9x$
$$5x+200-6x=9x$$
$$200-x=9x$$
$$200=10x$$
$$\frac{200}{10}=\frac{10x}{10}$$
$$20=x$$

11.
$$-2(2-3x)=76-2x$$
$$-4+6x=76-2x$$
$$-76-4+6x=-76+76-2x$$
$$-80+6x=-2x$$
$$-80+6x-6x=-2x-6x$$
$$-80=-8x$$
$$\frac{-80}{-8}=\frac{-8x}{-8}$$
$$10=x$$

12. $20-(2x+6)=5(2-x)+2x$
$$20-2x-6=10-5x+2x$$
$$-2x+14=-3x+10$$
$$3x-2x+14=3x-3x+10$$
$$x+14=10$$
$$x+14-14=10-14$$
$$x=-4$$

13.
$$2x-3=12-6x+3(2x+3)$$
$$2x-3=12-6x+6x+9$$
$$2x-3=21$$
$$2x-3+3=21+3$$
$$2x=24$$
$$\frac{2x}{2}=\frac{24}{2}$$
$$x=12$$

14.

$$\frac{1}{3}x - \frac{3}{4}x = \frac{1}{12}$$

$$12\left(\frac{1}{3}x - \frac{3}{4}x\right) = 12\left(\frac{1}{12}\right)$$

$$4x - 9x = 1$$

$$-5x = 1$$

$$\frac{-5x}{-5} = \frac{1}{-5}$$

$$x = -\frac{1}{5}$$

15.

$$\frac{3}{5}x + \frac{7}{10} = \frac{1}{3}x + \frac{3}{2}$$

$$30\left(\frac{3}{5}x + \frac{7}{10}\right) = 30\left(\frac{1}{3}x + \frac{3}{2}\right)$$

$$18x + 21 = 10x + 45$$

$$18x + 21 - 21 = 10x + 45 - 21$$

$$18x = 10x + 24$$

$$-10x + 18x = -10x + 10x + 24$$

$$8x = 24$$

$$\frac{8x}{8} = \frac{24}{8}$$

$$x = 3$$

16.

$$\frac{15x - 2}{28} = \frac{5x - 3}{7}$$

$$28\left(\frac{15x - 2}{28}\right) = 28\left(\frac{5x - 3}{7}\right)$$

$$15x - 2 = 4(5x - 3)$$

$$15x - 2 = 20x - 12$$

$$15x - 2 + 12 = 20x - 12 + 12$$

$$15x + 10 = 20x$$

$$-15x + 15x + 10 = -15x + 20x$$

$$10 = 5x$$

$$\frac{10}{5} = \frac{5x}{5}$$

$$2 = x$$

17.

$$\frac{2}{3}(x + 8) + \frac{3}{5} = \frac{1}{5}(11 - 6x)$$

$$15\left(\frac{2}{3}\right)(x + 8) + 15\left(\frac{3}{5}\right) = 15\left(\frac{1}{5}\right)(11 - 6x)$$

$$10(x + 8) + 9 = 3(11 - 6x)$$

$$10x + 80 + 9 = 33 - 18x$$

$$10x + 89 = 33 - 18x$$

$$10x + 18x + 89 = 33 - 18x + 18x$$

$$28x + 89 = 33$$

$$28x + 89 + (-89) = 33 + (-89)$$

$$28x = -56$$

$$\frac{28x}{28} = \frac{-56}{28}$$

$$x = -2$$

18.
$$A = 3w + 2P$$
$$A - 2P = 3w$$
$$\frac{A - 2P}{3} = w$$

19.
$$\frac{2w}{3} = 4 - \frac{1}{2}(x + 6)$$
$$\frac{2w}{3} = 4 - \frac{1}{2}x - 3$$
$$6\left(\frac{2w}{3}\right) = 6(4) - 6\left(\frac{1}{2}x\right) - 6(3)$$
$$4w = 24 - 3x - 18$$
$$4w = 3x + 6$$
$$w = \frac{-3x + 6}{4}$$

20.
$$A = \frac{1}{2}h(a + b)$$
$$2A = h(a + b)$$
$$2A = ha + hb$$
$$2A - hb = ha$$
$$\frac{2A - hb}{h} = a$$

21.
$$5ax(2 - y) = 3axy + 5$$
$$10ax - 5axy = 3axy + 5$$
$$10ax - 5 = 8axy$$
$$\frac{10ax - 5}{8ax} = y$$

22.
$$V = \frac{1}{3}Bh$$
$$3V = 3\left(\frac{1}{3}Bh\right)$$
$$3V = Bh$$
$$\frac{3V}{h} = \frac{Bh}{h}$$
$$\frac{3V}{h} = B$$

23. $B = \dfrac{3V}{h}$, $V = 140$, $h = 14$
$$B = \frac{3(140)}{14} = 30 \text{ square inches}$$

24.
$$3(x - 2) \geq 5x$$
$$3x - 6 \geq 5x$$
$$3x + (-5x) - 6 \geq 5x + (-5x)$$
$$-2x - 6 \geq 0$$
$$-2x \geq 6$$
$$\frac{-2x}{-2} \leq \frac{6}{-2}$$
$$x \leq -3$$

88

25. $2 - 7(x+1) - 5(x+2) < 0$

$$2 - 7x - 7 - 5x - 10 < 0$$

$$-12x - 15 < 0$$

$$-12x - 15 + 15 < 0 + 15$$

$$-12x < 15$$

$$\frac{-12x}{-12} > \frac{15}{-12}$$

$$x > -\frac{5}{4}$$

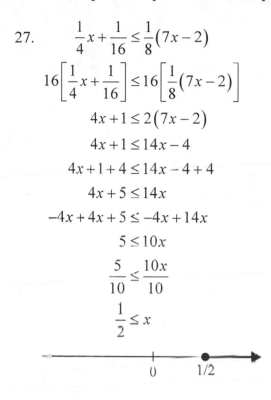

-5/4   0

26. $5 + 8x - 4 < 2x + 13$

$$8x + 1 < 2x + 13$$

$$8x + 1 - 1 < 2x + 13 - 1$$

$$8x < 2x + 12$$

$$2x + 8x < -2x + 2x + 12$$

$$6x < 12$$

$$\frac{6x}{6} < \frac{12}{6}$$

$$x < 2$$

0   2

27. $\quad \frac{1}{4}x + \frac{1}{16} \le \frac{1}{8}(7x - 2)$

$$16\left[\frac{1}{4}x + \frac{1}{16}\right] \le 16\left[\frac{1}{8}(7x - 2)\right]$$

$$4x + 1 \le 2(7x - 2)$$

$$4x + 1 \le 14x - 4$$

$$4x + 1 + 4 \le 14x - 4 + 4$$

$$4x + 5 \le 14x$$

$$-4x + 4x + 5 \le -4x + 14x$$

$$5 \le 10x$$

$$\frac{5}{10} \le \frac{10x}{10}$$

$$\frac{1}{2} \le x$$

0   1/2

Cumulative Test Chapters 0-2

1. $\frac{6}{7} - \frac{2}{3} = \frac{18}{21} - \frac{14}{21} = \frac{4}{21}$

2. $1\frac{3}{4} + 2\frac{1}{5} = 1\frac{15}{20} + 2\frac{4}{20}$

$$= \frac{35}{20} + \frac{44}{20} = \frac{79}{20}$$

$$= 3\frac{19}{20}$$

3. $3\frac{1}{5} \div 1\frac{1}{2} = \frac{16}{5} \cdot \frac{2}{3} = \frac{32}{15} = 2\frac{2}{15}$

4.   1.23

     $\times$ 0.56

      738

     615

   0.6888

5. $1.2\overline{)0.144}$ $\dfrac{0.12}{}$

      $\underline{12}$

      24

      $\underline{24}$

6. What is 4.3% of 830?

$0.043(830) = 35.69$

7. $(-3)(-5)(-1)(2)(-1) = (3)(5)(1)(2)(1)$

$ = 30$

8. $5ab - 7ab^2 - 3ab - 12ab^2 + 10ab - 9ab^2$

$= (5 - 3 + 10)ab + (-7 - 12 - 9)ab^2$

$= 12ab - 28ab^2$

9. $(5x)^2 = 5^2 (x)^2 = 25x^2$

10. $2\{3x - 4[5 - 3y(2 - x)]\}$

$= 2[3x - 4(5 - 6y + 3xy)]$

$= 2(3x - 20 + 24y - 12xy)$

$= 6x - 40 + 48y - 24xy$

11. $4(7 - 2x) = 3x - 12$

$28 - 8x = 3x - 12$

$28 - 8x + 8x = 3x + 8x - 12$

$28 = 11x - 12$

$28 + 12 = 11x - 12 + 12$

$40 = 11x$

$\dfrac{40}{11} = \dfrac{11x}{11}$

$\dfrac{40}{11} = x \text{ or } 3\dfrac{7}{11}$

12. $\dfrac{1}{3}(x + 5) = 2x - 5$

$3\left[\dfrac{1}{3}(x + 5)\right] = 3(2x - 5)$

$x + 5 = 6x - 15$

$x + 5 + 15 = 6x - 15 + 15$

$x + 20 = 6x$

$-x + x + 20 = -x + 6x$

$20 = 5x$

$\dfrac{20}{5} = \dfrac{5x}{5}$

$4 = x$

13. $\dfrac{2y}{3} - \dfrac{1}{4} = \dfrac{1}{6} + \dfrac{y}{4}$

$8y - 3 = 2 + 3y$

$5y = 5$

$y = 1$

14.
$$5a - 8b = 6 + 2a$$
$$5a + (-2a) - 8b = 6 + 2a + (-2a)$$
$$3a - 8b = 6$$
$$3a - 8b + 8b = 8b + 6$$
$$3a = 8b + b$$
$$\frac{3a}{3} = \frac{8b + 6}{3}$$
$$a = \frac{8b + 6}{3}$$

15.
$$II = \frac{2}{3}(b + 4a)$$
$$\frac{3H}{2} = b + 4a$$
$$\frac{3H}{2} - 4a = b \ \text{ or } \ b = \frac{3H - 8a}{2}$$

16. $I = P\,tr$
$$\frac{I}{\mathrm{Pr}} = t$$

17.
$$A = \frac{ha}{2} + \frac{hb}{2}$$
$$2A = ha + hb$$
$$2A - hb = ha$$
$$\frac{2A - hb}{h} = a \ \text{ or } \ a = \frac{2A}{h} - b$$

18.
$$-6x - 3 < 2x - 10x + 7$$
$$-6x - 3 < -8x + 7$$
$$8x - 6x - 3 < 8x - 8x + 7$$
$$2x - 3 < 7$$
$$2x - 3 + 3 < 7 + 3$$
$$2x < 10$$
$$\frac{2x}{2} < \frac{10}{2}$$
$$x < 5$$

19. $\frac{1}{2}(x - 5) \geq x - 4$
$$x - 5 \geq 2x - 8$$
$$-x \geq -3$$
$$x \leq 3$$

20.
$$4(2 - x) > 1 - 5x - 8$$
$$8 - 4x > -7 - 5x$$
$$-8 + 8 - 4x > -8 - 7 - 5x$$
$$-4x > -15 - 5x$$
$$-4x + 5x > -15 - 5x + 5x$$
$$x > -15$$

21. $x + \frac{5}{9} \leq \frac{1}{3} + \frac{7}{9}x$
$$9x + 5 \leq 3 + 7x$$
$$2x \leq -2$$
$$x \leq -1$$

22. $7x - 13 \le 3(4 - 5x)$

$7x - 13 \le 12 - 15x - 3$

$7x - 13 \le 9 - 15x$

$7x + 15x - 13 \le 9 - 15x + 15x$

$22x - 13 \le 9$

$22x - 13 + 13 \le 9 + 13$

$22x \le 22$

$\dfrac{22x}{22} = \dfrac{22}{22}$

$x \le 1$

23. $\dfrac{0 + 82 + 89 + 87 + x}{5} \ge 70$

$258 + x \ge 5(70)$

$x \ge 350 - 258$

$x \ge 92$

He must receive a 92 or better.

Chapter 3

3.1 Exercises

1. $x + 5$

3. $x - 6$

5. $\dfrac{x}{8}$

7. $2x$

9. $3 + \dfrac{1}{2}x$

11. $2x + 9$

13. $\dfrac{1}{3}(x + 7)$

15. $\dfrac{1}{3}x - 2x$

17. $3x - 7$

19. $x = $ value of a share of AT&T stock
$x + 74.50 = $ value of a share of IBM stock

21. $w = $ width of rectangle
$2w + 7 = $ length of rectangle

23. $x = $ number of boxes of cookies sold by Keiko
$x - 43 = $ number of boxes of cookies sold by Sarah
$x + 53 = $ number of boxes of cookes sold by Imelda

25. $s = $ measure of 2nd angle
$s - 16 = $ measure of 1st angle
$2s = $ measure of 3rd angle

27. $v = $ value of exports of Canada
$2v = $ value of exports of Japan

29. $x = $ 2nd angle
$3x = $ 1st angle
$x - 14 = $ 3rd angle

31. $A = $ area of Minnesota
$\dfrac{1}{2}A = $ area of Kentucky
$\dfrac{2}{5}A = $ area of Maine

33. $x = $ points for an arrow in the blue ring
$3x - 6 = $ points awarded for an arrow in the gold ring

35. $x = $ number of men aged 16 to 24
$x + 51 = $ number of men aged 25 to 34
$x - 60 = $ number of men aged 35 to 44
$x - 132 = $ number of men aged 45 and above

Cumulative Review

37. $x + \dfrac{1}{2}(x-3) = 9$

$2x + 2\left(\dfrac{1}{2}\right)(x-3) = 2(9)$

$2x + (x-3) = 18$

$2x + x - 3 = 18$

$3x - 3 = 18$

$3x - 3 + 3 = 18 + 3$

$3x = 21$

$\dfrac{3x}{3} = \dfrac{21}{3}$

$x = 7$

39. $5(x-8) = 13 + x - 5$

$5x - 40 = 13 + x - 5$

$5x - 40 = x + 8$

$4x = 48$

$x = 12$

3.2 Exercises

1. x = the number

$x - 543 = 718$

$x = 1261$

Check:

$1261 - 543 \overset{?}{=} 718$

$718 = 718$

The number is 1261.

3. x = the number

$\dfrac{x}{8} = 296$

$x = 2368$

Check:

$\dfrac{2368}{8} \overset{?}{=} 296$

$296 = 296$

The number is 2368.

5. x = the number

$x + 17 = 199$

$x = 182$

Check:

$182 + 17 \overset{?}{=} 199$

$199 = 199$

The number is 182.

7. x = the number

$2x + 7 = 93$

$2x = 86$

$x = 43$

Check:

$2(43) + 7 \overset{?}{=} 93$

$86 + 7 \overset{?}{=} 93$

$93 = 93$

The number is 43.

9. $x =$ the number

$$18 - \frac{2}{3}x = 12$$

$$54 - 2x = 36$$

$$-2x = -18$$

$$x = 9$$

Check:

$$18 - \frac{2}{3}(9) \stackrel{?}{=} 12$$

$$18 - 6 \stackrel{?}{=} 12$$

$$12 = 12$$

The number is 9.

11. $x =$ the number

$$2x - 5 = 3x$$

$$-5 = x$$

Check.

$$2(-5) - 5 \stackrel{?}{=} 3(-5)$$

$$-10 - 5 \stackrel{?}{=} -15$$

$$-15 = -15$$

The number is -5.

13. $x =$ the number

$$x + \frac{1}{2}x + \frac{1}{3}x = 22$$

$$6x + 3x + 2x = 132$$

$$11x = 132$$

$$x = 12$$

Check:

$$12 + \frac{1}{2}(12) + \frac{1}{3}(12) \stackrel{?}{=} 22$$

$$12 + 6 + 4 \stackrel{?}{=} 22$$

$$22 = 22$$

The number is 12.

15. $x =$ number of used bikes

$4x =$ number of new bikes

$$4x = 60$$

$$x = 15$$

Used bikes in stock: 15

17. $x =$ wildfires between 1/1/03 and 7/27/03

$$2x - 16,723 = 52,107$$

$$2x = 68,830$$

$$x = 34,415$$

34,415 wildfires between 1/1/03 and 7/27/03

19. $x =$ number of CDs

$$218 + 11x = 284$$

$$11x = 66$$

$$x = 6$$

Kyle purchased 6 CDs.

21. x = number of items of jewelry

$$2(38) + 49 + 11.50x = 171$$
$$76 + 49 + 11.50x = 171$$
$$125 + 11.50x = 171$$
$$11.50x = 46$$
$$x = 4$$

She could buy 4 items of jewelry.

23. $r = \dfrac{d}{t}$, $d = 6404$, $t = 20$

$$r = \frac{6404}{20} = 320.2$$

It traveled at 320.2 mi/hr

25. $J = 2.5E$, $E = 220$

$$J = 2.5(220) = 550 \text{ lb}$$

27. Nell: $r = 12$, $t = 2.5$

$$d = rt = 12(2.5) = 30$$

Kristin: $r = 14$, $t = 2.5$

$$d = rt = 14(2.5) = 35$$

Distance apart $= 35 - 30 = 5$ miles

29. r = rate

Highway route: $5r = 320$
$$r = 64$$

Highway route at 64 mph.

Mountain route: $6r = 312$
$$r = 52$$

Mountain route at 52 mph.

Difference: $64 - 52 = 12$ mph

31. x = temperature on the 9th day

$$101 + 100 + 102.5 + 103 + 108 + 109$$
$$+ 105.5 + 102 + x$$
$$= 831 + x$$
$$\frac{831 + x}{9} = 104$$
$$831 + x = 936$$
$$x = 105$$

It needs to be 105°F.

33. x = old station wagon mileage

$$\frac{38 + 21 + x}{3} = 22\frac{2}{3}$$
$$\frac{59 + x}{3} = \frac{68}{3}$$
$$59 + x = 68$$
$$x = 9 \text{ mpg}$$

35. x = number of cricket chirps

F = Fahrenheit temperature

(a) $F - 40 = \dfrac{x}{4}$

(b) $90 - 40 = \dfrac{x}{4}$

$$50 = \frac{x}{4}$$
$$x = 200 \text{ chirps}$$

(c) $F - 40 = \dfrac{148}{4}$

$$F - 40 = 37$$
$$F = 77^0$$

Cumulative Review

37. $-2a(ab - 3b + 5a) = -2a^2b + 6ab - 10a^2$

39. $5x^2y - 7xy^2 - 8xy - 9x^2y$
$$= (5 - 9)x^2y - 7xy^2 - 8xy$$
$$= -4x^2y - 7xy^2 - 8xy$$

41. x = number of people invited
$$23.75x = 1425$$
$$x = 60$$
She can invite 60 people.

3.3 Exercises

1. x = long length
$x - 17$ = short length
$$x + x - 17 = 47$$
$$2x = 64$$
$$x = 32$$
$$x - 17 = 15$$
The long piece is 32 m long.
The short piece is 15 m long.

3. x = Dave's salary
$x + 2600$ = Elsie's salary
$$x + x + 2600 = 71,200$$
$$2x + 2600 = 71,200$$
$$2x = 68,600$$
$$x = 34,300$$
$$x + 2600 = 34,300 + 2600 = 36,900$$
Dave earned \$34,300
Elsie earned \$36,900

5. x = hours David worked
$x + 15$ = hours Sarah worked
$x - 5$ = hours Kate worked
$$x + x + 15 + x - 5 = 100$$
$$3x + 10 = 100$$
$$3x = 90$$
$$x = 30$$
$$x + 15 = 45$$
$$x - 5 = 25$$

David worked 30 hours
Sarah worked 45 hours
Kate worked 25 hours

7. x = number born in Oklahoma

$x + 8$ = number born in Texas

$x - 9$ = number born in Arizona

$x + x + 8 + x - 9 = 32$

$\qquad 3x - 1 = 32$

$\qquad\quad 3x = 33$

$\qquad\qquad x = 11$

$x + 8 = 11 + 8 = 19$

$x - 9 = 11 - 9 = 2$

11 were born in Oklahoma

19 were born in Texas

2 were born in Arizona

9. x = width

$2x - 3$ = length

$P = 2L + 2W$

$42 = 2(2x - 3) + 2x$

$42 = 4x - 6 + 2x$

$42 = 6x - 6$

$48 = 6x$

$8 = x$

$2x - 3 = 2(8) - 3 = 16 - 3 = 13$

width $= 8$ meters

length $= 13$ meters

11. x = width

$3x + 20$ = length

$P = 2L + 2W$

$96 = 2(3x + 20) + 2x$

$96 = 6x + 40 + 2x$

$96 = 8x + 40$

$56 = 8x$

$7 = x$

$3x + 20 = 3(7) + 20 = 41$

width $= 7$ cm

length $= 41$ cm

13. w = width

$\qquad 3w - 35$ = length

$2w + 2(3w - 35) = 190$

$\qquad 2w + 6w - 70 = 190$

$\qquad\qquad\quad 8w = 260$

$\qquad\qquad\quad\; w = 32.5$

$\qquad\quad 3w - 35 = 62.5$

width $= 32.5$ cm

length $= 62.5$ cm

15. $x = $ speed of jackal

     $2x = $ speed of cheetah

     $x + 10 = $ speed of elk

     $x + 2x + x + 10 = 150$

         $4x + 10 = 150$

           $4x = 140$

            $x = 35$

           $2x = 70$

        $x + 10 = 45$

     35 mi/hr is the speed of the jackal.

     70 mi/hr is the speed of the cheetah.

     45 mi/hr is the speed of the elk.

17. $x = $ length C

     $2x = $ length A

     $1.5x = $ length B

     $x + 3 = $ length D

     $x + 2x + 1.5x + x + 3 = 58$

            $5.5x + 3 = 58$

                $x = 10$

      $x = $ length C $= 10"$

     $2x = $ length A $= 20"$

     $1.5x = $ length B $= 15"$

     $x + 3 = $ length D $= 13"$

     $x + 2x + 1.5x + x + 3 = 58$

     $x = 10"$

19. $x = $ time over land

     $x + 3 = $ time over water

     $x + x + 3 = 39$

       $2x + 3 = 39$

          $2x = 36$

           $x = 18$

     $x + 3 = 18 + 3 = 21$

     a.   18 hours over land

     b.   21 hours over water

     c.   rate over land $= r = \dfrac{d}{t} = \dfrac{684}{18} = 38$ mi/hr

         rate over water $= r = \dfrac{d}{t} = \dfrac{1197}{21} = 57$ mi/hr

         $57 - 38 = 19$ mi/hr faster over water

21. $x = $ length of side

     $x + 2 = $ length of new side

     $4(x + 2) = 5x - 3$

       $4x + 8 = 5x - 3$

         $11 = x$

     The original square was 11 m by 11 m.

Cumulative Review

23. $-4x(2x^2 - 3x + 8) = -8x^3 + 12x^2 - 32x$

25. $-7x + 10y - 12x - 8y - 2$

     $= (-7 - 12)x + (10 - 8)y - 2$

     $= -19x + 2y - 2$

27.   Professional L & C: $\dfrac{117}{650} = 0.18 = 18\%$

     Not professional L & C: $100\% - 18\% = 82\%$

How Am I Doing? Sections 3.1-3.3

1. $3x - 40$

2. $\dfrac{1}{2}x + 12$

3. $\dfrac{5x}{12}$

4. $\dfrac{1}{4}(x + 10)$

5. $x =$ the number

$$2x + 5 = -47$$
$$2x = -52$$
$$x = -26$$

The number is -26.

6. $x =$ the number

$$\dfrac{x}{2} - 9 = 43$$
$$\dfrac{x}{2} = 52$$
$$x = 104$$

The number is 104.

7. $x =$ number of months

$$310x = 12,400$$
$$x = 40$$

In 40 months

8. $x =$ hours of overtime

$$24(40) + \dfrac{1}{2}(24)x = 1140$$
$$960 + 12x = 1140$$
$$12x = 180$$
$$x = 15$$

9. $x =$ 4th person's salary

$x + 2500 =$ 5th person's salary

$40,000 + 13,000 =$ 3rd person's salary

$40,000 + 35,000 + 53,500 + x + x + 2500$
$$= 2x + 131,000$$
$$\dfrac{2x + 131,000}{5} = 50,200$$
$$2x + 131,000 = 251,000$$
$$2x = 120,000$$
$$x = 60,000$$

$x + 2500 = 60,000 + 2500 = 62,500$

The 4th person's salary was $60,000.

The 5th person's salary was $62,500.

10. $x =$ length of short piece

$2x + 18 =$ length of long piece

$$x + 2x + 18 = 84$$
$$3x + 18 = 84$$
$$3x = 66$$
$$x = 22$$

$2x + 18 = 2(22) + 18 = 62$

The long piece is 62 feet.

The short piece is 22 feet.

11. x = number of pages on Sunday

   $2x - 25$ = number of pages on Monday

   $3x - 15$ = number of pages on Tuesday

$$x + 2x - 25 + 3x - 15 = 260$$
$$6x - 40 = 260$$
$$6x = 300$$
$$x = 50$$
$$2x - 25 = 2(50) - 25 = 75$$
$$3x - 15 = 3(50) - 15 = 135$$

50 pages on Sunday

75 pages on Monday

135 pages on Tuesday

12. x = hours to plow 2nd field

   $3x$ = hours to plow 1st field

   $\dfrac{x}{4}$ = hours to plow 3rd field

$$x + 3x + \frac{x}{4} = 510$$
$$4x + 12x + x = 2040$$
$$17x = 120$$
$$x = 120$$
$$3x = 3(120) = 360$$
$$\frac{x}{4} = \frac{120}{4} = 30$$

2nd field takes 120 hours

1st field takes 360 hours

3rd field takes 30 hours

3.4 Exercises

1. x = number of bags

$$0.75x + 3(6.50) = 27.75$$
$$0.75x + 19.50 = 27.75$$
$$0.75x = 8.25$$
$$x = 11$$

He filled 11 bags.

3. x = overtime hours

$$6(40) + 9x = 303$$
$$240 + 9x = 303$$
$$9x = 63$$
$$x = 7$$

He needs 7 hours of overtime per week.

5. x = time to pay off the uniforms

$$600 + 105x = 1817.75$$
$$105x = 1217.75$$
$$x \approx 11.6$$

It will take about 12 weeks.

7. x = original price

$$0.28x = 100.80$$
$$x = 360$$

The original price was \$360.

9. x = last year's salary

   $0.03x$ = raise

$$x + 0.03x = 22,660$$
$$1.03x = 22,660$$
$$x = 22,000$$

Last year's salary was \$22,000

11. $x =$ investment

$0.09x =$ interest

$x + 0.09x = 6540$

$1.09x = 6540$

$x = 6000$

He invested $6000.

13. $x =$ amount earning 7%

$5000 - x =$ amount earning 5%

$0.07x + 0.05(5000 - x) = 310$

$0.07x + 250 - 0.05x = 310$

$0.02x + 250 = 310$

$0.02x = 60$

$x = 3000$

$5000 - x = 2000$

They invested $3000 at 7% and $2000 at 5%.

15. $x =$ amount invested at 12%

$400,000 - x =$ amount invested at 8%

$0.12x + 0.08(400,000 - x) = 38,000$

$0.12x + 32,000 - 0.08x = 38,000$

$0.04x + 32,000 = 38,000$

$0.04x = 6,000$

$x = 150,000$

$400,000 - x = 250,000$

They invested $150,000 at 12% and $250,000 at 8%.

17. $x =$ amount invested

$\dfrac{x}{2} =$ amount invested at 5%

$\dfrac{x}{3} =$ amount invested at 4%

$x - \dfrac{x}{2} - \dfrac{x}{3} = \dfrac{6x - 3x - 2x}{6} = \dfrac{x}{6} =$

amount invested at 3.5%

$0.05\left(\dfrac{x}{2}\right) + 0.04\left(\dfrac{x}{3}\right) + (0.035)\left(\dfrac{x}{6}\right) = 530$

$\left(\dfrac{0.05}{2} + \dfrac{0.04}{3} + \dfrac{0.035}{6}\right)x = 530$

$\dfrac{53}{1200}x = 530$

$x = 12,000$

He invested $12,000.

19. $x =$ number of quarters

$x - 4 =$ number of nickels

$0.25x + 0.05(x - 4) = 3.70$

$25x + 5(x - 4) = 370$

$25x + 5x - 20 = 370$

$30x = 390$

$x = 13$

$x - 4 = 9$

She has 13 quarters and 9 nickels.

21. $x =$ number of dimes

$x + 3 =$ number of quarters

$2(x + 3) = 2x + 6 =$ number of nickels

$0.25(x + 3) + 0.10x + 0.05(2x + 6) = 3.75$

$25(x + 3) + 10x + 5(2x + 6) = 375$

$25x + +75 + 10x + 10x + 30 = 375$

$45x + 105 = 375$

102

$$45x = 270$$
$$x = 6$$
$$x + 3 = 6 + 3 = 9$$
$$2x + 6 = 12 + 6 = 18$$

He has 9 quarters, 6 dimes, and 18 nickels

23. x = number of regular stamps

$x - 8$ = number of breast cancer stamps

$$0.37x + 0.4(x - 8) = 19.90$$
$$0.37x + 0.4x - 3.2 = 19.90$$
$$0.77x - 23.1$$
$$x = 30$$
$$x - 8 = 16$$
$$x + 3 = 30 - 8 = 22$$

30 regular stamps

22 breast cancer stamps

25. x = number of $10 bills

$2x$ = number of $20 bills

$x + 3$ = number of $100 bills

$$10x + 20(2x) + 100(x + 3) = 1500$$
$$10x + 40x + 100x + 300 = 1500$$
$$150x = 1200$$
$$x = 8$$
$$2x = 16$$
$$x + 3 = 11$$

Eight $10 bills, sixteen $20 bills, eleven $100 bills.

27. x = amount of sales

$$18,000 + 0.04x = 55,000$$
$$0.04x = 37,000$$
$$x = 925,000$$

She must sell $925,000 worth of furniture.

29. x = miles driven

Golden Gate has the better bargain when the miles driven exceeds the number which makes their total charge equal to that of the West Suburban Agency.

$$0.24x + 3(35) = 0.16x + 3(41)$$
$$24x + 10,500 = 16x + 12,300$$
$$8x = 1800$$
$$x = 225$$

The salesperson must drive more than 225 miles.

Cumulative Review

31. $5(3) + 6 \div (-2) = 15 + (-3) = 12$

33. If $x = -2$ and $y = 3$, then

$$2x^2 + 3xy - 2y^2$$
$$= 2(-2)^2 + 3(-2)(3) - 2(3)^2$$
$$= 2(4) - 18 - 2(9)$$
$$= 8 - 18 - 18 = -28$$

103

35. Discount $= 0.15(22,400) = 3360$

    Discounted cost $= 22,400 - 3360$

    $= \$19,040$

    Average cost $= \dfrac{19,040}{200} = \$95.20 / \text{part}$

3.5 Exercises

1. Perimeter is the <u>distance around</u> a plane figure.

3. Area is a measure of the amount of <u>surface</u> in a region.

5. The sum of the interior angles of any triangle is $\underline{180^0}$.

9. $a = 14, \ b = 7$

    $A = ba = (14)(7) = 98 \text{ in.}^2$

11. $A = 80, \ b = 16$

    $A = \dfrac{1}{2}ab$

    $80 = \dfrac{1}{2}a(16)$

    $80 = 8a$

    $10 = a$

    $a = 10 \text{ feet}$

13. $x = $ length of adjacent side

    $2(14) + 2x = 46$

    $28 + 2x = 46$

    $28 + 2x = 46$

    $2x = 18$

    $x = 9$

    The length is 9 inches.

15. $A = \pi r^2, \ r = 7.00$

    $A \approx (3.14)(7.00)^2 = 153.86 \text{ square feet}$

17. $C = \pi d, \ d = 3032$

    $C = (3.14)(3032)$

    $C = 9520.48 \text{ miles}$

19. $A = 600, \ b_1 = 20, \ b_2 = 30$

    $A = \dfrac{1}{2}a(b_1 + b_2)$

    $600 = \dfrac{1}{2}a(20 + 30)$

    $1200 = a(50)$

    $a = 24 \text{ in.}$

21. length $= 3(80) = 240$

    width $= 2(280) = 560$

    $A = LW = 240(560) = 134,400 \text{ m}^2$

23. $C = 2\pi r, \ C = 31.4$

    $31.4 = 2(3.14)r$

    $31.4 = 6.28r$

    $5 = r$

    Radius is 5 centimeters

104

25. $r = \dfrac{d}{2}$, $d = 64$

    $r = \dfrac{64}{2} = 32$

    $C = 2\pi r$, $r = 32$

    $C = 2(3.14)(32) = 200.96$ centimeters

27. x = measure of 3rd angle

    47 = measure of 1st angle

    59 = measure of 2nd angle

    Sum of the angles is $180°$

    $x + 47 + 59 = 180$

    $x + 106 = 180$

    $x = 74$

    The measure of the 3rd angle is $74°$

29. x = measure of 3rd angle

    $4x$ = measure of the equal angles

    Sum of the angles is $180°$

    $x + 4x + 4x = 180$

    $9x = 180$

    $x = 20$

    $4x = 80$

    The measure of the 3rd angle is $20°$

    The measure of the equal angles is $80°$

31. x = measure of the equal angles

    38 = measure of smallest angle

    Sum of the angles is $180°$

    $x + x + 38 = 180$

    $2x + 38 = 180$

    $2x = 142$

    $x = 71$

    The measure of the equal angles is $71°$

33. x = measure of 2nd angle

    $2x$ = measure of 1st angle

    $2(2x) + 19$ = measure of 3rd angle

    $x + 2x + 4x + 19 = 180$

    $7x + 19 = 180$

    $7x - 161$

    $x = 23$

    $2x = 46$

    $4x + 19 = 111$

    1st angle measures $46°$

    2nd angle measures $23°$

    3rd angle measures $111°$

35. x = the angle

    $x + 38 + 90 = 180$

    $x + 128 = 180$

    $x = 52$

    The angle is $52°$.

105

37. Number of cans of paint $= \dfrac{40}{20} = 2$

    Area painted $= 2(102) = 204$

    Area of one side $= \dfrac{204}{4} = 51$

    $A = \dfrac{1}{2}a(b_1 + b_2)$

    $51 = \dfrac{1}{2}a(8+9)$

    $102 = a(17)$

    $6 = a$

    Altitude is 6 feet.

39. $V = 235.5, \quad r = 15$

    $V = \pi r^2 h, \ r = 10, \ h = 8$

    $V = (3.14)(10)^2 (8)$

    $\quad = (3.14)(100)(8)$

    $\quad = 2512$

    The volume is 2512 cubic inches

41. $V = \dfrac{4}{3}\pi r^3, \ r = \dfrac{d}{2} = \dfrac{8}{2} = 4$

    $V = \dfrac{4}{3}(3.14)(4)^3 = 267.95$

    $267.95 > 175$

    Yes, it will stay aloft.

43. $\qquad r = 6, \ h = 4$

    (a) $V = 4\pi r^2 h$

    $\quad = 4(3.14)(6)^2 (4)$

    $\quad = 452.16$

    The volume is 452.16 cm^3

    (b) $S = 2\pi rh + 2\pi r^2$

    $\quad = 2(3.14)(6)(4) + 2(3.14)(6)^2$

    $\quad = 150.72 + 226.08$

    $\quad = 376.8$

    The total surface area is 376.8 cm^2

45. Area of the $\dfrac{3}{4}$ circle:

    $A = \dfrac{3}{4}\pi r^2, \ r = 8$

    $A = \dfrac{3}{4}(3.14)(8)^2 = 150.72$

    Area of the $\dfrac{1}{4}$ circle:

    $A = \dfrac{1}{4}\pi r^2, \ r = 4$

    $A = \dfrac{1}{4}(3.14)(4)^2 = 12.56$

    Total area $= 150.72 + 12.56$

    $\qquad\qquad = 163.28$

    Goat eats 163.28 square feet

47. (a) $A = l_1 w_1 + \frac{1}{4}\pi r^2 + l_2 w_2$

    $l_1 = 1.5, \ w_1 = 9.5, \ r = 1.5,$

    $l_2 = 1.5, \ w_2 = 4.5$

    $A = (1.5)(9.5) + \frac{1}{4}(3.14)(1.5)^2 + (1.5)(4.5)$

    $\quad = 14.25 + 1.77 + 6.75$

    $\quad = 22.77 \text{ yards}^2$

    (b) $\text{Cost} = (2.50)(22.77) = \$56.93$

49. a. $x = \text{length of straight edge}$

    $P = 2\pi r + 2x, \ r = 7, \ x = 15$

    $P = 2(3.14)(7) + 2(15) = 43.96 + 30 = 73.96$

    The perimeter is 73.96 inches.

    b. $V = (\pi r^2 + 2rx)h, \ h = 0.5$

    $V = \left[3.14(7)^2 + 2(7)(15)\right](0.5)$

    $V = 363.86(0.5)$

    $V = 181.93$ cubic inches of plastic

51. Perimeter $= \dfrac{120.93}{1.39} = 87$ feet

    $w = \text{width}, \ 4w - 3 = \text{length}$

    $2w + 2(4w - 3) = 87$

    $\quad 2w + 8w - 6 = 87$

    $\quad\quad 10w = 93$

    $\quad\quad\quad w = 9.3$

    $4w - 3 = 34.2$

    width is 9.3 feet, length is 34.2 feet

53. 1st possibility: 2 sides are 4 and one is 7.5

    Perimeter $= 4 + 4 + 7.5 = 15.5$ feet

    2nd possibility: one side is 4 and 2 are 7.5

    Perimeter $= 4 + 7.5 + 7.5 = 19$ feet

55. Moon's radius $= 1080(5280) = 5,702,400$

    4-ft poles: $C = 2\pi r, \ r = 5,702,404$

    $C = 2(3.14)(5,702,404) = 35,811,097.12$

    3-ft poles: $C = 2\pi r, \ r = 5,702,404$

    $C = 2(3.14)(5,702,403) = 35,811,090.84$

    $C_4 - C_3 = 35,811,097.12 - 35,811,090.84$

    $\quad = 6.28$ feet

Cumulative Review

57. $-5(x+3) - 2\left[4 + 3(x-1)\right]$

    $= -5x - 15 - 2(4 + 3x - 3)$

    $= -5x - 15 - 2(3x + 1)$

    $= -5x - 15 - 6x - 2$

    $= -11x - 17$

59. $-2\left\{x + 3\left[2 - 4(x-3)\right]\right\}$

    $= -2\left\{x + 3[2 - 4x + 12]\right\}$

    $= -2\left\{x + 3[-4x + 14]\right\}$

    $= -2\left\{x - 12x + 42\right\}$

    $= -2\left\{-11x + 42\right\}$

    $= 22x - 84$

3.6 Exercises

1. $x > 67,000$

3. $x \leq 120$

5. $h \leq 1500$

7. $x \geq 93$

9. 3rd length: x
    $87 + 64 + x \leq 291$
    $151 + x \leq 291$
    $x \leq 140$
    140 cm or less

11. $x =$ number of deliveries in week 6
    $$\frac{18 + 40 + 21 + 7 + 36 + x}{6} \geq 24$$
    $$\frac{122 + x}{6} \geq 24$$
    $122 + x \geq 144$
    $x \geq 22$

    She must make 22 or more deliveries.

13. $A = LW$, $W = 8$
    $8L \leq 60$
    $L \leq 7.5$
    Depth can be no more than 7.5 feet

15. $x =$ number of miles
    Cost for 2 days $= 2(37.50) = 75$
    $0.195x + 75 \leq 150$
    $0.195x \leq 75$
    $x \leq 384.6$
    They could drive no more than
    384.6 miles.

17. $\dfrac{5}{9}(F - 32) < 110$
    $5(F - 32) < 990$
    $F - 32 < 198$
    $F < 230$
    Temperature less than 230^0F.

19. $A = 9.2x + 77.1$, $A = 307.1$
    $9.2x + 77.1 > 307.1$
    $9.2x > 230$
    $x > 25$
    After $1980 + 25 = 2005$
    The budget will exceed $307.1 billion
    after 2005.

21. $x =$ hours of labor
    $840 + 45x \leq 1200$
    $45x \leq 360$
    $x \leq 8$
    It will take 8 hours or less.

23. $18n > 5000 + 7n$

    $11n > 5000$

    $n > 454.5$

    Need to manufacture and sell
    more than 455 discs.

Cumulative Review

25. $10 - 3x > 14 - 2x$

    $-x > 4$

    $x < -4$

27. $30 - 2(x+1) \le 4x$

    $30 - 2x - 2 \le 4x$

    $-6x \le -28$

    $x \ge \dfrac{14}{3}$

    $x \ge 4\dfrac{2}{3}$

29. a. $8(365) = 2920$ gallons wasted

    b. $\text{Cost} = \dfrac{2920}{1000}(8.50) = 24.82$

    He will pay $24.82 extra.

Putting Your Skills to Work

1. $a = \dfrac{22,766 - 15,303}{4} \approx 1865.75$

    $b = 15,303$

    $y = 1866x + 15,303$

2. $1995 - x = 1995 - 1986 = 9$

    $y = 1866(9) + 15,303$

    $y = 32,097$ caribou

    $1984 - x = 1984 - 1986 = -2$

    $y = 1866(-2) + 15,303$

    $y = 11,571$ caribou

3. $2003 - x = 2003 - 1986 = 17$

    $y = 1866(17) + 15,303$

    $y = 47,025$ caribou

    The measured value of 43,375 is
    $47,025 - 43,375 = 3650$ lower. The
    equation predicts a value that is too high
    for 2003.

4. $a = \dfrac{43,375 - 15,303}{17} \approx 1651$

    $y = 1651 \times 15,303$

Chapter 3 Review Problems

1. $x + 19$

2. $\dfrac{2}{3}x$

3. $\dfrac{1}{2}x$ or $\dfrac{x}{2}$

4. $x - 18$

5. $3(x + 4)$

6. $2x - 3$

7. number of retired people: r

   number of working people: $4r$

   number of unemployed people: $\dfrac{1}{2}r$

8. $w =$ width of the rectangle

   $3w + 5 =$ length of the redctangle

9. $\quad b =$ the number of degrees in angle B

   $\quad 2b =$ the number of degrees in angle A

   $b - 17 =$ the number of degrees in angle C

10. number of algebra students: a

    number of biology students: $a + 29$

    number of geology students: $\dfrac{1}{2}a$

11. $x =$ the number

    $2x - 18 = -8$

    $2x = 10$

    $x = 5$

    The number is 5.

12. $x =$ a number

    $3x - 6 = 15$

    $3x = 21$

    $x = 7$

    The number is 7.

13. $x =$ cost of chair

    $210 + 6x = 450$

    $6x = 240$

    $x = 40$

    1 chair costs \$40.

14. $x =$ David's age

    $2x =$ Jon's age

    $2x = 32$

    $x = 16$

    David is 16 years old.

15. $t_1 =$ time for first car

    $t_2 =$ time for other car

    $330 = 50t_1$

    $6.6 = t_1$

    $330 = 55t_2$

    $6 = t_2$

    The first car took 6.6 hours.

    The other car took 6 hours.

16. $x = \text{grade}$

$$\frac{85 + 78 + 65 + 92 + 70 + x}{6} = 80$$

$$\frac{390 + x}{6} = 80$$

$$390 + x = 480$$

$$x = 90$$

She needs a grade of 90.

17. x is the measure of the third sid

$$x + 2(31) = 85$$

$$x + 62 = 85$$

$$x = 23$$

The third side measures 23 feet

18. 1st angle: x

2nd angle: $3x$

3rd angle: $2x - 12$

$$x + 3x + 2x - 12 = 180$$

$$6x - 12 = 180$$

$$6x = 192$$

$$x = 32$$

$$3x = 3(32) = 96$$

$$2x - 12 = 2(32) - 12 = 52$$

32^0, 96^0, and 52^0, respectively.

19. $x = \text{length of one piece}$

$\dfrac{3}{5}x = \text{length of other}$

$$x + \frac{3}{5}x = 50$$

$$5x + 3x = 250$$

$$8x = 250$$

$$x = 31.25$$

$$\frac{3}{5}x = 18.75$$

The lengths are 31.25 yd and 18.75 yd.

20. $x = \text{Jon's salary}$

$3000 + \dfrac{1}{2}x = \text{Lauren's salary}$

$$x + 3000 + \frac{1}{2}x = 48,000$$

$$\frac{3}{2}x + 3000 = 48,000$$

$$\frac{3}{2}x = 45,000$$

$$x = 30,000$$

$$3000 + \frac{1}{2}x = 3000 + \frac{1}{2}(30,000) = 18,000$$

Jon: \$30,000; Lauren: \$18,000

21. $x = \text{number of kilowatt-hours}$

$$25 + 0.15x = 71.50$$

$$0.15x = 46.50$$

$$x = 310$$

310 kilowatt-hours

22. x = number of miles driven

$$0.25x + 39(3) = 187$$
$$0.25x + 117 = 187$$
$$0.25x = 70$$
$$x = 280$$

He drove 280 miles.

23. x = amount withdrawn

$$0.055(7400 - x) = 242$$
$$407 - 0.055x = 242$$
$$-0.055x = -165$$
$$x = 3000$$

They withdrew $3000.

24. x = original price

$$0.18x = 36$$
$$x = 200$$

The original price was $200.

25. x = amount invested at 12%

$9000 - x$ = amount at 8%

$$0.12x + 0.08(9000 - x) = 1000$$
$$12x + 8(9000 - x) = 100,000$$
$$12x + 72,000 - 8x = 100,000$$
$$4x = 28,000$$
$$x = 7000$$
$$9000 - x = 2000$$

They invested $7000 at 12% and $2000 at 8%.

26. x = amount at 4.5%

$5000 - x$ = amount at 6%

$$0.045x + 0.06(5000 - x) = 270$$
$$45x + 60(5000 - x) = 270,000$$
$$45x + 300,000 - 60x = 270,000$$
$$-15x = -30,000$$
$$x = 2000$$
$$5000 - x = 5000 - 2000 = 3000$$

$2000 at 4.5%; $3000 at 6%

27. x = number of dimes

$x + 3$ = number of quarters

$$2(x + 3) = 2x + 6 = \text{number of nickels}$$
$$0.05(2x + 6) + 0.10x + 0.25(x + 3) = 3.75$$
$$5(2x + 6) + 10x + 25(x + 3) = 375$$
$$10x + 30 + 10x + 25x + 75 = 375$$
$$45x = 270$$
$$x = 6$$

$$x + 3 = 6 + 3 = 9$$
$$2x + 6 = 2(6) + 6 = 18$$

She has 18 nickels, 6 dimes, 9 quarters

28. $d - 1 =$ number of nickels

    $d =$ number of dimes

    $d + 2 =$ number of quarters

    $0.05(d-1) + 0.10d + 0.25(d+2) = 3.65$

       $5(d-1) + 10d + 25(d+2) = 365$

         $5d - 5 + 10d + 25d + 50 = 365$

                $40d + 45 = 365$

                    $40d = 320$

                         $d = 8$

    $d - 1 = 8 - 1 = 7$

    $d + 2 = 8 + 2 = 10$

    7 nickels, 8 dimes, 10 quarters

29. $\text{S.A.} = 4\pi r^2, \; r = \dfrac{d}{2} = \dfrac{32}{2} = 16$

    $\text{S.A.} = 4(3.14)(16)^2$

    $\text{S.A.} = 3215.36$ sq. in.

30. $P = (\text{number of sides})(\text{length of side})$

    $P = 64$

    $P = 24$ feet

31. $x =$ measure of third angle

    $62 + 47 + x = 180$

       $109 + x = 180$

           $x = 71$

    The angle is 71^0.

32. $A = \dfrac{1}{2}ab$

    $= \dfrac{1}{2}(8)(10.5)$

    $= 42$

    42 mi^2

33. $l = 12, \; w = 8, \; h = 20$

    $V = lwh = 12(8)(20) = 1920$ ft^3

34. $V = \dfrac{4}{3}\pi r^3$

    $= \dfrac{4}{3}(3.14)(3)^3$

    $= 113.04$

    113.04 cm^3

35. $A = \pi r^2$

    $= 3.14\left(\dfrac{18.00}{2}\right)^2$

    $= 3.14(9)^2$

    $= 254.34$

    254.34 cm^2

36. $x =$ length of 3rd side

    $P =$ sum of sides

    $17 + 17 + x = 46$

       $34 + x = 46$

           $x = 12$

    The 3rd side is 12 in.

37. $C = 2.50 \left[2(18)(22) + 2(18)(19) - 100 \right]$

$\quad = 2.50(1376)$

$\quad = 3440$

$\quad \$3440$

38. $r = 5,\ h = 14$

$\quad S = 2\pi rh + 2\pi r^2$

$\quad = 2(3.14)(5)(14) + 2(3.14)(5)^2$

$\quad = 439.60 + 157.00$

$\quad = 596.60 \text{ m}^2$

$\quad \text{Cost} = 40(596.60) = \$23,864.00$

39. $x =$ miles driven

$\quad 0.15x + 2(35) \le 100$

$\quad\quad 15x + 7000 \le 10,000$

$\quad\quad\quad 15x \le 3000$

$\quad\quad\quad\quad x \le 200$

Distance must be no more than 200 miles.

40. $x =$ sales

$\quad 12,000 + 0.04x > 24,000$

$\quad\quad 0.04x > 12,000$

$\quad\quad\quad x > 300,000$

More than \$300,000 in sales

41. $d = rt$

$\quad 1590 = 8.75t + 20(t - 24)$

$\quad 1590 = 28.75t - 480$

$\quad 1590 = 28.75t - 480$

$\quad 2070 = 28.75t$

$\quad\quad 72 = t$

It took 72 months.

CP distance $= rt$

$\quad\quad = 8.75(72)$

$\quad\quad = 630$ miles

UP distance $= rt$

$\quad\quad = 20(72 - 24)$

$\quad\quad = 960$ miles

42. $x =$ amount spent on ties

$\quad 3(17.95) + x < 70$

$\quad\quad 53.85 + x < 70$

$\quad\quad\quad x < 16.15$

He must spend less than \$16.15 on ties.

43. $x =$ length of commercials

$\quad 4x + 4 =$ length of entertainment

$\quad x + 4x + 4 = 30$

$\quad\quad 5x = 26$

$\quad\quad\quad x = 5.2$

$\quad 4x + 4 = 4(5.2) + 4 = 24.8$

Entertainment was 24.8 min.

44. x = weight of each ball

    $3x = x + 8$

    $2x = 8$

    $x = 4$

    4 oz

45. x = number of years to even the cost

    $83x + 744 > 41x + 870$

    $42x + 744 > 870$

    $42x > 126$

    $x > 3$

    It will take more than 3 years.

46. x = number of months

    $1100x + 42,000 < 1800x$

    $42,000 < 700x$

    $60 < x$

    It will take more than 60 months.

47. x = height

    $2.5x$ = width

    $3(2.5x) + 2x = 38$

    $7.5x + 2x = 38$

    $9.5x = 38$

    $x = 4$

    $2.5x = 10$

    Width = 10 feet, height = 4 feet

48.

Year	Amount	Total
1	1200	1200
2	2400	3600
3	3600	7200
4	4800	12,000
5	6000	18,000
6	7200	25,200
7	8400	33,600
8	9600	43,200
9	10,800	54,000
10	12,000	66,000

49. x – number of free throws

    $3x$ = number of field goals

    $1x + 2(3x) + 3(12) = 99$

    $7x + 36 = 99$

    $7x = 63$

    $x = 9$

    $3x = 27$

    They made 9 free throws and 27 field goals.

50. x = width

    $2x - 10$ = length

    $P = 2L + 2W$

    $76 = 2(2x - 10) + 2x$

    $76 = 4x - 20 + 2x$

    $76 = 6x - 20$

    $96 = 6x$

    $16 = x$

    $2x - 10 = 22$

    Length = 22 feet

    Width = 16 feet

115

51. x = hours Carl worked

    $2x - 8$ = hours Ryan worked

    $x + 2x - 8 = 28$

    $3x - 8 = 28$

    $3x = 36$

    $x = 12$

    $2x - 8 = 2(12) - 8 = 16$

    Carl worked 12 hours.

    Ryan worked 16 hours.

52. x = amount invested at 9.75%

    $x + 2000$ = amount invested at 8.5%

    $0.0975x = 0.085x + 170$

    $0.0125x = 170$

    $x = 13,600$

    $x + 2000 = 13,600 + 2000 = 15,600$

    \$13,600 was invested at 9.75%.

    \$15,600 was invested at 8.5%.

53. x = measure of 2nd angle

    $x + 20$ = measure of 1st angle

    $2x$ = measure of 3rd angle

    $x + x + 20 + 2x = 180$

    $4x + 20 = 180$

    $4x = 160$

    $x = 40$

    $x + 20 = 60$

    $2x = 80$

    1st angle $= 60^0$

    2nd angle $= 40^0$

    3rd angle $= 80^0$

54. $A = \dfrac{1}{2}a(b_1 + b_2)$, $a = 12$, $b_1 = 15$, $b_2 = 9$

    $A = \dfrac{1}{2}(12)(15 + 9) = 6(34) = 204$

    Cost $= 6(204) = \$1224$

55. x = score on the final exam

    $\dfrac{88 + 77 + 95 + 92 + 2x}{6} = 90$

    $\dfrac{352 + 2x}{6} = 90$

    $352 + 2x = 540$

    $2x = 188$

    $x = 94$

    She must make 94 on the final exam.

56. x = business miles driven

    $2x$ = pleasure miles driven

    $x + 2x = 27,000$

    $3x = 27,000$

    $x = 9000$

    Deduction $= (0.33)(9000) = \$2970$

    No, her correct deduction was \$2970.

57. $d = rt$, $r = \dfrac{32}{3}$, $t = 60$

    $d = \dfrac{32}{3}(60) = 640$ miles

    Boston to Denver: $d = 1800$

    $1800 = \dfrac{32}{3}t$

    $169 \approx t$

    It will take about 169 minutes
    or 2 hr 49 min.

116

58. $d = rt$, $d = 80$, $r = 0.8\left(\dfrac{50}{6}\right)$

$$80 = 0.8\left(\dfrac{50}{6}\right)t$$

$$12 = t$$

It will take him 12 seconds.

59. $x = $ number of Explorers

$2x = $ number of Caravans

$$5x + 7(2x) = 95$$

$$5x + 14x = 95$$

$$19x = 95$$

$$x = 5$$

$$2x = 10$$

They need 5 Explorers and 10 Caravans.

60. $x = $ smallest angle

$3x = $ largest angle

$2x - 12 = $ third angle

$$x + 3x + 2x - 12 = 180$$

$$6x - 12 = 180$$

$$6x = 192$$

$$x = 32$$

$$3x = 3(32) = 96$$

$$2x - 12 = 2(32) - 12 = 52$$

Smallest angle $= 32°$

Largest angle $= 96°$

Third angle $= 52°$

61. $V = \dfrac{4}{3}\pi r^3$, $r = \dfrac{3}{2} = 1.5$

$$V = \dfrac{4}{3}(3.14)(1.5)^3$$

$$V = 14.13 \text{ cubic meters}$$

$$80 + 75 + 2(14.13) = 183.26 \text{ kg}$$

How Am I Doing? Chapter 3 Test

1. $x = $ number

$$2x - 11 = 59$$

$$2x = 70$$

$$x = 35$$

The number is 35.

2. $x = $ number

$$\dfrac{1}{2}x + \dfrac{1}{9}x + \dfrac{1}{12}x = 25$$

$$36\left(\dfrac{1}{2}x + \dfrac{1}{9}x + \dfrac{1}{12}x\right) = 36(25)$$

$$18x + 4x + 3x = 900$$

$$25x = 900$$

$$x = 36$$

The number is 36.

3. $x = $ number

$$2(x + 5) = 3x + 14$$

$$2x + 10 = 3x + 14$$

$$10 = x + 14$$

$$-4 = x$$

The number is -4.

4. $\frac{2}{3}x = $ 1st side

$x = $ 2nd side

$x - 14 = $ 3rd side

$\frac{2}{3}x + x + x - 14 = 66$

$\frac{8}{3}x - 14 = 66$

$\frac{8}{3}x = 80$

$x = 30$

$\frac{2}{3}x = \frac{2}{3}(30) = 20$

$x - 14 = 30 - 14 = 16$

20 m, 30 m, and 16 m, respectively.

5. $w = $ width

$2w + 7 = $ length

$2w + 2(2w + 7) = 134$

$2w + 4w + 14 = 134$

$6w + 14 = 134$

$6w = 120$

$w = 20$

$2w + 7 = 2(20) + 7 = 47$

width $= 20$ m

length $= 47$ m

6. $2x = $ 1st pollutant

$x = $ 2nd pollutant

$0.75x = $ 3rd pollutant

$2x + x + 0.75x = 15$

$3.75x = 15$

$x = 4$

$2x = 2(4) = 8$

$0.75x = 0.75(4) = 3$

1st pollutant: 8ppm;

2nd pollutant: 4 ppm;

3rd pollutant: 3 ppm

7. $x = $ number of months

$116x + 200 = 1940$

$116x = 1740$

$x = 15$

15 months

8. $x = $ last year's tuition

$x + 0.08x = 22,680$

$1.08x = 22,680$

$x = 21,000$

Last year's tuition was $21,000

9. x = amount at 14%

   $4000 - x$ = amount at 11%

$$0.14x + 0.11(4000 - x) = 482$$

$$100[0.14x + -.11(4000 - x)] = 100(482)$$

$$14x + 11(4000 - x) = 48,200$$

$$14x + 44,000 - 11x = 48,200$$

$$3x + 44,000 = 48,200$$

$$3x = 4200$$

$$x = 1400$$

$$4000 - x = 4000 - 1400 = 2600$$

$1400 at 14%; \$2600 at 11%

10. $2x$ = number of nickels

   $x - 1$ = number of dimes

   x = number of quarters

$$0.05(2x) + 0.10(x - 1) + 0.25(x) = 3.50$$

$$5(2x) + 10(x - 1) + 25x = 350$$

$$10x + 10x - 10 + 25x = 350$$

$$45x - 10 = 350$$

$$45x = 360$$

$$x = 8$$

$$2x = 2(8) = 16$$

$$x - 1 = 8 - 1 = 7$$

16 nickels; 7 dimes; 8 quarters

11. $C = 2\pi r,\ r = 34$

   $C \approx 2(3.14)(34) = 213.52$ inches

12. $A = \dfrac{1}{2}a(b_1 + b_2)$

$$= \frac{1}{2}(16)(10 + 14)$$

$$= 192$$

192 in.^{2}

13. $r = 10$

$$V = \frac{4}{3}\pi r^3$$

$$= \frac{4}{3}(3.14)(10)^3$$

$$= 4187 \text{ in.}^3$$

14. $A = ab,\ a = 8,\ b = 12$

   $A = 8(12)$

   $= 96$ square centimeters

15. $C = 12(1.5) + 9(2) + \dfrac{1}{2}(2)(1.5)$

$$= 18 + 18 + 1.5 = 37.5 \text{ yd}^2$$

$$\text{Cost} = 12(37.5) = \$450$$

16. x = score

$$\frac{76 + 84 + 78 + x}{4} \geq 80$$

$$\frac{238}{4} \geq 80$$

$$238 + x \geq 320$$

$$x \geq 82$$

At least an 82

17. $x = $ sales

$$15,000 + 0.05(x - 10,000) > 20,000$$
$$15,000 + 0.05x - 500 > 20,000$$
$$0.05x + 14,500 > 20,000$$
$$0.05x > 5500$$
$$x > 110,000$$

She must have sales of more than $110,000.

18. $A = LW$, $L = 150$, $W = 100$

$A = 150(100) = 15,000$ square feet

$$\text{Time} = \frac{15,000}{25} = 600 \text{ hours}$$

Cumulative Test for Chapters 0-3

1. $\begin{array}{r} 3.69 \\ 2.4\overline{)8.856} \end{array}$

$$\begin{array}{r} \underline{72} \\ 165 \\ \underline{144} \\ 216 \\ \underline{216} \end{array}$$

2. $\dfrac{3}{8} + \dfrac{5}{12} + \dfrac{1}{2} = \dfrac{9}{24} + \dfrac{10}{24} + \dfrac{12}{24}$

$$= \frac{9 + 10 + 12}{24}$$

$$= \frac{31}{24}$$

3. $3(2x - 3y + 6) + 2(-3x - 7y)$

$$= 6x - 9y + 18 - 6x - 14y$$
$$= -23y + 18$$

4. $12 - 3(2 - 4) + 12 \div 4$

$$= 12 - 3(-2) + 12 \div 4$$
$$= 12 + 6 + 3$$
$$= 21$$

5. $H = \dfrac{1}{2}(3a + 5b)$

$$2H = 2\left(\frac{1}{2}\right)(3a + 5b)$$

$$2H = 3a + 5b$$

$$2H + (-3a) = 3a + (-3a) + 5b$$

$$2H - 3a = 5b$$

$$\frac{2H - 3a}{5} = \frac{5b}{5}$$

$$\frac{2H - 3a}{5} = b$$

6. $5x - 3 \le 2(4x + 1) + 4$

$$5x - 3 \le 8x + 2 + 4$$
$$5x - 3 \le 8x + 6$$
$$5x \le 8x + 9$$
$$-3x \le 9$$
$$x \ge -3$$

7. x = the number

$$2x + 15 = 1$$
$$2x = -14$$
$$x = -7$$

The number is -7.

8. $x - 34$ = Psychology students

x = World History students

$$x + x - 34 = 134$$
$$2x - 34 = 134$$
$$2x = 168$$
$$x = 84$$
$$x - 34 = 84 - 34 = 50$$

50 Psychology students;

84 World History students

9. w = width

$3w + 11$ = length

$$P = 2L + 2W$$
$$2(3w + 11) + 2w = 78$$
$$6w + 22 + 2w = 78$$
$$8w = 56$$
$$w = 7$$
$$3w + 11 = 32$$

length = 32 cm, width = 7 cm

10. x = last year's sales

$$x + 0.35x = 182,250$$
$$1.35x = 182,250$$
$$x = 135,000$$

$135,000

11. x = amount invested at 15%

$7000 - x$ = amount invested at 7%

$$0.15x + 0.07(7000 - x) = 730$$
$$15x + 7(7000 - x) = 73,000$$
$$15x + 49,000 - 7x = 73,000$$
$$8x = 24,000$$
$$x = 3000$$
$$7000 - x = 4000$$

He invested $3000 at 15% and
$4000 at 7%.

12. $x + 3$ = number of nickels

$3x$ = number of dimes

x = number of quarters

$$0.05(x + 3) + 0.10(3x) + 0.25(x) = 2.55$$
$$5(x + 3) + 10(3x) + 25x = 255$$
$$5x + 15 + 30x + 25x = 255$$
$$60x + 15 = 255$$
$$60x = 240$$
$$x = 4$$

$$x + 3 = 4 + 3 = 7$$
$$3x = 3(4) = 12$$

7 nickels; 12 dimes; 4 quarters

13. $b = 25, \quad a = 13$

$$A = \frac{1}{2}ab = \frac{1}{2}(25)(13) = 162.5 \text{ m}^2$$

$$\text{Cost} = 4.50(162.5) = \$731.25$$

14. $V = \dfrac{4}{3}\pi r^3$

$ = \dfrac{4}{3}(3.14)(3.00)^3$

$ = 113.04 \text{ in.}^3$

weight $= (113.04)(1.50) = 169.56$

169.56 lb

15. $d = rt,\ d = 1625,\ r = 65$

$1625 = 65t$

$25 = t$

It will take 25 days.

Chapter 4

4.1 Exercises

1. When you multiply exponential expressions with the same base, keep the base the same and add the exponents.

3. $\dfrac{2^2}{2^3} \overset{?}{=} \dfrac{1}{2^{3-2}}$

   $\dfrac{4}{8} \overset{?}{=} \dfrac{1}{2}$

   $\dfrac{1}{2} = \dfrac{1}{2}$

5. $6x^{11}y$: Coefficient is 6, bases are x, y and exponents are 11, 1.

7. $2 \cdot 2 \cdot a \cdot a \cdot a \cdot b = 2^2 a^3 b$

9. $(-3)(a)(a)(b)(c)(b)(c)(c) = -3a^2 b^2 c^3$

11. $\left(7^4\right)\left(7^6\right) = 7^{4+6} = 7^{10}$

13. $\left(5^{10}\right)\left(5^{16}\right) = 5^{10+16} = 5^{26}$

15. $\left(x^4\right)\left(x^8\right) = x^{4+8} = x^{12}$

17. $\left(w^{12}\right)\left(w^{20}\right) = w^{12+20} = w^{32}$

19. $-5x^4\left(4x^2\right) = -20x^{4+2}$

    $= -20x^6$

21. $(5x)\left(10x^2\right) = (5 \cdot 10)x^{1+2}$

    $= 50x^3$

23. $\left(3x^2 y\right)\left(8x^3 y^3\right) = 24x^{2+3}y^{1+3}$

    $= 24x^5 y^4$

25. $\left(\dfrac{2}{5}xy^3\right)\left(\dfrac{1}{3}x^2 y^2\right) = \dfrac{2}{15}x^{1+2}y^{3+2}$

    $= \dfrac{2}{15}x^3 y^5$

27. $\left(1.1x^2 z\right)(-2.5xy) = (1.1)(-2.5)x^{2+1}yz$

    $= -2.75x^3 yz$

29. $(8a)\left(2a^3 b\right)(0) = 0$

31. $\left(-16x^2 y^4\right)\left(-5xy^3\right)$

    $= 80x^{2+1}y^{4+3}$

    $= 80x^3 y^7$

33. $\left(-8x^3 y^2\right)\left(3xy^5\right) = -24x^{3+1}y^{2+5}$

    $= -24x^4 y^7$

35. $\left(-2x^3 y^2\right)(0)\left(-3x^4 y\right) = 0$

123

37. $\left(8a^4b^3\right)\left(-3x^2y^5\right) = -24a^4b^3x^2y^5$

39. $\left(2x^2y\right)\left(-3y^3z^2\right)\left(5xz^4\right) = -30x^{2+1}y^3z^{2+4}$
$$= -30x^3y^3z^6$$

41. $\dfrac{y^{12}}{y^5} = y^{12-5}$
$$= y^7$$

43. $\dfrac{y^5}{y^8} = \dfrac{1}{y^{3-5}}$
$$= \dfrac{1}{y^3}$$

45. $\dfrac{11^{18}}{11^{30}} = \dfrac{1}{11^{30-18}} = \dfrac{1}{11^{12}}$

47. $\dfrac{3^{18}}{3^{14}} = 3^{18-14} = 3^4$

49. $\dfrac{a^{13}}{4a^5} = \dfrac{a^{13-5}}{4}$
$$= \dfrac{a^8}{4}$$

51. $\dfrac{x^7}{y^9} = \dfrac{x^7}{y^9}$

51. $\dfrac{-12x^5y^3}{-24xy^3} = \dfrac{x^{5-1}y^{3-3}}{2} = \dfrac{x^4}{2}$

53. $\dfrac{48x^5y^3}{24xy^3} = 2x^{5-1}y^{3-3} = 2x^4$

55. $\dfrac{16x^5y}{-32x^2y^3} = \dfrac{x^{5-2}}{-2y^{3-1}}$
$$= -\dfrac{x^3}{2y^2}$$

57. $\dfrac{1.8f^4g^3}{54f^2g^8} = \dfrac{f^{4-2}}{30g^{8-3}} = \dfrac{f^2}{30g^5}$

59. $\dfrac{-51x^6y^8}{17x^3y^8} = -3x^{6-3}y^{8-8} = -3x^3$

61. $\dfrac{8^0x^2y^3}{16x^5y} = \dfrac{y^{3-1}}{16x^{5-2}} = \dfrac{y^2}{16x^3}$

63. $\dfrac{18a^6b^3c^0}{24a^5b^3} = \dfrac{3}{4}a^{6-5}b^{3-3}c^0 = \dfrac{3}{4}a$

65. $\dfrac{85a^2b}{45c^3} = \dfrac{17a^2b}{9c^3}$

67. $\dfrac{81x^8y^2z^4}{-3x^3yz} = -27x^5yz^3$

so, $\left(-3x^3yz\right)\left(-27x^5yz^3\right) = 81x^8y^2z^4$

69. $\left(x^2\right)^6 = x^{2\cdot6} = x^{12}$

71. $\left(xy^2\right)^7 = x^7\left(y^2\right)^7 = x^7y^{14}$

73. $\left(rs^2\right)^6 = r^6 s^{2 \cdot 6} = r^6 s^{12}$

75. $\left(3a^3 b^2 c\right)^3 = 3^3 a^{3(3)} b^{2(3)} c^3$
$$= 27 a^9 b^6 c^3$$

77. $\left(-3a^4\right)^2 = \left(-3\right)^2 \left(a^4\right)^2 = 9a^8$

79. $\left(\dfrac{x}{2m^4}\right)^7 = \dfrac{x^7}{2^7 m^{4 \cdot 7}} = \dfrac{x^7}{128 m^{28}}$

81. $\left(\dfrac{5x}{7y^2}\right)^2 = \dfrac{5^2 x^2}{7^2 y^{2(2)}} = \dfrac{25x^2}{49y^4}$

83. $\left(-3a^2 b^3 c^0\right)^4 = \left(-3\right)^4 \left(a^2\right)^4 \left(b^3\right)^4$
$$= 81 a^8 b^{12}$$

85. $\left(-2x^3 y^0 z\right)^3 = \left(-2\right)^3 x^{3 \cdot 3} y^{0 \cdot 3} z^3$
$$= -8x^9 z^3$$

87. $\dfrac{\left(3x\right)^5}{\left(3x^2\right)^3} = \dfrac{3^5 x^5}{3^3 x^{2 \cdot 3}} = \dfrac{3^{5-3}}{x^{6-5}} = \dfrac{9}{x}$

89. $\left(3ab^2\right)^3 (ab) = \left(27 a^3 b^6\right)(ab) = 27 a^4 b^7$

91. $\left(\dfrac{8}{y^5}\right)^2 = \dfrac{8^2}{y^{5(2)}} = \dfrac{64}{y^{10}}$

93. $\left(\dfrac{2x}{y^3}\right)^4 = \dfrac{2^4 x^4}{y^{3 \cdot 4}} = \dfrac{16x^4}{y^{12}}$

95. $\left(\dfrac{ab^2}{c^3 d^4}\right)^4 = \dfrac{a^4 \left(b^2\right)^4}{\left(c^3\right)^4 \left(d^4\right)^4} = \dfrac{a^4 b^8}{c^{12} d^{16}}$

97. $a^3 = -27$ $3c = 12$
   $a = -3$ $c = 4$
   $\left(x^b\right)^3 = x^9$ $\left(z^d\right)^3 = z^{21}$
   $3b = 9$ $3d = 21$
   $b = 3$ $d = 7$
   $\left(y^c\right)^3 = y^{12}$ $-3x^3 y^4 z^7$

Cumulative Review

99. $-3 - 8 = -3 + \left(-8\right) = -11$

101. $\left(\dfrac{2}{3}\right)\left(-\dfrac{21}{8}\right) = \left(\dfrac{2}{3}\right)\left(\dfrac{-3 \cdot 7}{4 \cdot 2}\right) = -\dfrac{7}{4}$

103. $\text{Percentage} = \dfrac{1,500,000}{8,511,960}$
$$= 0.1762$$
$$= 17.6\%$$

105. 2.3% of $1,500,000$
   $0.023(1,500,000) = 34,500$
   $34,500$ sq km of rain forest lost

4.2 Exercises

1. $x^{-4} = \dfrac{1}{x^4}$

3. $3^{-4} = \dfrac{1}{3^4} = \dfrac{1}{81}$

5. $\dfrac{1}{y^{-8}} = y^8$

7. $\dfrac{x^{-4}y^{-5}}{z^{-6}} = \dfrac{z^6}{x^4 y^5}$

9. $x^{-5}y^6 = \dfrac{y^6}{x^5}$

11. $\left(2x^{-3}\right)^{-3} = 2^{-3}x^{-3(-3)}$

$\qquad = \dfrac{x^9}{2^3}$

$\qquad = \dfrac{x^9}{8}$

13. $3x^{-2} = \dfrac{3}{x^2}$

15. $\left(4x^2 y\right)^{-2} = \dfrac{1}{\left(4x^2 y\right)^2}$

$\qquad = \dfrac{1}{4^2 x^{2(2)} y^2}$

$\qquad = \dfrac{1}{16x^4 y^2}$

17. $\dfrac{3xy^{-2}}{z^{-3}} = \dfrac{3xz^3}{y^2}$

19. $\dfrac{(3x)^{-2}}{(3x)^{-3}} = \dfrac{(3x)^3}{(3x)^2}$

$\qquad = 3x$

21. $wx^{-5}y^3 z^{-2} = \dfrac{wy^3}{x^5 z^2}$

23. $\left(8^{-2}\right)\left(2^3\right) = \dfrac{1}{8^2} \cdot 2^3$

$\qquad = \dfrac{1}{64} \cdot 8$

$\qquad = \dfrac{1}{8}$

25. $\left(\dfrac{3x^0 y^2}{z^4}\right)^{-2} = \dfrac{3^{-2}x^{0(-2)}y^{2(-2)}}{z^{4(-2)}}$

$\qquad = \dfrac{x^0 y^{-4}}{3^2 z^{-8}}$

$\qquad = \dfrac{z^8}{9y^4}$

27. $\dfrac{x^{-2}y^{-3}}{x^4 y^{-2}} = \dfrac{y^2}{x^4 x^2 y^3}$

$\qquad = \dfrac{1}{x^6 y}$

29. $123,780 = 1.2378 \times 10^5$

31. $\left(-3x^{-4}y^2\right)^{-4} = \dfrac{1}{\left(-3x^{-4}y^2\right)^4}$

    $= \dfrac{1}{81x^{-16}y^8}$

    $= \dfrac{x^{16}}{81y^8}$

33. $889,610,000,000 = 8.8961\times10^{11}$

35. $0.00000001963 = 1.963\times10^{-8}$

37. $3.02\times10^5 = 302,000$

39. $4.7\times10^{-4} = 0.00047$

41. $9.83\times10^5 = 983,000$

43. $0.0000237 = 2.37\times10^{-5}$ miles per hour

45. $7\times10^{-6} = 0.000007$ m

47. $(56,000,000,000)(780,000,000)$

    $= \left(5.6\times10^{10}\right)\left(7.8\times10^8\right)$

    $= 43.68\times10^{18}$

    $= 4.368\times10^{19}$

49. $\dfrac{(5,000,000)(16,000)}{8,000,000,000} = \dfrac{\left(5\times10^6\right)\left(1.6\times10^4\right)}{8\times10^9}$

    $= \dfrac{8\times10^{10}}{8\times10^9}$

    $= 1.0\times10^1$

51. $(0.003)^4 = \left(3\times10^{-3}\right)^4$

    $= 3^4\times10^{-3(4)}$

    $= 81\times10^{-12}$

    $= 8.1\times10^{-11}$

53. $(150,000,000)(0.00005)(0.002)(30,000)$

    $= \left(1.5\times10^8\right)\left(5\times10^{-5}\right)\left(2\times10^{-3}\right)\left(3\times10^4\right)$

    $= 45\times10^4$

    $= 4.5\times10^5$

55. $\dfrac{6.816\times10^{12}}{2.92\times10^8} = 2.33\times10^4$ dollars

57. $d = (276)\left(3.09\times10^{13}\right)$

    $= \left(2.76\times10^2\right)\left(3.09\times10^{13}\right) = 8.528\times10^{15}$

    $r = 45,000 = 4.5\times10^4$

    $d = rt$

    $t = \dfrac{d}{r} = \dfrac{8.528\times10^{15}}{4.5\times10^4} = 1.90\times10^{11}$ hours

59. $d = rt$

    $d = (0.00000275)(24)$

    $= 2.75\times10^{-6}(24)$

    $= 66\times10^{-6}$

    $= 6.6\times10^{-5}$ miles

61. $\dfrac{3.2\times10^9}{20} = 0.16\times10^9$

    $= \$1.6\times10^8$

127

63. Percent increase $= \dfrac{9.36 \times 10^{11} - 3.61 \times 10^{11}}{3.61 \times 10^{11}}$

$= 1.593$

$= 159.3\%$

Cumulative Review

65. $-2.7 - (-1.9) = -2.7 + 1.9 = -0.8$

67. $-\dfrac{3}{4} + \dfrac{5}{7} = \dfrac{-21}{28} + \dfrac{20}{28} = \dfrac{-21 + 20}{28} = -\dfrac{1}{28}$

69. x = Mario's salary

$x + 12,460$ = Gina's salary

$x - 8742$ = Alfonso's salary

$x + x + 12,460 + x - 8742 = 112,000$

$3x + 3718 = 112,000$

$3x = 108,282$

$x = 36,094$

$x + 12,460 = 48,554$

$x - 8742 = 27,352$

Mario earns $36,094

Gina earns $48,554

Alfonso earns $27,352

4.3 Exercises

1. A polynomial in x is the sum of a finite number of terms of the form ax^n, where a is any real number and n is a whole number. An example is $3x^2 - 5x - 9$.

3. The degree of a polynomial in x is the largest exponent of x in any of the terms of the polynomial.

5. $6x^3 y$, degree 4: monomial

7. $20x^5 + 6x^3 - 7x$, degree 5: trinomial

9. $5xy^2 - 3x^2 y^3$, degree 5: binomial

11. $(-3x + 15) + (8x - 43)$

$= (-3 + 8)x + 15 - 43$

$= 5x - 28$

13. $(6x^2 + 5x - 6) + (-8x^2 - 3x + 5)$

$= 6x^2 + 5x - 6 - 8x^2 - 3x + 5$

$= -2x^2 + 2x - 1$

15. $\left(\dfrac{1}{2}x^2 + \dfrac{1}{3}x - 4\right) + \left(\dfrac{1}{3}x^2 + \dfrac{1}{6}x - 5\right)$

$= \left(\dfrac{1}{2} + \dfrac{1}{3}\right)x^2 + \left(\dfrac{1}{3} + \dfrac{1}{6}\right)x - 4 - 5$

$= \dfrac{5}{6}x^2 + \dfrac{1}{2}x - 9$

128

17. $\left(3.4x^3 - 5.6x^2 - 7.1x + 3.4\right)$

    $+\left(-1.7x^3 + 2.2x^2 - 6.1x - 8.8\right)$

    $= \left(3.4 - 1.7\right)x^3 + \left(-5.6 + 2.2\right)x^2$

    $+\left(-7.1 - 6.1\right)x + 3.4 - 8.8$

    $= 1.7x^3 - 3.4x^2 - 13.2x - 5.4$

19. $\left(2x - 19\right) - \left(-3x + 5\right)$

    $= \left(2x - 19\right) + \left(3x - 5\right)$

    $= \left(2 + 3\right)x - 19 - 5$

    $= 5x - 24$

21. $\left(\dfrac{2}{5}x^2 - \dfrac{1}{2}x + 5\right) - \left(\dfrac{1}{3}x^2 - \dfrac{3}{7}x \quad 6\right)$

    $= \dfrac{2}{5}x^2 - \dfrac{1}{2}x + 5 \quad \dfrac{1}{3}x^2 + \dfrac{3}{7}x + 6$

    $= \dfrac{1}{15}x^2 - \dfrac{1}{14}x + 11$

23. $\left(-3x^2 + 5x\right) - \left(2x^3 - 3x^2 + 10\right)$

    $= \left(-3x^2 + 5x\right) + \left(-2x^3 + 3x^2 - 10\right)$

    $= -2x^3 + \left(-3 + 3\right)x^2 + 5x - 10$

    $= -2x^3 + 5x - 10$

25. $\left(0.5x^4 - 0.7x^2 + 8.3\right) - \left(5.2x^4 + 1.6x + 7.9\right)$

    $= \left(0.5x^4 - 0.7x^2 + 8.3\right) + \left(-5.2x^4 - 1.6x - 7.9\right)$

    $= \left(0.5 - 5.2\right)x^4 - 0.7x^2 - 1.6x + 8.3 - 7.9$

    $= -4.7x^4 - 0.7x^2 - 1.6x + 0.4$

27. $\left(4x - 3\right) - \left(7x - 2\right) + \left(-5x + 8\right)$

    $= 4x - 3 - 7x + 2 - 5x + 8$

    $= -8x + 7$

29. $\left(5x^2y - 6xy^2 + 2\right) + \left(-8x^2y + 12xy^2 - 6\right)$

    $= \left(5 - 8\right)x^2y + \left(-6 + 12\right)xy^2 + 2 - 6$

    $= -3x^2y + 6xy^2 - 4$

31. $\left(3x^4 - 4x^2 - 18\right) - \left(2x^4 + 3x^3 + 6\right)$

    $= \left(3x^4 - 4x^2 - 18\right) + \left(-2x^4 - 3x^3 - 6\right)$

    $= \left(3 - 2\right)x^4 - 3x^3 - 4x^2 - 18 - 6$

    $= x^4 - 3x^3 - 4x^2 - 24$

33. $0.04x + 5.2$, $x = 1975 - 1970 = 5$

    $0.04\left(5\right) + 5.2 = 5.4$ mpg

35. $0.04x + 5.2 = 7.2$

    $0.04x = 2$

        $x = 50$

    year $= 1970 + 50 = 2020$

37. $1.8x^2 + 22.2x + 325$, $x = 1990 - 1980 = 10$

    $1.8\left(10\right)^2 - 22.2\left(10\right) + 325 = 727$

    $727,000$ prisoners

39. $1.8x^2 + 22.2x + 325$

$2002 - 1980 = 22, \ 2006 - 1980 = 26$

$2002 : 1.8(22)^2 + 22.2(22) + 325$

$= 1,684,600$

$2006 : 1.8(26)^2 + 22.2(26) + 325$

$= 2,119,000$

Increase: $2,119,000 - 1,684,600$

$= 434,400$ prisoners

41. $x^2 + 12x + 2x^2 = 3x^2 + 12x$

Cumulative Review

43. $3y - 8x = 2$

$-8x = -3y + 2$

$x = \dfrac{-3y + 2}{-8}$

$x = \dfrac{3y - 2}{8}$

45. $A = \dfrac{1}{2}h(b + c)$

$2A = h(b + c)$

$\dfrac{2A}{h} = b + c$

$\dfrac{2A}{h} - c = b \ $ or $ \ b = \dfrac{2A - hc}{h}$

47. $x =$ amount spent in 1990

$x + 0.9x = 1.324$

$1.9x = 1.324$

$x = 0.6968$

$696.8 billion was spent

How Am I Doing? Sections 4.1-4.3

1. $(-5xy)(3x^2y^5) = -15x^3y^6$

2. $-\dfrac{35xy^6}{25x^8y^3} = -\dfrac{7y^3}{5x^7}$

3. $\dfrac{60x^7y^0}{15x^2y^9} = \dfrac{4x^5}{y^9}$

4. $(-3x^5y)^4 = (-3)^4 x^{20}y^4 = 81x^{20}y^4$

5. $(-4x^{-3}y^4)^{-2} = 4^{-2}x^6y^{-8}$

$= \dfrac{x^6}{4^2 y^8}$

$= \dfrac{x^6}{16y^8}$

6. $\dfrac{3x^{-2}y^6}{9xy^{-9}} = \dfrac{y^{15}}{3x^3}$

7. $58,740 = 5.874 \times 10^4$

8. $0.00009362 = 9.362 \times 10^{-5}$

9. $(2x^2 + 0.5x - 2) + (0.3x^2 - 0.9x - 3.4)$

$= 2.3x^2 - 0.4x - 5.4$

130

10. $\left(5x^2 + 8x - 14\right) - \left(-2x^2 - 9x + 12\right)$

$= 5x^2 + 8x - 14 + 2x^2 + 9x - 12$

$= 7x^2 + 17x - 26$

11. $\left(\dfrac{1}{2}x^3 + \dfrac{1}{4}x^2 - 2x\right) - \left(\dfrac{1}{3}x^3 - \dfrac{1}{8}x^2 - 5x\right)$

$= \dfrac{1}{2}x^3 + \dfrac{1}{4}x^2 - 2x - \dfrac{1}{3}x^3 + \dfrac{1}{8}x^2 + 5x$

$= \dfrac{1}{6}x^3 + \dfrac{3}{8}x^2 + 3x$

12. $\left(\dfrac{1}{16}x^2 + \dfrac{1}{8}\right) + \left(\dfrac{1}{4}x^2 - \dfrac{3}{10}x - \dfrac{1}{2}\right)$

$= \dfrac{1}{16}x^2 + \dfrac{1}{8} + \dfrac{1}{4}x^2 - \dfrac{3}{10}x - \dfrac{1}{2}$

$= \dfrac{5}{16}x^2 - \dfrac{3}{10}x - \dfrac{3}{8}$

4.4 Exercises

1. $-2x\left(6x^3 - x\right) = -12x^4 + 2x^2$

3. $3x^2\left(7x - 3\right) = 21x^3 - 9x^2$

5. $2x^3\left(-2x^3 + 5x - 1\right)$

$= -4x^6 + 10x^4 - 2x^3$

7. $\dfrac{1}{2}\left(2x + 3x^2 + 5x^3\right)$

$= x + \dfrac{3}{2}x^2 + \dfrac{5}{2}x^3$

9. $\left(5x^3 - 2x^2 + 6x\right)\left(-3xy^2\right)$

$= -15x^4y^2 + 6x^3y^2 - 18x^2y^2$

11. $\left(3x^3 + x^2 - 8x\right)\left(3xy\right)$

$= 9x^4y + 3x^3y - 24x^2y$

13. $\left(x^3 - 3x^2 + 5x - 2\right)\left(3x\right)$

$= 3x^4 - 9x^3 + 15x^2 - 6x$

15. $\left(x^2y^2 - 6xy + 8\right)\left(-2xy\right)$

$= -2x^3y^3 + 12x^2y^2 - 16xy$

17. $\left(-7x^3 + 3x^2 + 2x - 1\right)\left(4x^2y\right)$

$= -28x^5y + 12x^4y + 8x^3y - 4x^2y$

19. $\left(3d^4 - 4d^2 + 6\right)\left(-2c^2d\right)$

$= -6c^2d^5 + 8c^2d^3 - 12c^2d$

21. $6x^3\left(2x^4 - x^2 + 3x + 9\right)$

$= 12x^7 - 6x^5 + 18x^4 + 54x^3$

23. $-7x^4\left(5x^3 - 8x^2 + 3x\right)$

$= -35x^7 + 56x^6 - 21x^5$

25. $(x + 10)(x + 3) = x^2 + 13x + 30$

27. $(x + 6)(x + 2) = x^2 + 8x + 12$

29. $(x - 8)(x + 2) = x^2 - 6x - 16$

31. $(x-5)(x-4) = x^2 - 9x + 20$

33. $(5x-2)(-4x-3) = -20x^2 - 7x + 6$

35. $(7yx-4)(x+2y) = 7x^2 + 14xy - 4x - 8y$

37. $(5x+2)(3x-y) = 15x^2 - 5xy + 6x - 2y$

39. $(4y+1)(5y-3) = 20y^2 - 7y - 3$

41. The signs are incorrect.
$(x-2)(-3) = -3x + 6$

43. $(5x+2)(5x+2) = 25x^2 + 20x + 4$

45. $(4x-3y)(5x-2y) = 20x^2 - 23xy + 6y^2$

47. $(7x-2)^2 = (7x-2)(7x-2)$
$= 49x^2 - 28x + 4$

49. $(4a+2b)^2 = (4a+2b)(4a+2b)$
$= 16a^2 + 16ab + 4b^2$

51. $(0.2x+3)(4x-0.3)$
$= 0.8x^2 - 0.06x + 12x - 0.9$
$= 0.8x^2 + 11.94x - 0.9$

53. $\left(\frac{1}{2}x+\frac{1}{3}\right)\left(\frac{1}{2}x-\frac{1}{4}\right) = \frac{1}{4}x^2 - \frac{1}{8}x + \frac{1}{6}x - \frac{1}{12}$
$= \frac{1}{4}x^2 + \frac{1}{24}x - \frac{1}{12}$

55. $(2a-3b)(x-5b) = 2ax - 10ab - 3bx + 15b^2$

57. $(7x+3y)(5x+9y) = 35x^2 + 78xy + 27y^2$

59. $(5y-3z)(4y-2z) = 20y^2 - 22yz + 6z^2$

61. $(4x-6)(7x+3) = 28x^2 + 12x - 42x - 18$
$= 28x^2 - 30x - 18$

Cumulative Review

63. $3(w-7)-(4-w) = 11w$
$3w - 21 - 4 + w = 11w$
$4w - 25 = 11w$
$-25 = 7w$
$-\frac{25}{7} = w$

65. $x =$ number of tiger's eye marbles
$2x =$ number of cat's eye marbles
$0.11x + 0.07(2x) = 6.00$
$0.11x + 0.14x = 6.00$
$0.25x = 6.00$
$x = 24$
$2x = 2(24) = 48$
24 tiger's eye marbles
48 cat's eye marbles

67. $1.2x + 16$, $x = 1994 - 1992 = 2$

    $1.2(2) + 16 = 2.4 + 16$

                 $= 18.4$

    They spent 18.4 hours.

69. $1.2x + 16$, $x = 2008 - 1992 = 16$

    $1.2(16) + 16 = 19.2 + 16$

                   $= 35.2$

    They will spent 32.5 hours.

4.5 Exercises

1. In the special case of $(a + b)(a - b)$, a binomial times a binomial is a <u>binomial</u>.

3. $(4x - 7)^2 = 16x^2 - 56x + 49$

    The student left out the middle term which comes from the product of the two outer terms and the product of the two inner terms.

5. $(y - 7)(y + 7) = y^2 - 7^2 = y^2 - 49$

7. $(x - 9)(x + 9) = x^2 - (9)^2 = x^2 - 81$

9. $(7x - 4)(7x + 4) = (7x)^2 - (4)^2 = 49x^2 - 16$

11. $(2x - 7)(2x + 7) = (2x)^2 - (7)^2 = 4x^2 - 49$

13. $(5x - 3y)(5x + 3y) = (5x)^2 - (3y)^2$

                         $= 25x^2 - 9y^2$

15. $(0.6x + 3)(0.6x - 3) = (0.6x)^2 - 3^2$

                         $= 0.36x^2 - 9$

17. $(3y + 1)^2 = (3y)^2 + 2(3y)(1) + 1^2$

               $= 9y^2 + 6y + 1$

19. $(5x - 4)^2 = (5x)^2 - 2(5x)(4) + 4^2$

               $= 25x^2 - 40x + 16$

21. $(7x + 3)^2 = (7x)^2 + 2(7x)(3) + 3^2$

               $= 49x^2 + 42x + 9$

23. $(3x - 7)^2 = (3x)^2 - 2(3x)(7) + 7^2$

               $= 9x^2 - 42x + 49$

25. $\left(\dfrac{2}{3}x + \dfrac{1}{4}\right)^2$

    $= \left(\dfrac{2}{3}x\right)^2 + 2\left(\dfrac{2}{3}x\right)\left(\dfrac{1}{4}\right) + \left(\dfrac{1}{4}\right)^2$

    $= \dfrac{4}{9}x^2 + \dfrac{1}{3}x + \dfrac{1}{16}$

27. $(9xy + 4z)^2 = (9xy)^2 + 2(9xy)(4z) + (4z)^2$

                    $= 81x^2 y^{22} + 72xyz + 16z^2$

29. $(7x + 3y)(7x - 3y) = (7x)^2 - (3y)^2$

          $= 49x^2 - 9y^2$

31. $(7c - 6d)^2 = (7c)^2 - 2(7c)(6d)$

               $= 49c^2 - 84cd + 36d^2$

33. $(9a-10b)(9a+10b)=(9a)^2-(10b)^2$
$$=81a^2-100b^2$$

35. $(5x+9y)^2=(5x)^2+2(5x)(9y)+(9y)^2$
$$=25x^2+90xy+81y^2$$

37. $(x^2+5x-3)(x-2)$
$$=x^3+5x^2-3x-2x^2-10x+6$$
$$=x^3+3x^2-13x+6$$

39. $(4x+1)(x^3-2x^2+x-1)$
$$=4x(x^3-2x^2+x-1)+1(x^3-2x^2+x-1)$$
$$=4x^4-8x^3+4x^2-4x+x^3-2x^2+x-1$$
$$=4x^4-7x^3+2x^2-3x-1$$

41. $(a^2-3a+2)(a^2+4a-3)$
$$=a^2(a^2+4a-3)-3a(a^2+4a-3)$$
$$+2(a^2+4a-3)$$
$$=a^4+4a^3-3a^2-3a^3-12a^2+9a+2a^2$$
$$+8a-6$$
$$=a^4+a^3-13a^2+17a-6$$

43. $(x+3)(x-1)(3x-8)$
$$=(x^2+2x-3)(3x-8)$$
$$=3x^3+6x^2-9x-8x^2-16x+24$$
$$=3x^3-2x^2-25x+24$$

45. $(3x+5)(x-2)(x-4)$
$$=(3x+5)(x^2-6x+8)$$
$$=3x(x^2-6x+8)+5(x^2-6x+8)$$
$$=3x^3-18x^2+24x+5x^2-30x+40$$
$$=3x^3-13x^2-6x+40$$

47. $(a-5)(2a+3)(a+5)$
$$=(2a^2-7a-15)(a+5)$$
$$=2a^3-7a^2-15a+10a^2-35a-75$$
$$=2a^3+3a^2-50a-75$$

49. $V=(2x+1)(3x-2)(4x+3)$
$$=(6x^2-x-2)(4x+3)$$
$$=24x^3-4x^2-8x+18x^2-3x-6$$
$$=24x^3+14x^2-11x-6$$

Cumulative Review

51. Let $x=$ amount invested at 7%
$18,000-x=$ amount invested at 11%
$0.07x+0.11(18,000-x)=1540$
$7x+11(18,000-x)=154,000$
$7x+198,000-11x=154,000$
$-4x=-44,000$
$x=11,000$
$18,000-x=7000$
She invested \$11,000 at 7% and
\$7000 at 11%.

53. $F = 1.8C + 32$

$F = 1.8(-33.4) + 32$

$F = -60.12 + 32$

$F = -28.12^{\circ} F$

Check: $(3x+5)(2x+1)$

$= 6x^2 + 3x + 10x + 5$

$= 6x^2 + 13x + 5$

4.6 Exercises

1. $\dfrac{25x^4 - 15x^2 + 20x}{5x} = \dfrac{25x^4}{5x} - \dfrac{15x^2}{5x} + \dfrac{20x}{5x}$

$= 5x^3 - 3x + 4$

11.

$$\require{enclose}\begin{array}{r}x - 3 \\ x-5 \enclose{longdiv}{x^2 - 8x - 17} \\ \underline{x^2 - 5x} \\ -3x - 17 \\ \underline{-3x + 15} \\ -32 \end{array}$$

3. $\dfrac{8y^4 - 12y^3 - 4y^2}{4y^2} = \dfrac{8y^4}{4y^2} - \dfrac{12y^3}{4y^2} - \dfrac{4y^2}{4y^2}$

$= 2y^2 - 3y - 1$

$\dfrac{x^2 - 8x - 17}{x - 5} = x - 3 - \dfrac{32}{x - 5}$

5. $\dfrac{81x^7 - 236x^5 - 63x^3}{9x^3} - \dfrac{81x^7}{9x^3} - \dfrac{36x^5}{9x^3} - \dfrac{63x^3}{9x^3}$

$= 79x^4 - 4x^2 - 7$

Check: $(x-5)\left(x - 3 - \dfrac{32}{x-5}\right)$

$= x^2 - 3x - 5x + 15 - 32$

$= x^2 - 8x - 17$

7. $\left(48x^7 - 54x^4 + 36x^3\right) \div 6x^3$

$= \dfrac{48x^7}{6x^3} - \dfrac{54x^4}{6x^3} + \dfrac{36x^3}{6x^3}$

$= 8x^4 - 9x + 6$

13.

$$\require{enclose}\begin{array}{r}3x^2 - 4x + 8 \\ x+1 \enclose{longdiv}{3x^3 - x^2 + 4x - 2} \\ \underline{3x^3 + 3x^2} \\ -4x^2 + 4x - 2 \\ \underline{-4x^2 - 4x} \\ 8x - 2 \\ \underline{8x + 8} \\ -10 \end{array}$$

9.

$$\require{enclose}\begin{array}{r}3x + 5 \\ 2x+1 \enclose{longdiv}{6x^2 + 13x + 5} \\ \underline{6x^2 + 3x} \\ 10x + 5 \\ \underline{10x + 5} \\ 0 \end{array}$$

$\dfrac{3x^3 - x^2 + 4x - 2}{x + 1} = 3x^2 - 4x + 8 - \dfrac{10}{x + 1}$

$\dfrac{6x^2 + 13x + 5}{2x + 1} = 3x + 5$

Check: $(x+1)\left(3x^2 - 4x + 8 - \dfrac{10}{x+1}\right)$

$= 3x^3 - x^2 + 4x + 8 - 10$

$= 3x^3 - x^2 + 4x - 2$

$\dfrac{10x^3 + 11x^2 - 11x + 2}{5x - 2} = 2x^2 + 3x - 1$

$$
\begin{array}{r}
2x^2 - 3x - 2 \\
15.\quad 2x+5{\overline{\smash{\big)}\,4x^3 + 4x^2 - 19x - 15}} \\
\underline{4x^3 + 10x^2} \\
-6x^2 - 19x \\
\underline{-6x^2 - 15x} \\
-4x - 15 \\
\underline{-4x - 10} \\
-5
\end{array}
$$

$$
\begin{array}{r}
6y^2 + 3y - 8 \\
19.\quad 2y-3{\overline{\smash{\big)}\,12y^3 - 12y^2 - 25y + 31}} \\
\underline{12y^3 - 18y^2} \\
6y^2 - 25y \\
\underline{6y^2 - 9y} \\
-16y + 31 \\
\underline{-16y + 24} \\
7
\end{array}
$$

$\dfrac{4x^3 + 4x^2 - 19x - 15}{2x + 5} = 2x^2 - 3x - 2 - \dfrac{5}{2x + 5}$

$\dfrac{12y^3 - 12y^2 - 25y + 31}{2y - 3}$

Check:

$(2x+5)\left(2x^2 - 3x - 2 - \dfrac{5}{2x+5}\right)$

$= 4x^3 + 4x^2 - 19x - 10 - 5$

$= 4x^3 + 4x^2 - 19x - 15$

$= 6y^2 + 3y - 8 + \dfrac{7}{2y - 3}$

$$
\begin{array}{r}
y^2 - 4y - 1 \\
21.\quad y+3{\overline{\smash{\big)}\,y^3 - y^2 - 13y - 12}} \\
\underline{y^3 + 3y^2} \\
-4y^2 - 13y - 12 \\
\underline{-4y^2 - 12y} \\
-y - 12 \\
\underline{-y - 3} \\
-9
\end{array}
$$

$$
\begin{array}{r}
2x^2 + 3x - 1 \\
17.\quad 5x-2{\overline{\smash{\big)}\,10x^3 + 11x^2 - 11x + 2}} \\
\underline{10x^3 - 4x^2} \\
15x^2 - 11x \\
\underline{15x^2 - 6x} \\
-5x + 2 \\
\underline{-5x + 2} \\
0
\end{array}
$$

$\left(y^3 - y^2 - 13y - 12\right) \div (y + 3)$

$= y^2 - 4y - 1 - \dfrac{9}{y + 3}$

23.
$$\require{enclose}
\begin{array}{r}
y^3 + 2y^2 - 5y - 10 \\[2pt]
y-2 \enclose{longdiv}{y^4 + 0y^3 - 9y^2 + 0y - 5} \\
\end{array}$$

$$\underline{y^4 - 2y^3}$$
$$2y^3 - 9y^2 + 0y - 5$$
$$\underline{2y^3 - 4y^2}$$
$$-5y^2 + 0y - 5$$
$$\underline{-5y^2 + 10y}$$
$$-10y - 5$$
$$\underline{-10y + 20}$$
$$-25$$

$$\left(y^4 - 9y^2 - 5\right) \div \left(y - 2\right)$$
$$= y^3 + 2y^2 - 5y - 10 - \frac{25}{y-2}$$

25.
$$\begin{array}{r}
2y^2 + \frac{1}{2}y + \frac{7}{8} \\[2pt]
4y-1 \enclose{longdiv}{8y^3 + 0y^2 + 3y - 7} \\
\end{array}$$

$$\underline{8y^3 - 2y^2}$$
$$2y^2 + 3y$$
$$\underline{2y^2 - \frac{1}{2}y}$$
$$\frac{7}{2}y - 7$$
$$\underline{\frac{7}{2}y - \frac{7}{8}}$$
$$-\frac{49}{8}$$

$$\frac{8y^3 + 3y - 7}{4y - 1} = 2y^2 + \frac{1}{2}y + \frac{7}{8} - \frac{49/8}{4y-1}$$

Cumulative Review

27. $110{,}000 - 0.3\left(110{,}000\right) = 77{,}000$

   $77{,}000$ gallons

29. x = number of cats in the study

   $0.92x = 184$

   $x = 200$

   200 cats were in the study

31. a. $\dfrac{4+1+9+6+1}{5} = \dfrac{21}{5}$

   $= 4.2$

   4.2 hurricanes per year

   b. $\dfrac{9+7+8+7+6}{5} = \dfrac{37}{5} = 7.4$

   7.4 hurricanes per year

   c. Percent increase $= \dfrac{7.4 - 4.2}{4.2}$

   $= 0.762$

   $= 76.2\%$

   d. $100\% + 76.2\% = 176.2\%$

   176.2% of $7.4 = 13.0$

   13.0 hurricanes

Putting Your Skills to Work

1. $45,678 - 32,152 = \$13,526$

2. $42(13,526) = \$568,082$

3. Percentage growth $= \dfrac{100,987 - 74,560}{74,560}$

$= \dfrac{26,427}{74,560}$

$= 0.3544$

$= 35.4\%$

4. $100\% + 35.4\% = 135.4\%$

135.4% of $100,987$

$1.354(100,987) = \$136,777$ in 2006

5. $I = 35x^3 - 620x^2 + 2820x + 43,112$

$x = 2004 - 1998 = 6$

$I = 35(6)^3 - 620(6)^2 + 2820(6) + 43,112$

$I = \$45,272$ in 2004

6. $x = 2006 - 1998 = 8$

$I = 35(8)^3 - 620(8)^2 + 2820(8) + 43,112$

$I = \$43,912$ in 2006

Chapter 4 Review Problems

1. $(-6a^2)(3a^5) = -18a^7$

2. $(5^{10})(5^{13}) = 5^{10+13} = 5^{23}$

3. $(3xy^2)(2x^3 y^4) = 6x^4 y^6$

4. $(2x^3 y^4)(-7xy^5) = -14x^4 y^9$

5. $\dfrac{7^{15}}{7^{27}} = \dfrac{1}{7^{27-15}} = \dfrac{1}{7^{12}}$

6. $\dfrac{x^{12}}{x^{17}} = \dfrac{1}{x^{17-12}} = \dfrac{1}{x^5}$

7. $\dfrac{y^{30}}{y^{16}} = y^{30-16} = y^{14}$

8. $\dfrac{9^{13}}{9^{24}} = \dfrac{1}{9^{11}}$

9. $\dfrac{-15xy^2}{25x^6 y^6} = -\dfrac{3}{5x^{6-1} y^{6-2}} = -\dfrac{3}{5x^5 y^4}$

10. $\dfrac{-12a^3 b^6}{18a^2 b^{12}} = -\dfrac{2a}{3b^6}$

11. $(x^3)^8 = x^{3(8)} = x^{24}$

12. $(b^5) = b^{30}$

13. $(-3a^3 b^2)^2 = (-3)^2 a^{3(2)} b^{2(2)} = 9a^6 b^4$

14. $(3x^3 y)^4 = 3^4 (x^3)^4 y^4$

$= 81x^{12} y^4$

15. $\left(\dfrac{5ab^2}{c^3}\right)^2 = \dfrac{5^2 a^2 \left(b^2\right)^2}{\left(c^3\right)^2} = \dfrac{25a^2 b^4}{c^6}$

16. $\left(\dfrac{x^0 y^3}{4w^5 z^2}\right)^3 = \dfrac{\left(y^3\right)^3}{4^3 \left(w^5\right)^3 \left(z^2\right)^3} = \dfrac{y^9}{64w^{15} z^6}$

17. $a^{-3} b^5 = \dfrac{b^5}{a^3}$

18. $m^8 p^{-5} = \dfrac{m^8}{p^5}$

19. $\dfrac{2x^{-6}}{y^{-3}} = \dfrac{2y^3}{x^6}$

20. $\left(3x^{-4} y^3\right)^{-2} = 3^{-2} \left(x^{-4}\right)^{-2} \left(y^3\right)^{-2}$

$= \dfrac{x^8 y^{-6}}{3^2}$

$= \dfrac{x^8}{9y^6}$

21. $\left(5x^2 y^{-4}\right)^{-2} = 5^{-2} \left(x^2\right)^{-2} \left(y^{-4}\right)^{-2}$

$= \dfrac{x^{-4} y^8}{5^2}$

$= \dfrac{y^8}{25x^4}$

22. $\dfrac{3x^{-3}}{y^{-2}} = \dfrac{3y^2}{x^3}$

23. $\dfrac{4x^{-5} y^{-6}}{w^{-2} z^8} = \dfrac{4w^2}{x^5 y^6 z^8}$

24. $\dfrac{3^{-3} a^{-2} b^5}{c^{-3} d^{-4}} = \dfrac{b^5 c^3 d^4}{3^3 a^2} = \dfrac{b^5 c^3 d^4}{27a^2}$

25. $156,340,200,000 = 1.563402 \times 10^{11}$

26. $179,632 = 1.79632 \times 10^5$

27. $0.0078 = 7.8 \times 10^{-3}$

28. $0.00006173 = 6.173 \times 10^{-5}$

29. $1.2 \times 10^5 = 120,000$

30. $6.034 \times 10^6 = 6,034,000$

31. $3 \times 10^6 = 3,000,000$

32. $2.5 \times 10^{-1} = 0.25$

33. $4.32 \times 10^{-5} = 0.0000432$

34. $6 \times 10^{-9} = 000000006 \times 10^{-9}$

$= 0.000000006$

139

35. $\dfrac{(28,000,000)(5,000,000,000)}{7,000}$

$= \dfrac{(2.8 \times 10^7)(5 \times 10^9)}{7 \times 10^3}$

$= \dfrac{14 \times 10^{16}}{7 \times 10^3} = 2 \times 10^{13}$

36. $(3.12 \times 10^5)(2.0 \times 10^6)(1.5 \times 10^8)$

$= 9.36 \times 10^{5+6+8} = 9.36 \times 10^{19}$

37. $(1.6 \times 10^{-3})(3.0 \times 10^{-5})(2.0 \times 10^{-2})$

$= 9.6 \times 10^{-10}$

38. $\dfrac{(0.00078)(0.000005)(0.00004)}{0.002}$

$= \dfrac{(7.8 \times 10^{-4})(5.0 \times 10^{-6})(4.0 \times 10^{-5})}{2.0 \times 10^{-3}}$

$= \dfrac{156 \times 10^{-15}}{2.0 \times 10^{-3}} = 78 \times 10^{-12} = 7.8 \times 10^{-11}$

39. $r = 40,000 = 4 \times 10^4$

$t = 365(24) = 8760 = 8.76 \times 10^3$

$d = rt = (4 \times 10^4)(8.76 \times 10^3)$

$= 35.04 \times 10^7$

$= 3.504 \times 10^8$ km

40. Seconds in one day $= 60 \times 60 \times 24 = 86,400$

$= 8.64 \times 10^4$

Cycles of radiation in one second

$= 9,192,631,770 = 9.19 \times 10^9$

Cycles of radiation in one day

$= (8.64 \times 10^4)(9.19 \times 10^9)$

$= 79.4016 \times 10^{13} = 7.94 \times 10^{14}$

41. $\dfrac{60}{1 \times 10^{-8}} = 60 \times 10^8 = 6 \times 10^9$

In one minute the computer can perform 6×10^9 operations.

42. $(4.3x^2 - 2.6x - 3.1) + (7.1x^2 - 4.7x + 8.4)$

$= 11.4x^2 - 7.3x + 5.3$

43. $(1.2x^2 - 3.4x + 6) + (5.5x^2 - 7.6x - 3)$

$= (1.2 + 5.5)x^2 + (-3.4 - 7.6)x + 6 - 3$

$= 6.7x^2 - 11x + 3$

44. $(x^3 + x^2 - 6x + 2) - (2x^3 - x^2 - 5x - 6)$

$= (x^3 + x^2 - 6x + 2) + (-2x^3 x^2 + 5x + 6)$

$= (x^3 - 2x^3) + (x^2 + x^2)$

$\quad + (-6x + 5x) + (2 + 6)$

$= -x^3 + 2x^2 - x + 8$

45. $(4x^3 - x^2 - x + 3) - (-3x^3 + 2x^2 + 5x - 1)$

$= (4x^3 - x^2 - x + 3) + (3x^3 - 2x^2 - 5x + 1)$

$= (4 + 3)x^3 + (-1 - 2)x^2 + (-1 - 5)x + 3 + 1$

$= 7x^3 - 3x^2 - 6x + 4$

46. $\left(\dfrac{3}{5}x^2y - \dfrac{1}{3}x + \dfrac{3}{4}\right) - \left(\dfrac{1}{2}x^2y + \dfrac{2}{7}x + \dfrac{1}{3}\right)$

$= \dfrac{3}{5}x^2y - \dfrac{1}{3}x + \dfrac{3}{4} - \dfrac{1}{2}x^2y - \dfrac{2}{7}x - \dfrac{1}{3}$

$= \dfrac{1}{10}x^2y - \dfrac{13}{21}x + \dfrac{5}{12}$

47. $\dfrac{1}{2}x^2 - \dfrac{3}{4}x + \dfrac{1}{5} - \left(\dfrac{1}{4}x^2 - \dfrac{1}{2}x + \dfrac{1}{10}\right)$

$= \dfrac{1}{2}x^2 - \dfrac{3}{4}x + \dfrac{1}{5} - \dfrac{1}{4}x^2 + \dfrac{1}{2}x - \dfrac{1}{10}$

$= \left(\dfrac{1}{2} - \dfrac{1}{4}\right)x^2 + \left(-\dfrac{3}{4} + \dfrac{1}{2}\right)x + \dfrac{1}{5} - \dfrac{1}{10}$

$= \dfrac{1}{4}x^2 - \dfrac{1}{4}x + \dfrac{1}{10}$

48. $\left(5x^2 + 3x\right) + \left(-6x^2 + 2\right) - \left(5x - 8\right)$

$= \left(5x^2 + 3x\right) + \left(-6x^2 + 2\right) + \left(-5x + 8\right)$

$= \left(5x^2 - 6x^2\right) + \left(3x - 5x\right) + \left(2 + 8\right)$

$= -x^2 - 2x + 10$

49. $\left(2x^2 - 7\right) - \left(3x^2 - 4\right) + \left(-5x^2 - 6x\right)$

$= \left(2x^2 - 7\right) + \left(-3x^2 + 4\right) + \left(-5x^2 - 6x\right)$

$= \left(2 - 3 - 5\right)x^2 - 6x - 7 + 4$

$= -6x^2 - 6x - 3$

50. $\left(3x + 1\right)\left(5x - 1\right) = 15x^2 - 3x + 5x - 1$

$= 15x^2 + 2x - 1$

51. $\left(7x - 2\right)\left(4x - 3\right) = 28x^2 - 21x - 8x + 6$

$= 28x^2 - 29x + 16$

52. $\left(2x + 3\right)\left(10x + 9\right)$

$= 20x^2 + 18x + 30x + 27$

$= 20x^2 + 48x + 27$

53. $5x\left(2x^2 - 6x + 3\right) = 10x^3 - 30x^2 + 15x$

54. $\left(6x^3 - 2x^2 + x - 4\right)\left(-3x\right)$

$= -18x^4 + 6x^3 - 3x^2 + 12x$

55. $\left(2xy^2 - 3xy - 4y\right)\left(-3x^2y\right)$

$= -6x^3y^3 + 9x^3y^2 + 12x^2y^2$

56. $\left(5a + 7b\right)\left(a - 3b\right) = 5a^2 - 15ab + 7ab - 21b^2$

$= 5a^2 - 8ab - 21b^2$

57. $\left(2x^2 - 3\right)\left(4x^2 - 5y\right)$

$= 8x^4 - 10x^2y - 12x^2 + 15y$

58. $-3x^2y\left(5x^4y + 3x^2 - 2\right)$

$= -3x^2y\left(5x^4y\right) - 3x^2y\left(3x^2\right) - 3x^2y\left(-2\right)$

$= -15x^6y^2 - 9x^4y + 6x^2y$

59. $\left(3x - 2\right)^2$

$= 9x^2 + 2\left(-2\right)\left(3\right)x + 4$

$= 9x^2 - 12x + 4$

60. $\left(5x + 3\right)\left(5x - 3\right) = \left(5x\right)^2 - 3^2 = 25x^2 - 9$

141

61. $(7x + 6y)(7x - 6y)$

$$= (7x)^2 - (6y)^2$$
$$= 49x^2 - 36y^2$$

62. $(5a - 2b)^2 = (5a)^2 - 2(5a)(2b) + (2b)^2$

$$= 25a^2 - 20ab + 4b^2$$

63. $(8x + 9y)^2 = 64x^2 + 2(8x)(9y) + 81y^2$

$$= 64x^2 + 144xy + 81y^2$$

64. $(x^2 + 7x + 3)(4x - 1)$

$$= 4x^3 + 28x^2 + 12x - x^2 - 7x - 3$$
$$= 4x^3 + 27x^2 + 5x - 3$$

65. $(x - 6)(2x - 3)(x + 4)$

$$= (2x^2 - 15x + 18)(x + 4)$$
$$= 2x^3 - 15x^2 + 18x + 8x^2 - 60x + 72$$
$$= 2x^3 - 7x^2 - 42x + 72$$

66. $(12y^3 + 18x^2 + 24y) \div (6y)$

$$= \frac{12y^3}{6y} + \frac{18y^2}{6y} + \frac{24y}{6y}$$
$$= 2y^2 + 3y + 4$$

67. $(30x^5 + 35x^4 - 90x^3) \div (5x^2)$

$$= \frac{30x^5}{5x^2} + \frac{35x^4}{5x^2} - \frac{90x^3}{5x^2}$$
$$= 6x^3 + 7x^2 - 18x$$

68. $(16x^3y^2 - 24x^2y + 32xy^2) \div (4xy)$

$$= \frac{16x^3y^2}{4xy} - \frac{24x^2y}{4xy} + \frac{32xy^2}{4xy}$$
$$= 4x^2y - 6x + 8y$$

69. $(106x^6 - 24x^5 + 38x^4 + 26x^3) \div (2x^3)$

$$= \frac{106x^6}{2x^3} - \frac{24x^5}{2x^3} + \frac{38x^4}{2x^3} + \frac{26x^3}{2x^3}$$
$$= 53x^3 - 12x^2 + 19x + 13$$

70.

$$
\begin{array}{r}
3x - 2 \\
5x + 7 \overline{)15x^2 + 11x - 14} \\
\underline{15x^2 + 21x} \\
-10x - 14 \\
\underline{-10x - 14} \\
0
\end{array}
$$

$$\frac{15x^2 + 11x - 14}{5x + 7} = 3x - 2$$

71.

$$
\begin{array}{r}
3x - 7 \\
4x + 9 \overline{)12x^2 - x - 62} \\
\underline{12x^2 + 27x} \\
-28x - 63 \\
\underline{-28x - 63} \\
0
\end{array}
$$

$$\frac{12x^2 - x - 63}{4x + 9} = 3x - 7$$

72.

$$\require{enclose}
\begin{array}{r}
3x^2 + 2x + 4 \\
2x-1 \enclose{longdiv}{6x^3 + x^2 + 6x + 5} \\
\underline{6x^3 - 3x^2} \\
4x^2 + 6x \\
\underline{4x^2 - 2x} \\
8x + 5 \\
\underline{8x - 4} \\
9
\end{array}$$

$$\left(6x^3 + x^2 + 6x + 5\right) \div \left(2x - 1\right)$$

$$= 3x^2 + 2x + 4 + \frac{9}{2x-1}$$

73.

$$\begin{array}{r}
2x^2 - 5x + 13 - \frac{27}{x+2} \\
x+2 \enclose{longdiv}{2x^3 - x^2 + 3x - 1} \\
\underline{2x^3 + 4x^2} \\
-5x^2 + 3x \\
\underline{-5x^2 - 10x} \\
13x - 1 \\
\underline{13x + 26} \\
-27
\end{array}$$

74.

$$\begin{array}{r}
4x + 1 \\
3x+2 \enclose{longdiv}{12x^2 + 11x + 2} \\
\underline{12x^2 + 8x} \\
3x + 2 \\
\underline{3x + 2} \\
\end{array}$$

$$\left(12x^2 + 11x + 2\right) \div \left(3x + 2\right) = 4x + 1$$

75.

$$\begin{array}{r}
4x - 5 + \frac{11}{2x+1} \\
2x+1 \enclose{longdiv}{8x^2 - 6x + 6} \\
\underline{8x^2 + 4x} \\
-10x + 6 \\
\underline{-10x - 5} \\
11
\end{array}$$

76.

$$\begin{array}{r}
x^2 + 3x + 8 \\
x-3 \enclose{longdiv}{x^3 + 0x^2 - x - 24} \\
\underline{x^3 - 3x^2} \\
3x^2 - x \\
\underline{3x^2 - 9x} \\
8x - 24 \\
\underline{8x - 24}
\end{array}$$

77.

$$\begin{array}{r}
2x^2 + 4x + 5 \\
x-2 \enclose{longdiv}{2x^3 + 0x^2 - 3x + 1} \\
\underline{2x^3 - 4x^2} \\
4x^2 - 3x \\
\underline{4x^2 - 8x} \\
5x + 1 \\
\underline{5x - 10} \\
11
\end{array}$$

$$\left(2x^3 - 3x + 1\right) \div \left(x - 2\right)$$

$$= 2x^2 + 4x + 5 + \frac{11}{x-2}$$

78. $\left(4^6\right)\left(4^{23}\right) = 4^{29}$

79. $\dfrac{6^{50}}{6^{35}} = 6^{15}$

80. $\left(-5x^3y^4\right)\left(-25x^5y^{10}\right) = 125x^8y^{14}$

81. $\dfrac{-36x^6y^5}{18xy^8} = -\dfrac{2x^5}{y^3}$

82. $\left(-4x^5y^6\right)^3 = (-4)^3\left(x^5\right)^3\left(y^6\right)^3$

$\qquad = -64x^{15}y^{18}$

83. $0.0000786 = 7.86 \times 10^{-5}$

84. $\left(-6x^3 - 7x + 8\right) - \left(-2x^3 + 5x - 9\right)$

$\qquad = -6x^3 - 7x + 8 + 2x^3 - 5x + 9$

$\qquad = -4x^3 - 12x + 17$

85. $-6x^2\left(2x^3 + 5x^2 - 2\right)$

$\qquad = -12x^5 - 30x^4 + 12x^2$

86. $(7x - 3)(2x - 1)(x + 2)$

$\qquad = \left(14x^2 - 13x + 3\right)(x + 2)$

$\qquad = 14x^3 - 13x^2 + 3x + 28x^2 - 26x + 6$

87.

$$
\begin{array}{r}
2x^2 + 5x + 3 \\
3x - 2 \overline{\smash{\big)}\, 6x^3 + 11x^2 - x - 2} \\
\underline{6x^3 - 4x^2} \\
15x^2 - x \\
\underline{15x^2 - 10x} \\
9x - 2 \\
\underline{9x - 6} \\
4
\end{array}
$$

$\dfrac{6x^3 + 11x^2 - x - 2}{3x - 2} = 2x^2 + 5x + 3 + \dfrac{4}{3x - 2}$

88. $\dfrac{\$12.9 \times 10^9}{2.8 \times 10^8 \text{ people}} = \$4.607 \times 10^1/\text{person}$

$\qquad\qquad\qquad = \$46.07/\text{person}$

89. $1.132 \times 10^9 + 1.31 \times 10^8$

$\qquad = 1.132 \times 10^9 + 0.131 \times 10^9$

$\qquad = 1.263 \times 10^9 \text{ people}$

90. $\left(9.11 \times 10^{-28}\right)(30{,}000)$

$\qquad = \left(9.11 \times 10^{-28}\right)\left(3 \times 10^4\right)$

$\qquad = 27.33 \times 10^{-24}$

$\qquad = 2.733 \times 10^{-23} \text{ grams}$

91. $\left(3.9 \times 10^{26}\right)(60)(60)(24)$

$= 3.9 \times 10^{26}\left(8.64 \times 10^{4}\right)$

$= 33.696 \times 10^{30}$

$= 3.3696 \times 10^{31}$ joules

7. $\left(\dfrac{7a^{7}b^{2}}{3c^{0}}\right)^{2} = \dfrac{7^{2}\,a^{7(2)}b^{2(2)}}{3^{2}\,c^{0(2)}} = \dfrac{49a^{14}b^{4}}{9}$

8. $\dfrac{\left(3x^{2}\right)^{3}}{\left(6x\right)^{2}} = \dfrac{3^{3}\left(x^{2}\right)^{3}}{6^{2}x^{2}} = \dfrac{27x^{6}}{36x^{2}} = \dfrac{3x^{4}}{4}$

92. $A = 2x(2y+1) - xy$

$= 4xy + 2x - xy$

$= 3xy + 2x$

9. $4^{-3} = \dfrac{1}{4^{3}} = \dfrac{1}{64}$

93. $A = 2x(x) - 4y(y) = 2x^{2} - 4y^{2}$

10. $8(x+d) = 3(y-d)$

$8x + 8d = 3y - 3d$

$8x + 11d = 3y$

$11d = 3y - 8x$

$d = \dfrac{3y - 8x}{11}$

How Am I Doing? Chapter 4 Test

1. $\left(3^{10}\right)\left(3^{24}\right) = 3^{10+24} = 3^{34}$

2. $\dfrac{25^{18}}{25^{34}} = \dfrac{1}{25^{16}}$

11. $\dfrac{3x^{-3}y^{2}}{x^{-4}y^{-5}} = 3xy^{7}$

3. $\left(8^{4}\right)^{6} = 8^{4 \cdot 6} = 8^{24}$

12. $0.0005482 = 5.482 \times 10^{-4}$

4. $\left(-3xy^{4}\right)\left(-4x^{3}y^{6}\right) = 12x^{1+3}y^{4+6} = 12x^{4}y^{10}$

13. $(5x+6)(4x-3) = 20x^{2} + 9x - 18$

5. $\dfrac{-35x^{8}y^{10}}{25x^{5}y^{10}} = -\dfrac{7x^{3}}{5}$

14. $\left(4.0 \times 10^{-3}\right)\left(3.0 \times 10^{-8}\right)\left(2.0 \times 10^{4}\right)$

$= 24.0 \times 10^{-7} = 2.4 \times 10^{-6}$

6. $\left(-5xy^{6}\right)^{3} = (-5)^{3}x^{3}\left(y^{6}\right)^{3} = -125x^{3}y^{18}$

15. $\left(2x^{2} - 3x - 6\right) + \left(-4x^{2} + 8x + 6\right)$

$= (2-4)x^{2} + (-3+8)x + 6 - 6$

$= -2x^{2} + 5x$

16. $\left(3x^3 - 4x^2 + 3\right) - \left(14x^3 + -7x + 11\right)$

     $= 3x^2 - 4x^2 + 3 - 14x^3 - 7x - 11$

     $= -11x^3 - 4x^2 + 7x - 8$

17. $-7x^2\left(3x^3 - 4x^2 + 6x - 2\right)$

     $= -21x^5 + 28x^4 - 42x^3 + 14x^2$

18. $\left(5x^2 y^2 - 6xy + 2\right)\left(3x^2 y\right)$

     $= 5x^2 y^2\left(3x^2 y\right) - 6xy\left(3x^2 y\right) + 2\left(3x^2 y\right)$

     $= 15x^4 y^3 - 18x^3 y^2 + 6x^2 y$

19. $\left(5a - 4b\right)\left(2a + 3b\right)$

     $= 10a^2 + 15ab - 8ab - 12b^2$

     $= 10a^2 + 7ab - 12b^2$

20. $\left(3x + 2\right)\left(2x + 1\right)\left(x - 3\right)$

     $= \left(6x^2 + 7x + 2\right)\left(x - 3\right)$

     $= 6x^3 + 7x^2 + 2x - 18x^2 - 21x - 6$

     $= 6x^3 - 11x^2 - 19x - 6$

21. $\left(7x^2 + 2y^2\right)^2$

     $= 49x^4 + 2\left(7x^2\right)\left(2y^2\right) + 4y^4$

     $= 49x^4 + 28x^2 y^2 + 4y^4$

22. $\left(5s - 11t\right)\left(5s + 11t\right) = \left(5s\right)^2 - \left(11t\right)^2$

                         $= 25s^2 - 121t^2$

23. $\left(3x - 2\right)\left(4x^3 - 2x^2 + 7x - 5\right)$

     $= 3x\left(4x^3 - 2x^2 + 7x - 5\right)$

     $-2\left(4x^3 - 2x^2 + 7x - 5\right)$

     $= 12x^4 - 6x^3 + 21x^2 - 15x - 8x^3 + 4x^2$

     $-14x + 10$

     $= 12x^4 - 14x^3 + 25x^2 - 29x + 10$

24. $\left(3x^2 - 5xy\right)\left(x^2 + 3xy\right)$

     $= 3x^4 + 9x^3 y - 5x^3 y - 15x^2 y^2$

     $= 3x^4 + 4x^3 y - 15x^2 y^2$

25. $\dfrac{15x^6 - 5x^4 + 25x^3}{5x^3} = \dfrac{15x^6}{5x^3} - \dfrac{5x^4}{5x^3} + \dfrac{25x^3}{5x^3}$

                       $= 3x^3 - x + 5$

26.
$$
\begin{array}{r}
2x^2 - 7x + 4 \\
4x+3 \overline{\smash{)}8x^3 - 22x^2 - 5x + 12} \\
\underline{8x^3 + 6x^2} \\
-28x^2 - 5x \\
\underline{-28x^2 - 21x} \\
16x + 12 \\
\underline{16x + 12}
\end{array}
$$

     $\dfrac{8x^3 - 22x^2 - 5x + 12}{4x + 3} = 2x^2 - 7x + 4$

146

27.

$$\begin{array}{r} 2x^2 + 6x + 12 \\ x-3{\overline{\smash{\big)}\,2x^3 + 0x^2 - 6x - 36}} \\ \underline{2x^3 - 6x^2} \\ 6x^2 - 6x \\ \underline{6x^2 - 18x} \\ 12x - 36 \\ \underline{12x - 36} \end{array}$$

$$\frac{2x^3 - 6x - 36}{x-3} = 2x^2 + 6x + 12$$

28. $\dfrac{2.618 \times 10^{11}}{86} = 0.03044 \times 10^{11}$

$$= 3.044 \times 10^9 \text{ barrels per year}$$

29. $d = rt$

$$= 2.49 \times 10^4 \,(7)(24)$$

$$= 418 \times 10^4$$

$$= 4.18 \times 10^6 \text{ miles}$$

Cumulative Test for Chapters 0-4

1. $\dfrac{5}{12} - \dfrac{7}{8} = \dfrac{10}{24} - \dfrac{21}{24} = -\dfrac{11}{24}$

2. $(-3.7) \times (0.2) = -0.74$

3. $\left(-4\dfrac{1}{2}\right) \div \left(5\dfrac{1}{4}\right) = \left(-\dfrac{9}{2}\right) \div \left(\dfrac{21}{4}\right)$

$$= \left(-\dfrac{3 \cdot 3}{2}\right)\left(\dfrac{2 \cdot 2}{3 \cdot 7}\right)$$

$$= -\dfrac{6}{7}$$

4. 6% of $1842.5 = 0.06(1842.5)$

$$= 110.55$$

5. $7x(3x - 4) - 5x(2x - 3) - (3x)^2$

$$= 21x^2 - 28x - 10x^2 + 15x - 9x^2$$

$$= 2x^2 - 13x$$

6. $2x^2 - 3xy + y^2 = 2(-2)^2 - 3(-2)(3) + 3^2$

$$= 2(4) + 18 + 9$$

$$= 8 + 18 + 9 = 35$$

7. $7x - 3(4 - 2x) = 14x - (3 - x)$

$$7x - 12 + 6x = 14x - 3 + x$$

$$13x - 12 = 15x - 3$$

$$-9 = 2x$$

$$-\dfrac{9}{2} = x$$

8. $\qquad \dfrac{2}{3}x + 6 = 4(x - 11)$

$$3\left(\dfrac{2}{3}x\right) + 3(6) = 3(4)(x - 11)$$

$$2x + 18 = 12x - 132$$

$$18 = 10x - 132$$

$$150 = 10x$$

$$15 = x$$

9. $4 - 7x < 11$

   $-7x < 7$

   $x > -1$

10. $8(x + d) = 3(y - d)$

   $8x + 8d = 3y - 3d$

   $8x + 11d = 3y$

      $11d = 3y - 8x$

        $d = \dfrac{3y - 8x}{11}$

11. $\dfrac{11,904}{x} = 0.96$

   $11,904 = 0.96x$

   $12,400 = x$

   VBM has 12,400 employees.

12. $(0.06)(3320) = 199.20$

   $199.20

13. $(5x + 6)(4x - 3) = 20x^2 + 9x - 18$

14. $(3x - 5)^2 = (3x)^2 - 2(3x)(5) + 5^2$

          $= 9x^2 - 30x + 25$

15. $(3x + 2)(2x + 1)(x - 4)$

   $= (3x + 2)(2x^2 - 7x - 4)$

   $= 6x^3 - 21x^2 - 12x + 4x^2 - 14x - 8$

   $= 6x^3 - 17x^2 - 26x - 8$

16. $\left(-4x^2y^5\right)\left(5xy^3\right) = (-4)(5)x^{2+1}y^{5+3}$

   $= -20x^3y^8$

17. $\dfrac{14x^8y^3}{-21x^5y^{12}} = -\dfrac{2x^3}{3y^9}$

18. $\left(-2x^3y^2z^0\right)^4 = (-2)^4\left(x^3\right)^4\left(y^2\right)^4\left(z^0\right)^4$

           $= 16x^{12}y^8$

19. $\dfrac{9x^{-3}y^{-4}}{w^2z^{-8}} = \dfrac{9z^8}{x^3y^4w^2}$

20. $1,360,000,000,000,000 = 1.36 \times 10^{15}$

21. $0.00056 = 5.6 \times 10^{-4}$

22. $\dfrac{\left(2.0 \times 10^{-12}\right)\left(8.0 \times 10^{-20}\right)}{4.0 \times 10^3} = \dfrac{16.0 \times 10^{-32}}{4.0 \times 10^3}$

   4.0×10^{-35}

23. $\left(x^3 - 3x^2 - 5x + 20\right) - \left(-4x^3 - 10x^2 + x - 30\right)$

   $= \left(x^3 - 3x^2 - 5x + 20\right) + \left(4x^3 + 10x^2 - x + 30\right)$

   $= \left(x^3 + 4x^3\right) + \left(-3x^2 + 10x^2\right) + (-5x - x)$

      $+ (20 + 30)$

   $= 5x^3 + 7x^2 - 6x + 50$

24. $-6xy^2\left(6x^2 - 3xy + 8y^2\right)$

   $= -36x^3y^2 + 18x^2y^3 - 48xy^4$

25. $\left(2x^2 - 3x + 1\right)(3x - 5)$

   $= 6x^3 - 9x^2 + 3x - 10x^2 + 15x - 5$

   $= 6x^3 - 19x^2 + 18x - 5$

26.

$$
\begin{array}{r}
x+5 \\
x-3\overline{\smash{\big)}\,x^2+2x-12} \\
\underline{x^2-3x} \\
5x-12 \\
\underline{5x-12} \\
3
\end{array}
$$

$$
\frac{2x^3-6x-36}{x-3}=2x^2+6x+12
$$

Chapter 5

1. $3x^2$ and $5x^3$ are called <u>factors</u>.

3. The factoring is not complete because $6a^3 + 3a^2 - 9a$ contains a common factor of $3a$.

5. $3a^2 + 3a = 3a(a+1)$
   Check:
   $3a(a+1) = 3a^2 + 3a$

7. $21abc - 14ab^2 = 7ab(3c - 2b)$
   Check:
   $7ab(3c - 2b) = 21abc - 14ab^2$

9. $2\pi rh + 2\pi r^2 = 2\pi r(h+r)$

11. $5x^3 + 25x^2 - 15x = 5x(x^2 + 5x - 3)$
    Check:
    $5x(x^2 + 5x - 3) = 5x^3 + 25x^2 - 15x$

13. $12ab - 28bc + 20ac = 4(3ab - 7bc + 5ac)$
    Check:
    $4(3ab - 7bc + 5ac) = 12ab - 28bc + 20ac$

15. $16x^5 + 24x^3 - 32x^2 = 8x^2(2x^3 + 3x - 4)$

17. $14x^2 y - 35xy - 63x = 7x(2xy - 5y - 9)$

19. $54x^2 - 45xy + 18x = 9x(6x - 5y + 2)$

21. $3xy^2 - 2ay + 5xy - 2y$
    $= y(3xy - 2a + 5x - 2)$
    Check:
    $y(3xy - 2a + 5x - 2)$
    $= 3xy^2 - 2ay + 5xy - 2y$

23. $24x^2 y - 40xy^2 = 8xy(3x - 5y)$

25. $7x^3 y^2 + 21x^2 y^2 = 7x^2 y^2(x+3)$

27. $9x^2 y - 18xy^2 - 27xy = 9xy(x - 2y - 3)$

29. $7a(x+2y) - b(x+2y) = (7a - b)(x+2y)$

31. $3x(x-4) - 2(x-4) = (x-4)(3x-2)$

33. $6b(2a - 3c) - 5d(2a - 3c)$
    $= (2a - 3c)(6b - 5d)$

35. $7c(b - a^2) - 5d(b - a^2) + 2f(b - a^2)$
    $= (b - a^2)(7c - 5d + 2f)$

37. $2a(xy-3)-4(xy-3)-z(xy-3)$
    $=(xy-3)(2a-4-z)$

39. $4a^3(a-3b)+(a-3b)=(a-3b)(4a^3+1)$

41. $(2a+3)-7x(2a+3)=(2a+3)(1-7x)$

43. $A=2.786a+2.786b+2.786c+2.786d$
    $=2.786(a+b+c+d)$ in^2

Cumulative Review

45. $x=$ 1st odd integer
    $x+2=$ 2nd odd integer
    $x+4=$ 3rd odd integer
    $x+x+2+x+4=x+40$
    $3x+6=x+40$
    $2x=34$
    $x=17$
    $x+2=19,\ x+4=21$
    The 3 integers are 17, 19, 21

47. $l=rt,\ l_1=l_2,\ r_1=6.72,\ t_1=2,\ t_2=6$
    $6.72(2)=r_2(6)$
    $r_2=2.24$ feet per minute

49. 15% of 258,000,000
    $=-0.15(258,000,000)$
    $=38,700,000$ tons

51. $\dfrac{38,700,000}{174,000,000}=0.2224$ tons per person
    $\dfrac{0.2224\text{ tons}}{1\text{ person}}\times\dfrac{2000\text{ pounds}}{1\text{ ton}}$
    $=445$ pounds/person

5.2 Exercises

1. We must remove a common factor of 5 from the last two terms.
   $3x^2-6xy+5x-10y$
   $=3x(x-2y)+5(x-2y)$
   $=(x-2y)(3x+5)$

3. $ab-3a+4b-12=a(b-3)+4(b-3)$
   $=(a+4)(b-3)$
   Check:
   $(a+4)(b-3)=ab-3a+4b-12$

5. $x^3-4x^2+3x-12$
   $=x^2(x-4)+3(x-4)$
   $=(x-4)(x^2+3)$
   Check:
   $(x-4)(x^2+3)=x^3+3x-4x^2-12$
   $=x^3-4x^2+3x-12$

151

7. $2ax + 6bx - ay - 3by$

    $= 2x(a + 3b) - y(a + 3b)$

    $= (a + 3b)(2x - y)$

    Check:

    $(a + 3b)(2x - y) = 2ax - ay + 6bx - 3by$

    $= 2ax + 6bx - ay - 3by$

9. $3ax + bx - 6a - 2b$

    $= x(3a + b) - 2(3a + b)$

    $= (3a + b)(x - 2)$

    Check:

    $(3a + b)(x - 2)$

    $= 3ax - 6a + bx - 2b$

    $= 3ax + bx - 6a - 2b$

11. $5a + 12bc + 10b + 6ac$

    $= 5a + 10b + 6ac + 12bc$

    $= 5(a + 2b) + 6c(a + 2b)$

    $= (a + 2b)(5 + 6c)$

    Check:

    $(a + 2b)(5 + 6c)$

    $= 5a + 6ac + 10b + 12bc$

    $= 5a + 12bc + 10b + 6ac$

13. $5a - 5b - 2ax + 2xb$

    $= 5(a - b) - 2x(a - b)$

    $= (a - b)(5 - 2x)$

    Check:

    $(a - b)(5 - 2x)$

    $= 5a - 2ax - 5b + 2bx$

    $= 5a - 5b - 2ax + 2xb$

15. $y^2 - 2y - 3y + 6$

    $= y(y - 2) - 3(y - 2)$

    $= (y - 2)(y - 3)$

17. $14 - 7y + 2y - y^2$

    $= 7(2 - y) + y(2 - y)$

    $= (7 + y)(2 - y)$

19. $6ax - y + 2ay - 3x$

    $= 6ax - 3x + 2ay - y$

    $= 3x(2a - 1) + y(2a - 1)$

    $= (2a - 1)(3x + y)$

21. $2x^2 + 8x - 3x - 12$

    $= 2x(x + 4) - 3(x + 4)$

    $= (2x - 3)(x + 4)$

23. $t^3 - t^2 + t - 1 = t^2(t - 1) + (t - 1)$

    $\qquad\qquad = (t - 1)(t^2 + 1)$

25. $28x^2 + 8xy^2 + 21xw + 6y^2w$

    $= 4x(7x + 2y^2) + 3w(7x + 2y^2)$

    $= (7x + 2y^2)(4x + 3w)$

27. Rearrange the terms so that factoring gives the same expression in parentheses.

    $6a^2 - 12bd - 8ad + 9ab$

    $= 6a^2 - 8ad + 9ab - 12bd$

    $= 2a(3a - 4d) + 3b(3a - 4d)$

    $= (3a - 4d)(2a + 3b)$

152

Cumulative Review

29. $x =$ number of seconds

$$73 - 4x = 41$$
$$-4x = -32$$
$$x = 8$$

The brakes were applied for 8 seconds

31. $x =$ dollar value in 1997

$$0.119x = 15.1$$
$$x = 126.9$$

The dollar value in 1997 was
$126.9 million

33. $100\% + 33\% = 133\%$

$2000 : 133\%$ of 5.5 million

$$= 1.33(5,500,000)$$
$$= 7,315,000 \text{ tons}$$

$100\% + 28\% = 128\%$

$2005 : 128\%$ of 7,315,000

$$= 1.28(7,315,000)$$
$$= 9,363,000 \text{ tons}$$

5.3 Exercises

1. Find two numbers whose <u>product</u> is 6 and whose <u>sum</u> is 5.

3. $x^2 + 2x + 1$; Product: 1, Sum: 2, + signs

$$x^2 + 2x + 1 = (x+1)(x+1)$$

5. $x^2 + 12x + 20$; Product: 20, Sum: 12, + signs

$$x^2 + 12x + 20 = (x+10)(x+2)$$

7. $x^2 - 4x + 3$; Product: 3, Sum: -4, $-$ signs

$$x^2 - 4x + 3 = (x-1)(x-3)$$

9. $x^2 - 11x + 28$; Product: 28, Sum: -11, $-$ signs

$$x^2 - 11x + 28 = (x-4)(x-7)$$

11. $x^2 + x - 20$; Product: -20, Sum: 1,
Opposite signs with larger absolute value +

$$x^2 + x - 20 = (x+5)(x-4)$$

13. $x^2 - 13x - 14$; Product: -14, Sum: -13,
Opposite signs with larger absolute value $-$.

$$x^2 - 13x - 14 = (x-14)(x+1)$$

15. $x^2 + 2x - 35$; Product: -35, Sum: 2
Opposite signs with larger absolute value +.

$$x^2 + 2x - 35 = (x+7)(x-5)$$

17. $x^2 - 2x - 24$; Product: -24, Sum: -2
Opposite signs with larger absolute value $-$.

$$x^2 - 2x - 24 = (x-6)(x+4)$$

19. $x^2 + 12x + 32$; Product: 32, Sum: 12,
+ signs

$$x^2 + 12x + 32 = (x+4)(x+8)$$

21. $x^2 - 10x + 24 = (x-6)(x-4)$

     Check: $(x-6)(x-4) = x^2 - 4x - 6x + 24$

     $= x^2 - 10x + 24$

23. $x^2 + 13x + 30 = (x+3)(x+10)$

     Check: $(x+3)(x+10) = x^2 + 10x + 3x + 30$

     $= x^2 + 13x + 30$

25. $x^2 - 6x + 5$; Product: 5, Sum: -6,

     $-$ signs

     $x^2 - 6x + 5 = (x-1)(x-5)$

27. $a^2 + 6a - 16 = (a+8)(a-2)$

     Check: $(a+8)(a-2) = a^2 - 2a + 8a - 16$

     $= a^2 + 6a - 16$

29. $x^2 - 12x + 32 = (x-4)(x-8)$

     Check: $(x-4)(x-8) = x^2 - 8x - 4x + 32$

     $= x^2 - 12x + 32$

31. $x^2 + 4x - 21 = (x+7)(x-3)$

     Check: $(x+7)(x-3) = x^2 - 3x + 7x - 21$

     $= x^2 + 4x - 21$

33. $x^2 + 15x + 56 = (x+7)(x+8)$

     Check: $(x+7)(x+8) = x^2 + 8x + 7x + 56$

     $= x^2 + 15x + 56$

35. $x^2 - 21x - 46 = (x-23)(x+2)$

     Check: $(x-23)(x+2) = x^2 + 2x - 23x - 46$

     $= x^2 - 21x - 46$

37. $x^2 + 9x - 36 = (x+12)(x-3)$

     Check: $(x+12)(x-3) = x^2 - 3x + 12x - 36$

     $= x^2 + 9x - 36$

39. $x^2 - 2xy - 15y^2 = (x-5y)(x+3y)$

     Check:

     $(x-5y)(x+3y) = x^2 + 3xy - 5xy - 15y^2$

     $= x^2 - 2xy - 15y^2$

41. $x^2 - 16xy + 63y^2 = (x-9y)(x-7y)$

     Check:

     $(x-9y)(x-7y) = x^2 - 7xy - 9xy + 63y^2$

     $= x^2 - 16xy + 63y^2$

43. $4x^2 + 24x + 20 = 4(x^2 + 6x + 5)$

     $= 4(x+1)(x+5)$

45. $6x^2 + 18x + 12 = 6(x^2 + 3x + 2)$

     $= 6(x+2)(x+1)$

47. $2x^2 - 20x + 42 = 2(x^2 - 10x + 21)$

     $= 2(x-7)(x-3)$

49. $3x^2 - 6x - 72 = 3(x^2 - 2x - 24)$

     $3(x-6)(x+4)$

51. $7x^2 + 21x - 70 = 7(x^2 + 3x - 10)$

     $= 7(x+5)(x-2)$

154

53. $3x^2 - 18x + 15 = 3(x^2 - 6x + 5)$

        $= 3(x - 5)(x - 1)$

55. $A = x^2 - \pi r^2,\ r = \dfrac{x}{2}$

    $A = x^2 - \pi \left(\dfrac{x}{2}\right)^2$

    $A = x^2 \left(1 - \dfrac{3.14}{4}\right) = 64(0.215)$

       $= 13.76$ sq. in.

57. $A = lw$

    $A = 10(12) - x(x + 2)$

      $= 120 - x^2 - 2x$

      $= 120 - 2x - x^2$

      $= (10 - x)(12 + x)$

59. $A = P + rPt$

    $A - P = rPt$

    $\dfrac{A - P}{rP} - t$

61. $c =$ car's speed

    $c = \dfrac{d}{t} = \dfrac{d}{2}$

    $c + 20 =$ train's speed

    $\dfrac{d}{2} + 20 = \dfrac{d}{1.5}$

    $1.5d + 60 = 2d$

    $60 = 0.5d$

    $120 = d$

    120 miles

63. $x =$ number of 30-min periods after midnight

    $4(65) + 85x = 515$

    $260 + 85x = 515$

    $85x = 255$

    $x = 3$

    The reception ended at 1:30 a.m.

65. $M = 3$

    $T = 19 + 2M$

    $T = 19 + 2(3)$

    $T = 25$

    $25^0\,\mathrm{C}$

5.4 Exercises

1. $4x^2 + 13x + 3$; Grouping number: 12

    $4x^2 + 13x + 3 = 4x^2 + 12x + x + 3$

              $= 4x(x + 3) + 1(x + 3)$

              $= (4x + 1)(x + 1)$

Check:

$(4x + 1)(x + 3) = 4x^2 + 12x + x + 3$

               $= 4x^2 + 13x + 3$

3. $5x^2 + 7x + 2$; Grouping number: 10

    $5x^2 + 7x + 2 = 5x^2 + 5x + 2x + 2$

           $= 5x(x + 1) + 2(x + 1)$

           $= (5x + 2)(x + 1)$

Check:

$(5x + 2)(x + 1) = 5x^2 + 5x + 2x + 2$

            $= 5x^2 + 7x + 2$

5. $3x^2 - 4x - 7$; Grouping number: -21

$$3x^2 - 4x - 7 = 3x^2 - 7x + 3x - 7$$
$$= x(3x - 7) + (3x - 7)$$
$$= (3x - 7)(x + 1)$$

Check:

$$(3x - 7)(x + 1) = 3x^2 + 3x - 7x - 7$$
$$= 3x^2 - 4x - 7$$

7. $2x^2 - 5x - 3$; Grouping number: -6

$$2x^2 - 5x - 3 = 2x^2 - 6x + x - 3$$
$$= 2x(x - 3) + (x - 3)$$
$$= (x - 3)(2x + 1)$$

Check:

$$(x - 3)(2x + 1) = 2x^2 + x - 6x - 3$$
$$= 2x^2 - 5x - 3$$

9. $9x^2 + 9x + 2$; Grouping number: 18

$$9x^2 + 9x + 2 = 9x^2 + 3x + 6x + 2$$
$$= 3x(3x + 1) + 2(3x + 1)$$
$$= (3x + 1)(3x + 2)$$

Check:

$$(3x + 1)(3x + 2) = 9x^2 + 6x + 3x + 2$$
$$= 9x^2 + 9x + 2$$

11. $15x^2 - 34x + 15$; Grouping number: 225

$$15x^2 - 34x + 15 = 15x^2 - 25x - 9x + 15$$
$$= 5x(3x - 5) - 3(3x - 5)$$
$$= (5x - 3)(3x - 5)$$

Check:

$$(5x - 3)(3x - 5) = 15x^2 - 25x - 9x + 15$$
$$= 15x^2 - 34x + 15$$

13. $2x^2 + 3x - 20$; Grouping number: -40

$$2x^2 + 3x - 20 = 2x^2 + 8x - 5x - 20$$
$$= 2x(x + 4) - 5(x + 4)$$
$$= (x + 4)(2x - 5)$$

Check:

$$(x + 4)(2x - 5) = 2x^2 - 5x + 8x - 20$$
$$= 2x^2 + 3x - 20$$

15. $8x^2 + 10x - 3$; Grouping number: -24

$$8x^2 + 10x - 3 = 8x^2 + 12x - 2x - 3$$
$$= 4x(2x + 3) - (2x + 3)$$
$$= (2x + 3)(4x - 1)$$

Check:

$$(2x + 3)(4x - 1) = 8x^2 - 2x + 12x - 3$$
$$= 9x^2 + 10x - 3$$

17. $6x^2 - 5x - 6$; Grouping number: -36

$6x^2 - 5x - 6 = 6x^2 - 9x + 4x - 6$

$\qquad = 3x(2x-3) + 2(2x-3)$

$\qquad = (2x-3)(3x+2)$

Check:

$(2x-3)(3x+2) = 6x^2 + 4x - 9x - 6$

$\qquad\qquad = 6x^2 - 5x - 6$

19. $6x^2 + x - 15 = 6x^2 + 10x - 9x - 15$

$\qquad = 2x(3x+5) - 3(3x+5)$

$\qquad = (3x+5)(2x-3)$

21. $7x^2 - 5x - 18 = 7x^2 - 14x + 9x - 18$

$\qquad = 7x(x-2) + 9(x-2)$

$\qquad = (7x+9)(x-2)$

23. $9y^2 - 13y + 4 = 9y^2 - 9y - 4y + 4$

$\qquad = 9y(y-1) - 4(y-1)$

$\qquad = (y-1)(9y-4)$

25. $5a^2 - 13a - 6 = 5a^2 - 15a + 2a - 6$

$\qquad = 5a(a-3) + 2(a-3)$

$\qquad = (a-3)(5a+2)$

27. $12x^2 - 20x + 3 = 12x^2 - 18x - 2x + 3$

$\qquad = 6x(2x-3) - (2x-3)$

$\qquad = (2x-3)(6x-1)$

29. $15x^2 + 4x - 4 = 15x^2 + 10x - 6x - 4$

$\qquad = 5x(3x+2) - 2(3x+2)$

$\qquad = (3x+2)(5x-2)$

31. $12x^2 + 28x + 15 = 12x^2 + 18x + 10x + 15$

$\qquad = 6x(2x+3) + 5(2x+3)$

$\qquad = (6x+5)(2x+3)$

33. $12x^2 - 16x - 3 = 12x^2 + 2x - 18x - 3$

$\qquad = 2x(6x+1) - 3(6x+1)$

$\qquad = (6x+1)(2x-3)$

35. $2x^4 + 15x^2 - 8 = 2x^4 + 16x^2 - x^2 - 8$

$\qquad = 2x^2(x^2 + 8) - (x^2 + 8)$

$\qquad = (x^2 + 8)(2x^2 - 1)$

37. $2x^2 + 11xy + 15y^2$

$\qquad = 2x^2 + 6xy + 5xy + 15y^2$

$\qquad = 2x(x+3y) + 5y(x+3y)$

$\qquad = (x+3y)(2x+5y)$

39. $5x^2 + 16xy - 16y^2 = 5x^2 + 20xy - 4xy - 16y^2$

$\qquad = 5x(x+4y) - 4y(x+4y)$

$\qquad = (x+4y)(5x-4y)$

41. $4x^2 + 34x + 42$

$\qquad = 2(2x^2 + 17x + 21)$

$\qquad = 2(x+7)(2x+3)$

43. $8x^2 - 26x + 6$

$= 2(4x^2 - 13x + 3)$

$= 2(x - 3)(4x - 1)$

45. $10x^2 - 25x - 15 = 5(2x^2 - 5x - 3)$

$= 5(2x^2 - 6x + x - 3)$

$= 5[2x(x - 3) + 1(x - 3)]$

$= 5(2x + 1)(x - 3)$

47. $6x^3 + 9x^2 - 60x = 3x(2x^2 + 3x - 20)$

$= 3x(2x - 5)(x + 4)$

49. $5x^2 + 3x - 2 = 5x^2 + 5x - 2x - 2$

$= 5x(x + 1) - 2(x + 1)$

$= (x + 1)(5x - 2)$

51. $12x^2 - 38x + 20 = 2(6x^2 - 19x + 10)$

$= 2(6x^2 - 15x - 4x + 10)$

$= 2[3x(2x - 5) - 2(2x - 5)]$

$= 2(2x - 5)(3x - 2)$

53. $12x^2 - 20x + 3 = 12x^2 - 18x - 2x + 3$

$= 6x(2x - 3) - (2x - 3)$

$= (2x - 3)(6x - 1)$

55. $8x^2 + 16x - 10 = 2(4x^2 + 8x - 5)$

$= 2(4x^2 + 10x - 2x - 5)$

$= 2[2x(2x + 5) - (2x + 5)]$

$= 2(2x + 5)(2x - 1)$

Cumulative Review

57. $7x - 3(4 - 2x) = 2(x - 3) - (5 - x)$

$7x - 12 + 6x = 2x - 6 - 5 + x$

$13x - 12 = 3x - 11$

$10x = 1$

$x = \dfrac{1}{10}$

59. Percent increase $= \dfrac{1809 - 1430}{1430}$

$= 0.265$

$= 26.5\%$

61. China:

Percent increase $= \dfrac{1131 - 778}{778}$

$= 0.454$

$= 45.5\%$

China had the greatest percent.

How Am I Doing? Sections 5.1-5.4

1. $6xy - 15z + 21 = 3(2xy - 5z + 7)$

2. $20x^2 - 32xy + 12x = 4x(5x - 8y + 3)$

3. $7(4x - 5) - b(4x - 5) = (4x - 5)(7 - b)$

4. $2x(8y + 3z) - 5y(8y + 3z)$
   $= (8y + 3z)(2x - 5y)$

5. $18 + 3x - 6y - xy = 3(6 + x) - y(6 + x)$
   $\qquad\qquad\qquad = (6 + x)(3 - y)$

6. $15x - 9xb + 20w - 12bw$
   $= 3x(5 - 3b) + 4w(5 - 3b)$
   $= (5 - 3b)(3x + 4w)$

7. $x^3 - 5x^2 - 3x + 15 = x^2(x - 5) - 3(x - 5)$
   $\qquad\qquad\qquad = (x - 5)(x^2 - 3)$

8. $7a + 21b + 2ab + 6b^2 = 7(a + 3b) + 2b(a + 3b)$
   $\qquad\qquad\qquad = (a + 3b)(7 + 2b)$

9. $x^2 - 15x + 56 = x^2 - 7x - 8x + 56$
   $\qquad\qquad = x(x - 7) - 8(x - 7)$
   $\qquad\qquad = (x - 7)(x - 8)$

10. $x^2 + 12x - 64 = x^2 + 16x - 4x - 64$
    $\qquad\qquad = x(x + 16) - 4(x + 16)$
    $\qquad\qquad = (x + 16)(x - 4)$

11. $x^2 + 13xy + 40y^2 = x^2 + 8xy + 5xy + 40y^2$
    $\qquad\qquad = x(x + 8y)5y(x + 8y)$
    $\qquad\qquad = (x + 8y)(x + 5y)$

12. $7x^2 - 14x - 245 = 7(x^2 - 2x - 35)$
    $\qquad\qquad = 7(x^2 - 7x + 5x - 35)$
    $\qquad\qquad = 7[x(x - 7) + 5(x - 7)]$
    $\qquad\qquad = 7(x - 7)(x + 5)$

13. $10x^2 + x - 2 = 10x^2 + 5x - 4x - 2$
    $\qquad\qquad = 5x(2x + 1) - 2(2x + 1)$
    $\qquad\qquad = (2x + 1)(5x - 2)$

14. $3x^2 - 23x + 14 = 3x^2 - 21x - 2x + 14$
    $\qquad\qquad = 3x(x - 7) - 2(x - 7)$
    $\qquad\qquad = (x - 7)(3x - 2)$

15. $6x^2 + 17xy + 12y^2 = 6x^2 + 9xy + 8xy + 12y^2$
    $\qquad\qquad = 3x(2x + 3y) + 4y(2x + 3y)$
    $\qquad\qquad = (2x + 3y)(3x + 4y)$

159

16. $14x^3 - 20x^2 - 16x = 2x(7x^2 - 10x - 8)$

$\qquad = 2x(7x^2 - 14x \_ 4x - 8)$

$\qquad = 2x[7x(x-2) + 4(x-2)]$

$\qquad = 2x(x-2)(7x+4)$

19. $25a^2 - 81b^2 = (5a)^2 - (9b)^2$

$\qquad = (5a + 9b)(5a - 9b)$

21. $9x^2 + 6x + 1 = (3x)^2 + 2(3x)(1) + (1)^2$

$\qquad = (3x+1)^2$

5.5 Exercises

1. $9x^2 - 1 = (3x)^2 - (1)^2 = (3x+1)(3x-1)$

23. $y^2 - 10y + 25 = y^2 - 2(y)(5) + (5)^2$

$\qquad = (y-5)^2$

3. $81x^2 - 16 = (9x)^2 - (4)^2 = (9x+4)(9x-4)$

25. $36x^2 - 60x + 25 = (6x)^2 - 2(6x)(5) + (5)^2$

$\qquad = (6x-5)^2$

5. $x^2 - 49 = (x)^2 - (7)^2 = (x+7)(x-7)$

7. $4x^2 - 25 = (2x)^2 - (5)^2 = (2x+5)(2x-5)$

27. $49x^2 + 28x + 4 = (7x)^2 + 2(7x)(2) + 2^2$

$\qquad = (7x+2)^2$

9. $x^2 - 25 = (x)^2 - (5)^2 = (x+5)(x-5)$

29. $x^2 + 14x + 49 = (x)^2 + 2(x)(7) + (7)^2$

$\qquad = (x+7)^2$

11. $1 - 16x^2 = (1)^2 - (4x)^2 = (1+4x)(1-4x)$

13. $16x^2 - 49y^2 = (4x)^2 - (7y)^2$

$\qquad = (4x+7y)(4x-7y)$

31. $25x^2 - 40x + 16 = (5)^2 - 2(5x)(4) + 4^2$

$\qquad = (5x-4)^2$

33. $81x^2 + 36xy + 4y^2$

$\qquad = (9x)^2 + 2(9x)(2y) + (2y)^2$

$\qquad = (9x+2y)^2$

15. $36x^2 - 169y^2 = (6x)^2 - (13y)^2$

$\qquad = (6x+13y)(6x-13y)$

17. $81x^2 - 100 = (9x)^2 - (10)^2$

$\qquad = (9x+10)(9x-10)$

35. $25x^2 - 30xy + 9y^2$

$\qquad = (5x)^2 - 2(5x)(3y) + (3y)^2$

$\qquad = (5x-3y)^2$

37. $16a^2 + 72ab + 81b^2$

$\quad = (4a)^2 + 2(4a)(9b) + (9b)^2$

$\quad = (4a + 9b)^2$

39. $49x^2 - 42xy + 9y^2$

$\quad = (7x)^2 - 2(7x)(3y) + (3y)^2$

$\quad = (7x - 3y)^2$

41. $49x^2 + 42x + 9 = (7x)^2 + 2(7x)(3) + (3)^2$

$\quad\quad\quad\quad\quad = (7x + 3)^2$

43. $49x^2 - 9 - (7x)^2 - (3)^2$

$\quad\quad\quad = (7x + 3)(7x - 3)$

45. $x^4 - 36 = (x^2)^2 - (6)^2 = (x^2 + 6)(x^2 - 6)$

47. $9x^4 - 12x^2 + 4 = (3x^2)^2 - 2(3x)(2) + (2)^2$

$\quad\quad\quad\quad\quad = (3x^2 - 2)^2$

49. You cannot factor $9x^2 + 1$ because there are no combinations of the product of two binomials that give $9x^2 + 1$.

51. $16 = 4^2$

$\quad 56 = (2)(4)(7)$

$\quad c = 7^2$

$\quad c = 49$

There is only one answer.

53. $16x^2 - 36 = 4(4x^2 - 9)$

$\quad\quad\quad\quad = 4(2x + 3)(2x - 3)$

55. $147x^2 - 3y^2 = 3(49x^2 - y^2)$

$\quad\quad\quad\quad\quad = 3\left[(7x)^2 - y^2\right]$

$\quad\quad\quad\quad\quad = 3(7x - y)(7x + y)$

57. $12x^2 - 36x + 27 = 3(4x^2 - 12x + 9)$

$\quad\quad\quad\quad\quad\quad = 3(2x - 3)^2$

59. $98x^2 + 84x + 18 = 2(49x^2 + 42x + 9)$

$\quad\quad\quad\quad\quad\quad = 2(7x + 3)^2$

61. $x^2 - 15x + 44 = x^2 - 11x - 4x + 44$

$\quad\quad\quad\quad\quad = x(x - 11) - 4(x - 11)$

$\quad\quad\quad\quad\quad = (x - 11)(x - 4)$

63. $2x^2 + 5x - 3 = (2x - 1)(x + 3)$

65. $16x^2 - 121 = (4x + 11)(4x - 11)$

67. $9x^2 + 42x + 49 = (3x + 7)^2$

69. $3x^2 + 6x - 45 = 3(x^2 + 2x - 15)$

$\quad\quad\quad\quad\quad = 3(x + 5)(x - 3)$

71. $5x^2 - 80 = 5(x^2 - 16)$

$\quad\quad\quad\quad = 5(x + 4)(x - 4)$

73. $7x^2 + 42x + 63 = 7(x^2 + 6x + 9)$

$$= 7\left[(x^2) + 2(x)(3) + (3)^2\right]$$

$$= 7(x+3)^2$$

75. $2x^2 - 32x + 126 = 2(x^2 - 16x + 63)$

$$= 2(x-9)(x-7)$$

Cumulative Review

77.
$$\require{enclose}
\begin{array}{r}
x^2 + 3x + 4 \\
x-2 \enclose{longdiv}{x^3 + x^2 - 2x - 11} \\
\underline{x^3 - 2x^2} \\
3x^2 - 2x \\
\underline{3x^2 - 6x} \\
4x - 11 \\
\underline{4x - 8} \\
-3
\end{array}$$

$(x^3 + x^2 - 2x - 11) \div (x-2)$

$= x^2 + 3x + 4 - \dfrac{3}{x-2}$

79. Daily diet $= 0.2(150) = 3$ ounces

$.4(3) = 1.2$ ounces of greens

$.35(3) = 1.05$ ounces of bulk vegtable

$.25(3) = 0.75$ ounces of fruit

81. $A = 6288 - 700M$

$A = 6288 - 700(3.5)$

$A = 6288 - 2450$

$A = 3838$

3838 feet above sea level

5.6 Exercises

1. $6a^2 + 2ab - 3a = a(6a + 2b - 3)$

Check: $a(6a + 2b) = 6a^2 + 2ab - 3a$

3. $16x^2 - 25y^2 = (4x)^2 - (5y)^2$

$$= (4x + 5y)(4x - 5y)$$

Check:

$(4x + 5y)(4x - 5y) = (4x)^2 - (5y)^2$

$$= 16x^2 - 25y^2$$

5. $9x^2 - 12xy + 4y^2 = (3x - 2y)^2$

Check:

$(3x - 2y)^2 = 9x^2 + 2(3x)(-2y) + (-2y)^2$

$$= 9x^2 - 12xy + 4y^2$$

7. $x^2 + 8x + 15 = (x+5)(x+3)$

Check:

$(x+5)(x+3) = x^2 + 3x + 5x + 15$

$$= x^2 + 8x + 15$$

9. $15x^2 + 7x - 2 = (5x - 1)(3x + 2)$
Check:
$(5x - 1)(3x + 2) = 15x^2 + 10x - 3x - 2$
$$= 15x^2 + 7x - 2$$

11. $ax - 3cx + 3ay - 9cy$
$= x(a - 3c) + 3y(a - 3c)$
$= (a - 3c)(x + 3y)$
Check:
$(x + 3y)(a - 3c) = ax - 3cx + 3ay - 9cy$

13. $y^2 + 14y + 49 = (y)^2 + 2(y)(7) + (7)^2$
$$= (y + 7)^2$$

15. $4x^2 - 12x + 9 = (2x - 3)(2x - 3)$
$$= (2x - 3)^2$$

17. $2x^2 - 11x + 12 = (2x - 3)(x - 4)$

19. $x^2 - 3xy - 70y^2 = (x - 10y)(x + 7y)$

21. $ax - 5a + 3x - 15 = a(x - 5) + 3(x - 5)$
$$= (a + 3)(x - 5)$$

23. $45x - 5x^3 = 5x(9 - x^2)$
$$= 5x(3 + x)(3 - x)$$

25. $5x^3y^3 - 10x^2y^3 + 5xy^3 = 5xy^3(x^2 - 2x + 1)$
$$= 5xy^3(x - 1)^2$$

27. $27xyz^2 - 12xy = 3xy(9z^2 - 4)$
$$= 3xy(3z + 2)(3z - 2)$$

29. $3x^2 + 6x - 105 = 3(x^2 + 2x - 35)$
$$= 3(x + 7)(x - 5)$$

31. $3x^3 + 3x^2 - 36x = 3x(x^2 + x - 12)$
$$= 3x(x^2 + 4x - 3x - 12)$$
$$= 3x[x(x + 4) - 3(x + 4)]$$
$$= 3x(x + 4)(x - 3)$$

33. $7x^2 - 2x^4 + 4 = -1(2x^4 - 7x^2 - 4)$
$$= -1(2x^2 + 1)(x^2 - 4)$$
$$= -1(2x^2 + 1)(x + 2)(x - 2)$$

35. $6x^2 - 3x + 2$ is prime.

37. $5x^2 + 10xy - 30y = 5(x^2 + 2xy - 6y)$

39. $30x^3 + 3x^2y - 6xy^2 = 3x(10x^2 + xy - 2y^2)$
$$= 3x(2x + y)(5x - 2)$$

41. $24x^2 - 58x + 30 = 2(12x^2 - 29x + 15)$
$$= 2(12x^2 - 20x - 9x + 15)$$
$$= 2[4x(3x - 5) - 3(3x - 5)]$$
$$= 2(3x - 5)(4x - 3)$$

43. A polynomial that cannot be factored by the methods of this chapter is called <u>prime</u>.

Check:

$$(-3)^2 - 4(-3) - 21 \overset{?}{=} 0 \qquad (7)^2 - 4(7) - 21 \overset{?}{=} 0$$

$$9 + 12 - 21 \overset{?}{=} 0 \qquad 49 - 28 - 21 \overset{?}{=} 0$$

$$0 = 0 \qquad\qquad 0 = 0$$

Cumulative Review

45. 20% of what $= 19.56$

$$0.2x = 19.56$$

$$x = 97.8$$

Sale price $= 97.80 - 19.56 = \$78.24$

47. Percentage increase $= \dfrac{65 - 57}{57}$

$$= 0.140$$

$$= 14\%$$

$$2010 : 100\% + 14\% = 114\%$$

$$114\% \text{ of } 65 = 1.14(65) = \$74$$

49. Average rate of change $= \dfrac{65 - 57}{10} = 0.8$

$$y = 0.8x + 57$$

5.7 Exercises

1. $x^2 - 4x - 21 = 0$

$$(x + 3)(x - 7) = 0$$

$$x + 3 = 0 \qquad x - 7 = 0$$

$$x = -3 \qquad\quad x = 7$$

3. $x^2 + 16x + 39 = 0$

$$(x + 13)(x + 3) = 0$$

$$x + 13 = 0 \qquad x + 3 = 0$$

$$x = -13 \qquad\quad x = -3$$

Check:

$$(-13)^2 + 16(-13) + 39 \overset{?}{=} 0$$

$$169 - 208 + 39 \overset{?}{=} 0$$

$$0 = 0$$

$$(-3)^2 + 16(-3) + 39 \overset{?}{=} 0$$

$$9 - 48 + 39 \overset{?}{=} 0$$

$$0 = 0$$

5. $2x^2 - 7x + 6 = 0$

$$2x^2 - 3x - 4x + 6 = 0$$

$$x(2x - 3) - 2(2x - 3) = 0$$

$$(2x - 3)(x - 2) = 0$$

$$2x - 3 = 0 \qquad x - 2 = 0$$

$$x = \dfrac{3}{2} \qquad\qquad x = 2$$

Check:

$$2\left(\frac{3}{2}\right)^2 - 7\left(\frac{3}{2}\right) + 6 \overset{?}{=} 0 \qquad 2(2)^2 - 7(2) + 6 \overset{?}{=} 0$$

$$\frac{9}{2} - \frac{21}{2} + \frac{12}{2} \overset{?}{=} 0 \qquad\qquad 8 - 14 + 6 \overset{?}{=} 0$$

$$0 = 0 \qquad\qquad\qquad\qquad 0 = 0$$

7. $6x^2 - 13x = -6$

$$6x^2 - 13x + 6 = 0$$

$$(3x - 2)(2x - 3) = 0$$

$$3x - 2 = 0 \qquad 2x - 3 = 0$$

$$3x = 2 \qquad\quad 2x = 3$$

$$x = \frac{2}{3} \qquad\quad x = \frac{3}{2}$$

Check:

$$6\left(\frac{2}{3}\right)^2 - 13\left(\frac{2}{3}\right) \overset{?}{=} -6 \qquad 6\left(\frac{3}{2}\right)^2 - 13\left(\frac{3}{2}\right) \overset{?}{=} -6$$

$$\frac{8}{3} - \frac{26}{3} \overset{?}{=} -6 \qquad\qquad \frac{27}{2} - \frac{39}{2} \overset{?}{=} -6$$

$$-6 = -6 \qquad\qquad\qquad -6 = -6$$

9. $x^2 + 13x = 0$

$$x(x + 13) = 0$$

$$x = 0 \qquad\qquad x + 13 = 0$$

$$x = -13$$

Check:

$$(-13)^2 + (13)(-13) \overset{?}{=} 0 \qquad 0^2 + 13(0) \overset{?}{=} 0$$

$$169 - 169 \overset{?}{=} 0 \qquad\qquad\qquad 0 \overset{?}{=} 0$$

$$0 = 0$$

11. $8x^2 = 72$

$$8x^2 - 72 = 0$$

$$8(x^2 - 9) = 0$$

$$8(x - 3)(x + 3) = 0$$

$$x - 3 = 0 \qquad\qquad x + 3 = 0$$

$$x = 3 \qquad\qquad\quad x = -3$$

Check:

$$8(-3)^2 \overset{?}{=} 72 \qquad\qquad 8(3)^2 \overset{?}{=} 72$$

$$72 = 72 \qquad\qquad\qquad 72 = 72$$

13. $5x^2 + 3x = 8x$

$$5x^2 - 5x = 0$$

$$5x(x - 1) = 0$$

$$5x = 0 \qquad\qquad x - 1 = 0$$

$$x = 0 \qquad\qquad\quad x = 1$$

Check:

$$5(0)^2 + 3(0) \overset{?}{=} 8(0) \qquad 5(1)^2 + 3(1) \overset{?}{=} 8(1)$$

$$0 + 0 \overset{?}{=} 0 \qquad\qquad\qquad 5 + 3 \overset{?}{=} 8$$

$$0 = 0 \qquad\qquad\qquad\qquad 8 = 8$$

15. $6x^2 = 16x - 8$

$$6x^2 - 16x + 8 = 0$$

$$2(3x^2 - 8x + 4) = 0$$

$$2(2x - 2)(x - 2) = 0$$

$$3x - 2 = 0 \qquad\qquad x - 2 = 0$$

$$3x = 2 \qquad\qquad\quad x = 2$$

$$x = \frac{2}{3}$$

Check:

$$6\left(\frac{2}{3}\right)^2 \overset{?}{=} 16\left(\frac{2}{3}\right) - 8$$

$$\frac{24}{9} \overset{?}{=} \frac{32}{3} - \frac{24}{3}$$

$$\frac{8}{3} = \frac{8}{3}$$

$$6(2)^2 \overset{?}{=} 16(2) - 8$$

$$24 \overset{?}{=} 32 - 8$$

$$24 = 24$$

19. $$4x^2 - 3x + 1 = -7x$$

$$4x^2 + 4x + 1 = 0$$

$$(2x + 1)(2x + 1) = 0$$

$$2x + 1 = 0$$

$$2x = -1$$

$$x = -\frac{1}{2}$$

Check:

$$4\left(-\frac{1}{2}\right)^2 - 3\left(-\frac{1}{2}\right) + 1 \overset{?}{=} -7\left(-\frac{1}{2}\right)$$

$$1 + \frac{3}{2} + 1 \overset{?}{=} \frac{7}{2}$$

$$\frac{7}{2} = \frac{7}{2}$$

21. $$\frac{x^2}{2} - 8 + x = -8$$

$$x^2 - 16 + 2x = -16$$

$$x^2 + 2x = 0$$

$$x(x + 2) = 0$$

$$x = 0 \qquad\qquad x + 2 = 0$$

$$x = -2$$

Check:

$$\frac{(0)^2}{2} - 8 + (0) \overset{?}{=} -8 \qquad\qquad \frac{(-2)^2}{2} - 8 + (-2) \overset{?}{=} -8$$

$$0 - 8 + 0 \overset{?}{=} -8 \qquad\qquad 2 - 8 - 2 \overset{?}{=} -8$$

$$-8 = -8 \qquad\qquad -8 = -8$$

23. $$\frac{x^2 + 7x}{4} = -3$$

$$x^2 + 7x = -12$$

$$x^2 + 7x + 12 = 0$$

$$(x + 4)(x + 3) = 0$$

$$x + 4 = 0 \qquad\qquad x + 3 = 0$$

$$x = -4 \qquad\qquad x = -3$$

Check:

$$\frac{(-4)^2 + 7(-4)}{4} \overset{?}{=} -3 \qquad\qquad \frac{(-3)^2 + 7(-3)}{4} \overset{?}{=} -3$$

$$\frac{16 - 28}{4} \overset{?}{=} -3 \qquad\qquad \frac{9 - 21}{4} \overset{?}{=} -3$$

$$\frac{-12}{4} \overset{?}{=} -3 \qquad\qquad \frac{-12}{4} \overset{?}{=} -3$$

$$-3 = -3 \qquad\qquad -3 = -3$$

25. $$\frac{10x^2 - 25x}{12} = 5$$

$$10x^2 - 25x = 60$$

$$10x^2 - 25x - 60 = 0$$

$$5(2x^2 - 5x - 12) = 0$$

$$5(2x + 3)(x - 4) = 0$$

$$2x + 3 = 0 \qquad x - 4 = 0$$

$$x = -\frac{3}{2} \qquad x = 4$$

Check:

$$\frac{9\left(-\frac{5}{3}\right)^2 - 12\left(-\frac{5}{3}\right)}{3} \overset{?}{=} 15 \qquad \frac{9(3)^2\, 12(3)}{3} \overset{?}{=} 15$$

$$\frac{25 + 20}{3} \overset{?}{=} 15 \qquad \frac{81 - 36}{3} \overset{?}{=} 15$$

$$15 = 15 \qquad\qquad 15 = 15$$

27. An equation in the form $ax^2 + bx = 0$ can always be solved by factoring out x.

29.
$$x = \text{length}$$
$$\frac{1}{2}x + 3 = \text{width}$$

$$x\left(\frac{1}{2}x + 3\right) = 140$$

$$\frac{x^2}{2} + 3x = 140$$

$$x^2 + 6x = 280$$

$$x^2 + 6x - 280 = 0$$

$$(x + 20)(x - 14) = 0$$

$$x + 20 = 0 \qquad x - 14 = 0$$

$$x = -20 \qquad x = 14$$

Width not negative $\quad \frac{1}{2}x + 3 = 10$

The length is 14 m and the width is 10 m.

31. $G = \dfrac{x^2 - 3x + 2}{2}, \quad x = 13$

$$G = \frac{13^2 - 3(13) + 2}{2}$$

$$G = \frac{169 - 39 + 2}{2}$$

$$G = 66 \text{ groups}$$

33. $G = \dfrac{x^2 - 3x + 2}{2}$

$$72 = x^2 - 3x + 2$$

$$0 = x^2 - 3x - 70$$

$$0 = (x - 10)(x + 7)$$

$$x \quad 10 = 0 \qquad x + 7 = 0$$

$$x = 10 \qquad\qquad x = -7$$

$$\text{Not possible}$$

There are 10 students.

35.
$$s = -5t^2 + vt + h$$
$$v = 13 \qquad h = 6$$
$$s = -5t^2 + 13t + 6$$

When the ball hits the ground $s = 0$.

$$0 = -5t^2 + 13t + 6$$

$$0 = 5t^2 - 13t - 6$$

$$0 = (5t + 2)(t - 3)$$

$$5t + 2 = 0 \qquad t - 3 = 0$$

$$t = -\frac{2}{5} \qquad\qquad t = 3$$

Time can't be negative.

The ball will hit the ground at $t = 3$ sec.

$s = -5(2)^2 + 13(2) + 6$

$\quad = -20 + 26 + 6$

$\quad = 12$

After 2 seconds the ball is 12 m from the ground.

37. $C = 2x^2 - 7x$

$15 = 2x^2 - 7x$

$2x^2 - 7x - 15 = 0$

$(2x + 3)(x - 5) = 0$

$2x + 3 = 0 \qquad x - 5 = 0$

$x = -\dfrac{3}{2} \qquad x = 5$

The number cannot be negative, so 5 additional helicopters were produced.

Use $T = 0.5(x^2 - x)$ in Exercise 37.

39. $x = 70$

$T = 0.5\left[(70)^2 - 70\right]$

$\quad = 0.5(4900 - 70)$

$\quad = 2415$ telephone calls

41. $\qquad\qquad T = 153$

$0.5(x^2 - x) = 306$

$x^2 - x - 306 = 0$

$(x + 17)(x - 18) = 0$

$x + 17 = 0 \qquad x - 18 = 0$

$x = -17 \qquad x = 18$

41. The negative number of people is not allowed. 18 people worked that day.

Cumulative Review

43. $\left(2x^2y^3\right)\left(-5x^3y\right) = -10x^5y^4$

45. $\dfrac{21a^5b^{10}}{-14ab^{12}} = -\dfrac{3a^4}{2b^2}$

Putting Your Skills to Work

1. Increase from 2001 to 2002 = $294 - 258 = 36/$ yr
    Reviews in 2005 = $294 + 3(36) = 402$

2. Increase from 2001 to 2002 = $94 - 89 = 5$
    Reviews in 2006 = $94 + 4(5) = 114$

3. 1999: Percentage reversals = $\dfrac{57}{195} = 0.29 = 29\%$

    2000: Percentage reversals = $\dfrac{84}{247} = 0.34 = 34\%$

    The percentage increased by 5.

4. 2001: Percentage reversals = $\dfrac{89}{258} = 0.34 = 34\%$

    2002: Percentage reversals = $\dfrac{94}{294} = 0.32 = 32\%$

    The percentage decreased by 2.

5. $y = 30x + 294, \; x = 2$

    $y = 30(2) + 294$

    $y = 354$

168

6. $y = 11x + 99, \; x = 3$

    $y = 11(3) + 99$

    $y = 132$

7. $y = 30x + 294$

    $y = 6(5x + 49)$

8. $y = 11x + 99$

    $y = 11(x + 9)$

Chapter 5 Review Problems

1. $12x^3 - 20x^2 y = 4x^2(3x - 5y)$

2. $10x^3 - 35x^3 y = 5x^3(2 - 7y)$

3. $7x^2 y - 14xy^2 - 21x^3 y^3$

    $= 7xy(x - 2y - 3x^2 y^2)$

4. $50a^4 b^5 - 25a^4 b^4 + 75a^5 b^5$

    $= 25a^4 b^4(2b - 1 + 3ab)$

5. $3a^3 + 6a^2 - 9ab + 12a = 3a(a^2 + 2a - 3b + 4)$

6. $2x - 4y + 6z + 12 = 2(x - 2y + 3z + 6)$

7. $2a(a + 3b) - 5(a + 3b) = (a + 3b)(2a - 5)$

8. $15x^3 y + 6xy^2 + 3xy = 3xy(5x^2 + 2y + 1)$

9. $3ax - 7a - 6x + 14 = a(3x - 7) - 2(3x - 7)$

    $= (3x - 7)(a - 2)$

10. $a^2 + 5ab - 4a - 20b = a(a + 5b) - (4a + 5b)$

    $= (a + 5b)(a - 4)$

11. $x^2 y + 3y - 2x^2 - 6 = y(x^2 + 3) - 2(x^2 + 3)$

    $= (x^2 + 3)(y - 2)$

12. $30ax - 15ay + 42x - 21y$

    $= 3(10ax - 5ay + 14x - 7y)$

    $= 3[5a(2x - y) + 7(2x - y)]$

    $= 3(2x - y)(5a + 7)$

13. $15x^2 - 3x + 10x - 2 = 3x(5x - 1) + 2(5x - 1)$

    $= (5x - 1)(3x + 2)$

14. $30w^2 - 18w + 5wz - 3z$

    $= 6w(5w - 3) + z(5w - 3)$

    $= (5w - 3)(6w + z)$

15. $x^2 - 2x - 35 = (x - 7)(x + 5)$

16. $x^2 - 10x + 24 = (x - 6)(x - 4)$

17. $x^2 + 14x + 48 = (x + 6)(x + 8)$

18. $x^2 + 8xy + 15y^2 = (x + 3y)(x + 5y)$

19. $x^4 + 13x^2 + 42 = (x^2 + 6)(x^2 + 7)$

20. $x^4 - 2x^2 - 35 = (x^2 - 7)(x^2 + 5)$

21. $6x^2 + 30x + 36 = 6(x^2 + 5x + 6)$
$$= 6(x + 2)(x + 3)$$

22. $3x^2 + 39x + 36 = 3(x^2 + 13x + 12)$
$$= 3(x + 12)(x + 1)$$

23. $2x^2 - 28x + 96 = 2(x^2 - 14x + 48)$
$$= 2(x - 8)(x - 6)$$

24. $4x^2 - 44x + 120 = 4(x^2 - 11x + 30)$
$$= 4(x - 6)(x - 5)$$

25. $4x^2 + 7x - 15 = (4x - 5)(x + 3)$

26. $12x^2 + 11x - 5 = 12x^2 - 4x + 15x - 5$
$$= 4x(3x - 1) + 5(3x - 1)$$
$$= (3x - 2)(2x - 3)$$

27. $15x^2 + 7x - 4 = (3x - 1)(5x + 4)$

28. $6x^2 - 13x + 6 = 6x^2 - 4x - 9x + 6$
$$= 2x(3x - 2) - 3(3x - 2)$$
$$= (3x - 2)(2x - 3)$$

29. $2x^2 - x - 3 = (2x - 3)(x + 1)$

30. $3x^2 + 2x - 8 = (3x - 4)(x + 2)$

31. $20x^2 + 48x - 5 = (10x - 1)(2x + 5)$

32. $20x^2 + 21x - 5 = 20x^2 - 4x + 25x - 5$
$$= 4x(5x - 1) + 5(5x - 1)$$
$$= (5x - 1)(4x + 5)$$

33. $6a^2 + 11a - 10 = (3a - 2)(2a + 5)$

34. $6a^2 - 19a + 10 = (3a - 2)(2a - 5)$

35. $6x^2 + 4x - 10 = 2(3x^2 + 2x - 5)$
$$= 2(3x + 5)(x - 1)$$

36. $6x^2 - 4x - 10 = 2(3x^2 - 2x - 5)$
$$= 2(3x^2 - 5x + 3x - 5)$$
$$= 2[x(3x - 5) + 1(3x - 5)]$$
$$= 2(3x - 5)(x + 1)$$

37. $4x^2 - 26x + 30 = 2(2x^2 - 13x + 15)$
$$= 2(2x - 3)(x - 5)$$

38. $4x^2 - 20x - 144 = 4(x^2 - 5x - 36)$
$$= 4(x - 9)(x + 4)$$

39. $12x^2 - 22x - 20 = 2(6x^2 - 11x - 10)$
$$= 2(3x + 2)(2x - 5)$$

40. $18x^2 + 51x - 42 = 3\left(6x^2 + 17x - 14\right)$
$$= 3(3x - 2)(2x + 7)$$

41. $6x^2 - 19xy + 10y^2 = (2x - 5y)(3x - 2y)$

42. $6x^2 - 32xy + 10y^2 = 2\left(3x^2 - 16xy + 5y^2\right)$
$$= 2\left(3x^2 - 15xy - xy + 5y^2\right)$$
$$= 2\left[3x(x - 5y) - y(x - 5y)\right]$$
$$= 2(x - 5y)(3x - y)$$

43. $49x^2 - y^2 = (7x)^2 - (y)^2$
$$= (7x + y)(7x - y)$$

44. $16x^2 - 36y^2 = 4\left(4x^2 - 9y^2\right)$
$$= 4\left[(2x)^2 - (3y)^2\right]$$
$$= 4(2x - 3y)(2x + 3y)$$

45. $25x^2 + 30x + 9 = (5x + 3)^2$

46. $49x^2 - 28x + 4 = (7x - 2)^2$

47. $25x^2 - 36 = (5x)^2 - (6)^2$
$$= (5x + 6)(5x - 6)$$

48. $100x^2 - 9 = (10x)^2 - 3^2$
$$= (10x - 3)(10x + 3)$$

49. $y^2 - 36x^2 = (y + 6x)(y - 6x)$

50. $9y^2 - 25x^2 = (3y + 5x)(3y - 5x)$

51. $36x^2 + 12x + 1 = (6x + 1)^2$

52. $25x^2 - 20x + 4 = (5x)^2 - 2(5x)(2) + 2^2$
$$= (5x - 2)^2$$

53. $16x^2 - 24xy + 9y^2 = (4x - 3y)^2$

54. $49x^2 - 28xy + 4y^2$
$$= (7x)^2 - 2(7x)(2y) + (2y)^2$$
$$= (7x - 2y)^2$$

55. $2x^2 - 18 = 2\left(x^2 - 9\right) = 2(x + 3)(x - 3)$

56. $3x^2 - 75 = 3\left(x^2 - 25\right)$
$$= 3\left(x^2 - 5^2\right)$$
$$= 3(x - 5)(x + 5)$$

57. $72x^2 - 192x + 128 = 8\left(9x^2 - 24x + 16\right)$
$$= 8(3x - 4)^2$$

58. $50x^2 - 120x + 72 = 2\left(25x^2 - 60x + 36\right)$
$$= 2(5x - 6)^2$$

59. $4x^2 - 9y^2 = (2x)^2 - (3y)^2$
$$= (2x + 3y)(2x - 3y)$$

60. $x^2 + 6x + 9 = x^2 + 2(x)(3) + 3^2$
$$= (x + 3)^2$$

61. $x^2 - 9x + 18 = (x - 6)(x - 3)$

62. $x^2 + 13x - 30 = (x + 15)(x - 2)$

63. $6x^2 + x - 7 = (6x + 7)(x - 1)$

64. $10x^2 + x - 2 = 10x^2 - 4x + 5x - 2$
$$= 2x(5x - 2) + 1(5x - 2)$$
$$= (5x - 2)(2x + 1)$$

65. $24x - 60 = 12(2x - 5)$

66. $8x^2 y^2 - 4xy = 4xy(2xy - 1)$

67. $50x^3 y^2 + 30x^2 y^2 - 10x^2 y^2$
$$= 50x^3 y^2 + 20x^2 y^2$$
$$= 10x^2 y^2 (5x + 2)$$

68. $26a^3 b - 13ab^3 + 52a^2 b^4$
$$= 13ab(2a^2 - b^2 + 4ab^3)$$

69. $x^3 - 16x^2 + 64x = x(x^2 - 16x + 64)$
$$= x(x - 8)^2$$

70. $2x^2 + 40x + 200 = 2(x^2 + 20x + 100)$
$$= 2\left[x^2 + 2(x)(10) + 10^2 \right]$$
$$= 2(x + 10)^2$$

71. $3x^2 - 18x + 27 = 3(x^2 - 6x + 9)$
$$= 3(x - 3)^2$$

72. $25x^3 - 60x^2 + 36x = x(25x^2 - 60x + 36)$
$$= x\left[(5x)^2 - 2(5x)(6) + 6^2 \right]$$
$$= x(5x - 6)^2$$

73. $7x^2 - 9x - 10 = (7x + 5)(x - 2)$

74. $4x^2 - 13x - 12 = (4x + 3)(x - 4)$

75. $9x^3 y - 4xy^3 = xy(9x^2 - 4y^2)$
$$= xy(3x + 2y)(3x - 2y)$$

76. $3x^3 a^3 - 11x^4 a^2 - 20x^5 a$
$$= x^3 a(3a^2 - 11xa - 20x^2)$$
$$= x^3 a(3a^2 + 4xa - 15xa - 20x^2)$$
$$= x^3 a\left[a(3a + 4x) - 5x(3a + 4x) \right]$$
$$= x^3 a(3a + 4x)(a - 5x)$$

77. $12a^2 + 14ab - 10b^2 = 2(6a^2 + 7ab - 5b^2)$
$$= 2(3a + 5b)(2a - b)$$

78. $121a^2 + 66ab + 9b^2 = (11a + 3b)^2$

79. $7a - 7 - ab + b = 7(a-1) - b(a-1)$
$$= (a-1)(7-b)$$

80. $8b - 10 + 28bc - 35c$
$$= 2(4b-5) + 7c(4b-5)$$
$$= (4b-5)(2+7c)$$

81. $18b - 21 + 14x - 12bx$
$$= 18b - 21 - 12bx + 14x$$
$$= 3(6b-7) - 2x(6b-7)$$
$$= (6b-7)(3-2x)$$

82. $5xb - 35x + 4by - 28y$
$$= 5x(b-7) + 4y(b-7)$$
$$= (b-7)(5x+4y)$$

83. $2a^2x - 15ax + 7x = x(2a^2 - 15a + 7)$
$$= x(2a-1)(a-7)$$

84. $x^5 - 17x^3 + 16x = x(x^4 - 17x^2 + 16)$
$$= x(x^2 - 16)(x^2 - 1)$$
$$= x(x^2 - 4^2)(x^2 - 1^2)$$
$$= x(x-4)(x+4)(x-1)(x+1)$$

85. $x^4 - 81y^{12} = (x^2)^2 - (9y^6)^2$
$$= (x^2 + 9y^6)(x^2 - 9y^6)$$
$$= (x^2 + 9y^6)(x + 3y^3)(x - 3y^3)$$

86. $6x^4 - x^2 - 15 = 6x^4 - 10x^2 + 9x^2 - 15$
$$= 2x^2(3x^2 - 5) + 3(3x^2 - 5)$$
$$= (3x^2 - 5)(2x^2 + 3)$$

87. $28yz - 16xyz + x^2yz = yz(28 - 16x + x^2)$
$$= yz(14 - x)(2 - x)$$

88. $12x^3 + 17x^2 + 6x = x(12x^2 + 17x + 6)$
$$= x(12x^2 + 8x + 9x + 6)$$
$$= x[4x(3x+2) + 3(3x+2)]$$
$$= x(3x+2)(4x+3)$$

89. $16w^2 - 2w - 5 = (2w+1)(8w-5)$

90. $12w^2 - 12w + 3 = 3(4w^2 - 4w + 1)$
$$= 3[(2w)^2 - 2(2w)(1) + 1^2]$$
$$= 3(2w-1)^2$$

91. $4y^3 + 10y^2 - 6y = 2y(2y^2 + 5y - 3)$
$$= 2y(2y-1)(y+3)$$

92. $10y^2 + 33y - 7 = 10y^2 - 2y + 35y - 7$
$$= 2y(5y-1) + 7(5y-1)$$
$$= (5y-1)(2y+7)$$

93. $8y^{10} - 16y^8 = 8y^8(y^2 - 2)$

173

94. $9x^4 - 144 = 9(x^2 - 16)$
$$= 9(x+4)(x-4)$$

95. $x^2 - 6x + 12$ is prime.

96. $8x^2 - 19x - 6$ is prime.

97. $8y^5 + 4y^3 - 60y = 4y(2y^4 + y^2 - 15)$
$$= 4y(2y^2 - 5)(y^2 + 3)$$

98. $9xy^2 + 3xy - 42x = 3x(3y^2 + y - 14)$
$$= 3x(3y^2 + 7y - 6y - 14)$$
$$= 3x[y(3y+7) - 2(3y+7)]$$
$$= 3x(3y+7)(y-2)$$

99. $16x^4y^2 - 56x^2y + 49 = (4x^2y - 7)^2$

100. $128x^3y - 2xy = 2xy(64x^2 - 1)$
$$= 2xy[(8x)^2 - 1^2]$$
$$= 2xy(8x-1)(8x+1)$$

101. $2ax + 5a - 10b - 4bx$
$$= a(2x+5) - 2b(2x+5)$$
$$= (2x+5)(a-2b)$$

102. $2x^3 - 9 + x^2 - 18x = 2x^3 + x^2 - 18x - 9$
$$= x^2(2x+1) - 9(2x+1)$$
$$= (2x+1)(x^2-9)$$
$$= (2x+1)(x^2-3^2)$$
$$= (2x+1)(x-3)(x+3)$$

103. $\quad x^2 - 3x - 18 = 0$
$$(x-6)(x+3) = 0$$
$$x - 6 = 0 \qquad x + 3 = 0$$
$$x = 6 \qquad x = -3$$

104. $\quad 2x^2 + 5x - 12 = 0$
$$(2x-3)(x+4) = 0$$
$$2x - 3 = 0 \qquad x + 4 = 0$$
$$2x = 3 \qquad x = -4$$
$$x = \frac{3}{2}$$

105. $\qquad 5x^2 = 2x - 7x^2$
$$12x^2 - 2x = 0$$
$$2x(6x-1) = 0$$
$$2x = 0 \qquad 6x - 1 = 0$$
$$x = 0 \qquad x = \frac{1}{6}$$

106. $5x^2 - x = 4x^2 + 12$

$$x^2 - x = 12$$

$$x^2 - x - 12 = 0$$

$$(x - 4)(x + 3) = 0$$

$$x - 4 = 0 \qquad x + 3 = 0$$

$$x = 4 \qquad\qquad x = -3$$

107. $2x^2 + 9x - 5 = 0$

$$(2x - 1)(x + 5) = 0$$

$$2x - 1 = 0 \qquad x + 5 = 0$$

$$x = \frac{1}{?} \qquad\qquad x = -5$$

108. $x^2 + 11x + 24 = 0$

$$(x + 8)(x + 3) = 0$$

$$x + 8 = 0 \qquad x + 3 = 0$$

$$x = -8 \qquad x = -3$$

109. $x^2 + 14x + 45 = 0$

$$(x + 9)(x + 5) = 0$$

$$x + 9 = 0 \qquad x + 5 = 0$$

$$x = -9 \qquad\qquad x = -5$$

110. $5x^2 = 7x + 6$

$$5x^2 - 7x - 6 = 0$$

$$(5x + 3)(x - 2) = 0$$

$$5x + 3 = 0 \qquad x - 2 = 0$$

$$5x = -3 \qquad x = 2$$

$$x = -\frac{3}{5} \qquad x = 2$$

111. $3x^2 + 6x = 2x^2 - 9$

$$x^2 + 6x + 9 = 0$$

$$(x + 3)^2 = 0$$

$$x + 3 = 0$$

$$x = -3$$

112. $4x^2 + 9x - 9 = 0$

$$(4x - 3)(x + 3) = 0$$

$$4x - 3 = 0 \qquad x + 3 = 0$$

$$4x = 3 \qquad\qquad x = -3$$

$$x = \frac{3}{4} \qquad\qquad x = -3$$

113. $5x^2 - 11x + 2 = 0$

$$(5x - 1)(x - 2) = 0$$

$$5x - 1 = 0 \qquad x - 2 = 0$$

$$x = \frac{1}{5} \qquad\qquad x = 2$$

114. $x = $ altitude

$$x + 3 = \text{base}$$

$$A = \frac{1}{2}ab$$

$$35 = \frac{1}{2}x(x + 3)$$

$$70 = x^2 + 3x$$

$$0 = x^2 + 3x - 70$$

$$0 = (x + 10)(x - 7)$$

175

$x + 10 = 0$　　　$x - 7 = 0$

$x = -10$　　　　$x = -7$

Since length cannot be negative,

$x = 7$ and $x + 3 = 7 + 3 = 10$.

altitude: 7 cm; base 10 cm

115.　　$x = $ width

$2x + 1 = $ length

$A = $ length $\times$ width

$105 = x(2x + 1)$

$105 = 2x^2 + x$

$0 = 2x^2 + x - 105$

$0 = (2x + 15)(x - 7)$

$2x + 15 = 0$　or　$x - 7 = 0$

$x = -\dfrac{15}{2}$　　　$x = 7$

　　　　　　$2x + 1 = 15$

Length cannot be negative so width

$= 7$ feet and length $= 15$ feet.

116.　$h = -16t^2 + 80t + 96$

$0 = -16t^2 + 80t + 96$

$0 = -16(t^2 - 5t - 6)$

$0 = -16(t - 6)(t + 1)$

$t - 6 = 0$　　　　$t + 1 = 0$

$t = 6$　　　　　$t = -1$

Since the time must be positive, $t = 6$

seconds.

117.　　　　　　$480 = -5x^2 + 100x$

$5x^2 - 100x + 480 = 0$

$5(x^2 - 20x + 96) = 0$

$x - 12 = 0$　or　$x - 8 = 0$

$x = 12$　　　　$x = 8$

The current is 12 amperes or 8 amperes.

How Am I Doing? Chapter 5 Test

1.　$x^2 + 12x - 28 = (x + 14)(x - 2)$

2.　$16x^2 - 81 = (4x + 9)(4x - 9)$

3.　$10x^2 + 27x + 5 = 10x^2 + 2x + 25x + 5$

$= 2x(5x + 1) + 5(5x + 1)$

$= (5x + 1)(2x + 5)$

4.　$9a^2 - 30ab + 25b^2$

$= (3a)^2 - 2(3a)(5b) + (5b)^2$

$= (3a - 5b)^2$

5.　$7x - 9x^2 + 14xy = x(7 - 9x + 14y)$

6.　$10xy + 15by - 8x - 12b$

$= 5y(2x + 3b) - 4(2x + 3b)$

$= (2x + 3b)(5y - 4)$

7. $6x^3 - 20x^2 + 16x = 2x(3x^2 - 10x + 8)$

     $= 2x(3x^2 - 6x - 4x + 8)$

     $= 2x[3x(x-2) - 4(x-2)]$

     $= 2x(x-2)(3x-4)$

8. $5a^2c - 11ac + 2c = c(5a^2 - 11a + 2)$

               $= c(5a-1)(a-2)$

9. $81x^2 - 100 = (9x+10)(9x-10)$

10. $9x^2 - 15x + 4 = (3x-1)(3x-4)$

11. $20x^2 - 45 = 5(4x^2 - 9)$

           $= 5(2x+3)(2x-3)$

12. $36x^2 + 1 = (6x)^2 + (1)^2$

    It is prime.

13. $3x^3 + 11x^2 + 10x = x(3x^2 + 11x + 10)$

              $= x(3x+5)(x+2)$

14. $60xy^2 - 20x^2y - 45y^3$

     $= -5y(-12xy + 4x^2 + 9y^2)$

     $= -5y(4x^2 - 12xy + 9y^2)$

     $= -5y[(2x)^2 - 2(2x)(3y) + (3y)^2]$

     $= -5y(2x-3y)^2$

15. $81x^2 - 1 = (9x)^2 - (1)^2$

          $= (9x+1)(9x-1)$

16. $81y^4 - 1 = (9y^2 + 1)(9y^2 - 1)$

             $= (9y^2 + 1)(3y+1)(3y-1)$

17. $2ax + 6a - 5x - 15 = 2a(x+3) - 5(x+3)$

                  $= (x+3)(2a-5)$

18. $aw^2 - 8b + 2bw^2 - 4a$

     $= aw^2 - 4a + 2bw^2 - 8b$

     $= a(w^2 - 4) + 2b(w^2 - 4)$

     $= (w^2 - 4)(a + 2b)$

     $= (w-2)(w+2)(a+2b)$

19. $3x^2 - 3x - 90 = 3(x^2 - x - 30)$

              $= 3(x-6)(x+5)$

20. $2x^3 - x^2 - 15x = x(2x^2 - x - 15)$

         $= x(2x^2 - 6x + 5x - 15)$

         $= x[2x(x-3) + 5(x-3)]$

         $= x(x-3)(2x+5)$

21. $x^2 + 14x + 45 = 0$

    $(x+9)(x+5) = 0$

    $x + 9 = 0$ $x + 5 = 0$

       $x = -9$ $x = -5$

22. $14 + 3x(x+2) = -7x$

$14 + 3x^2 + 6x = -7x$

$3x^2 + 13x + 14 = 0$

$(3x+7)(x+2) = 0$

$3x + 7 = 0 \qquad x + 2 = 0$

$3x = -7 \qquad\quad x = -2$

$x = -\dfrac{7}{3} \qquad\quad x = -2$

23. $2x^2 + x - 10 = 0$

$(2x+5)(x-2) = 0$

$2x + 5 = 0 \qquad x - 2 = 0$

$x = -\dfrac{5}{2} \qquad\quad x = 2$

24. $x^2 - 3x - 28 = 0$

$(x-7)(x+4) = 0$

$x - 7 = 0 \qquad x + 4 = 0$

$x = 7 \qquad\quad x = -4$

25. $x = \text{width}$

$2x - 1 = \text{length}$

$x(2x - 1) = 91$

$2x^2 - x = 91$

$2x^2 - x - 91 = 0$

$(2x + 13)(x - 7) = 0$

$2x + 13 = 0 \qquad x - 7 = 0$

$2x = -13 \qquad\quad x = 7$

$x = -\dfrac{13}{2}$

Since the width cannot be negative, $x = 7$
and $2x - 1 = 2(7) - 1 = 13$.
width = 7 miles, length = 13 miles.

Cumulative Test Chapters 0 - 5

1. $\dfrac{72}{480} = 0.15 = 15\%$

2. $(0.13)(3.8) = 0.494$

3. $4.3 - 2(3.5 - 7.2) - 6.1$

$= 4.3 - 2(-3.8) - 6.1$

$= 4.3 + 7.6 - 6.1$

$= 5.8$

4. $\left(-2x^3 y^4\right)\left(-4xy^6\right) = (-2)(-4)x^{3+1}y^{4+6}$

$= 8x^4 y^{10}$

5. $(-3)^4 = 81$

6. $(9x - 4)(3x + 2) = 27x^2 + 18x - 12x - 8$

$= 27x^2 + 6x - 8$

7. $\left(2x^2 - 6x + 1\right)(x - 3)$

$= 2x^3 - 6x^2 + x - 6x^2 + 18x - 3$

$= 2x^3 - 12x^2 + 19x - 3$

8. $3x - 4 \geq 6x + 5$

$-4 \geq 3x + 5$

$-9 \geq 3x$

$-3 \geq x$

9. $3x - (7 - 5x) = 3(4x - 5)$

$3x - 7 + 5x = 12x - 15$

$-7 + 8x = 12x - 15$

$8 = 4x$

$2 = x$

10. $\dfrac{1}{2}x - 3 = \dfrac{1}{4}(3x + 3)$

$4\left(\dfrac{1}{2}x - 3\right) = 4\left[\dfrac{1}{4}(3x + 3)\right]$

$2x - 12 = 3x + 3$

$-12 = x + 3$

$-15 = x$

11. $3(q + 1) = 8q - p$

$3q + 3 = 5q - p$

$p + 3 = 5q$

$\dfrac{p + 3}{5} = q$

12. $6x^2 - 5x + 1 = 6x^2 - 3x - 2x + 1$

$= 3x(2x - 1) - 1(2x - 1)$

$= (3x + 2)(3x - 1)$

13. $6x^2 + 5x - 4 = (3x + 4)(2x - 1)$

14. $9x^2 + 3x - 2 = 9x^2 + 6x - 3x - 2$

$= 3x(3x + 2) - 1(3x + 2)$

$= (3x + 2)(3x - 1)$

15. $121x^2 - 64y^2 = (11x)^2 - (8y)^2$

$= (11x + 8y)(11x - 8y)$

16. $4x + 120 - 80x^2 = -80x^2 + 4x + 120$

$= -4(20x^2 - x - 30)$

$= -4(20x^2 + 24x - 25x - 30)$

$= -4[4x(5x + 6) - 5(5x + 6)]$

$= -4(5x + 6)(4x - 5)$

17. $x^2 + 5x + 9$ is prime.

18. $16x^3 + 40x^2 + 25x = x(16x^2 + 40x + 25)$

$= x\left[(4x)^2 + 2(4x)(5) + 5^2\right]$

$= x(4x + 5)^2$

19. $81x^4 - 16b^4 = (9x^2)^2 - (4b^2)^2$

$= (9x^2 + 4b^2)(9x^2 - 4b^2)$

$= (9x^2 + 4b^2)(3x + 2b)(3x - 2b)$

20. $2ax - 4bx + 3a - 6b$

$= 2x(a - 2b) + 3(a - 2b)$

$= (a - 2b)(2x + 3)$

179

21. $15x^2 + 6x - 9 = 3(5x^2 + 2x - 3)$
$$= 3(x^2 + 5)(x^2 + 3)$$

22. $x^2 + 5x - 24 = 0$

$(x + 8)(x - 3) = 0$

$x + 8 = 0 \qquad x - 3 = 0$

$\qquad x = -8 \qquad\quad x = 3$

23. $3x^2 - 11x + 10 = 0$

$(3x - 5)(x - 2) = 0$

$3x - 5 = 0 \qquad\qquad x - 2 = 0$

$\qquad x = \dfrac{5}{3} \qquad\qquad\quad x = 2$

24. $\qquad x = $ length

$x - 5 = $ width

$\qquad A = LW$

$\quad 300 = x(x - 5)$

$\quad 300 = x^2 - 5x$

$\qquad 0 = x^2 - 5x - 300$

$\qquad 0 = (x - 20)(x + 15)$

$x - 20 = 0 \qquad\qquad x + 15 = 0$

$\qquad x = 20 \qquad\qquad\quad x = -15$

$\qquad\qquad\qquad\qquad$ Not possible

$x - 5 = 15$

length $= 20$ ft., width $= 15$ ft.

Chapter 6

6.1 Exercises

1. $\dfrac{3a-9b}{a-3b} = \dfrac{3(a-3b)}{a-3b} = 3$

3. $\dfrac{6x+18}{x^2+3x} = \dfrac{6(x+3)}{x(x+3)} = \dfrac{6}{x}$

5. $\dfrac{9x^2+6x+1}{1-9x^2} = \dfrac{(3x+1)(3x+1)}{(1+3x)(1-3x)} = \dfrac{3x+1}{1-3x}$

7. $\dfrac{3a^2b(a-2b)}{6ab^2} = \dfrac{a(a-2b)}{2b}$

9. $\dfrac{x^2+x-2}{x^2-x} = \dfrac{(x+2)(x-1)}{x(x-1)} = \dfrac{x+2}{x}$

11. $\dfrac{x^2-3x-10}{3x^2+5x-2} = \dfrac{(x-5)(x+2)}{(3x-1)(x+2)}$

$\qquad = \dfrac{x-5}{3x-1}$

13. $\dfrac{x^2+4x-21}{x^3-49x} = \dfrac{(x+7)(x-3)}{x(x^2-49)}$

$\qquad = \dfrac{(x+7)(x-3)}{x(x+7)(x-7)}$

$\qquad = \dfrac{x-3}{x(x-7)}$

15. $\dfrac{3x^2+7x-6}{x^2+7x+12} = \dfrac{(3x-2)(x+3)}{(x+4)(x+3)} = \dfrac{3x-2}{x+4}$

17. $\dfrac{3x^2-8x+5}{4x^2-5x+1} = \dfrac{(3x-5)(x-1)}{(4x-1)(x-1)} = \dfrac{3x-5}{4x-1}$

19. $\dfrac{5x^2-27x+10}{5x^2+3x-2} = \dfrac{(5x-2)(x-5)}{(5x-2)(x+1)}$

$\qquad = \dfrac{x-5}{x+1}$

21. $\dfrac{10-2x}{4x^2-20x} = \dfrac{2(5-x)}{4x(x-5)}$

$\qquad = \dfrac{-2(x-5)}{4x(x-5)}$

$\qquad = \dfrac{-1}{2x}$

23. $\dfrac{2x^2-7x-15}{25-x^2} = \dfrac{(2x+3)(x-5)}{(5-x)(5+x)}$

$\qquad = \dfrac{-2x-3}{x+5} = \dfrac{-2x-3}{5+x}$

25. $\dfrac{(4x+5)^2}{8x^2+6x-5} = \dfrac{(4x+5)^2}{(4x+5)(2x-1)}$

$\qquad = \dfrac{(4x+5)(4x+5)}{(4x+5)(2x-1)} = \dfrac{4x+5}{2x-1}$

27. $\dfrac{2x^2+9x-18}{30-x-x^2} = \dfrac{2x^2+9x-18}{-(x^2+x-30)}$

181

$$= \frac{(2x-3)(x+6)}{-(x+6)(x-5)}$$

$$= \frac{2x-3}{-x+5}$$

29. $\dfrac{a^2 + 2ab - 3b^2}{2a^2 + 5ab - 3b^2} = \dfrac{(a+3b)(a-b)}{(2a-b)(a+3b)} = \dfrac{a-b}{2a-b}$

31. $\dfrac{9x^2 - 4y^2}{9x^2 + 12xy + 4y^2} = \dfrac{(3x-2y)(3x+2y)}{(3x+2y)(3x+2y)}$

$$= \frac{3x-2y}{3x+2y}$$

33. $\dfrac{x^3 - bx^2 - abx + ax^2}{bx^2 - b^2x - b^2c + bcx} = \dfrac{x\left(x^2 - bx - ab + ax\right)}{b\left(x^2 - bx - bc + cx\right)}$

$$= \frac{x\left[x(x-b)+a(-b+x)\right]}{b\left[x(-b)+c(-b+x)\right]}$$

$$= \frac{x(x-b)(x+a)}{b(x-b)(x+c)}$$

$$= \frac{x(x+a)}{b(x+c)}$$

Cumulative Review

35. $(3x-7)^2 = (3x)^2 - 2(3x)(7) + (7)^2$

$$= 9x^2 - 42x + 49$$

37. $(2x+3)(x-4)(x-2)$

$$= (2x+3)(x^2 - 6x + 8)$$

$$= 2x^3 - 12x^2 + 16x + 3x^2 - 18x + 24$$

$$= 2x^3 - 9x^2 - 2x + 24$$

39. $\dfrac{4\frac{7}{8}}{3} = \dfrac{\frac{39}{8}}{\frac{3}{1}} = \dfrac{39}{8} \cdot \dfrac{1}{3} = \dfrac{13}{8} = 1\dfrac{5}{8}$ acre

41. Spanish $= 341 + 17 = 358$ million

Chinese Mandarin $= 2(358) + 158 = 874$

$874,000,000$ people

6.2 Exercises

1. Factor the numerator and denominator completely and divide out any common factors.

3. $\dfrac{2x-10}{x-4} \cdot \dfrac{x^2 + 5x + 4}{x^2 - 4x - 5} = \dfrac{2(x-5)}{x-4} \cdot \dfrac{(x+4)(x+1)}{(x-5)(x+1)}$

$$= \frac{2(x+4)}{x-4}$$

5. $\dfrac{24x^3}{4x^2 - 36} \cdot \dfrac{2x^2 + 6x}{16x^2} = \dfrac{3\left(8x^3\right)}{4\left(x^2 - 9\right)} \cdot \dfrac{2x(x+3)}{2 \cdot 8x^2}$

$$= \frac{3 \cdot 8x^3}{4(x+3)(x-3)} \cdot \frac{2x(x+3)}{2 \cdot 8x^2}$$

$$= \frac{3x^2}{4(x-3)}$$

7. $\dfrac{x^2 + 3x - 10}{x^2 + x - 20} \cdot \dfrac{x^2 - 3x - 4}{x^2 + 4x + 3}$

$$= \frac{(x-2)(x+5)}{(x-4)(x+5)} \cdot \frac{(x-4)(x+1)}{(x+3)(x+1)}$$

$$= \frac{x-2}{x+3}$$

182

9. $\dfrac{x+6}{x-8} \div \dfrac{x+5}{x^2-6x-16} = \dfrac{x+6}{x-8} \cdot \dfrac{x^2-6x-16}{x+5}$

$= \dfrac{x+6}{x-8} \cdot \dfrac{(x-8)(x+2)}{x+5}$

$= \dfrac{(x+6)(x+2)}{x+5}$

11. $(6x-5) \div \dfrac{36x^2-25}{6x^2+17x+10}$

$= \dfrac{6x-5}{1} \cdot \dfrac{6x^2+17x+10}{36x^2-25}$

$= \dfrac{6x-5}{1} \cdot \dfrac{(6x+5)(x+2)}{(6x+5)(6x-5)}$

$= x+2$

13. $\dfrac{3x^2+12xy+12y^2}{x^2+4xy+3y^2} \div \dfrac{4x+8y}{x+y}$

$= \dfrac{3(x+2y)(x+2y)}{(x+3y)(x+y)} \div \dfrac{4(x+2y)}{x+y}$

$= \dfrac{3(x+2y)(x+2y)}{(x+3y)(x+y)} \cdot \dfrac{x+y}{4(x+2y)} = \dfrac{3(x+2y)}{4(x+3y)}$

15. $\dfrac{(x+5)^2}{3x^2-7x+2} \cdot \dfrac{x^2-4x+4}{(x+5)}$

$= \dfrac{(x+5)(x+5)}{(3x-1)(x-2)} \cdot \dfrac{(x-2)(x-2)}{(x+5)}$

$= \dfrac{(x+5)(x-2)}{3x-1}$

17. $\dfrac{x^2+x-30}{10-2x} \div \dfrac{x^2+4x-12}{5x+15}$

$= \dfrac{x^2+x-30}{10-2x} \cdot \dfrac{5x+15}{x^2+4x-12}$

$= \dfrac{(x+6)(x-5)}{2(5-x)} \cdot \dfrac{5(x+3)}{(x+6)(x-2)}$

$= -\dfrac{5(x+3)}{2(x-2)}$

19. $\dfrac{y^2+4y-12}{y^2+2y-24} \cdot \dfrac{y^2-16}{y^2+2y-8}$

$= \dfrac{(y+6)(y-2)}{(y+6)(y-4)} \cdot \dfrac{(y+4)(y-4)}{(y+4)(y-2)}$

$= 1$

21. $\dfrac{x^2+7x+12}{2x^2+9x+4} \div \dfrac{x^2+6x+9}{2x^2-x-1}$

$= \dfrac{(x+4)(x+3)}{(2x+1)(x+4)} \cdot \dfrac{(2x+1)(x-1)}{(x+3)(x+3)}$

$= \dfrac{x-1}{x+3}$

23. By definition, the denominator of a rational expression cannot have the value zero. So the original expression cannot have a replacement value of 2 (or the first denominator would be zero). If we multiply the first fraction by the reciprocal of the second fraction, then the denominator $x+7$ cannot be zero. Thus x also cannot have a replacement value of -7.

Cumulative Review

6.3 Exercises

25. $6x^2 + 3x - 18 = 5x - 2 + 6x^2$

$$3x - 18 = 5x - 2$$
$$-18 = 2x - 2$$
$$-16 = 2x$$
$$-8 = x$$

1. The LCD would be a product that contains each factor. However, any repeated factor in any one denominator must be repeated the greatest number of times it occurs in any one denominator. So the LCD would be $(x+5)(x+3)^2$.

27. $\dfrac{1}{16}(80) = 5$

5 milligrams of medication

3. $\dfrac{x}{x+5} + \dfrac{2x+1}{5+x} = \dfrac{x+2x+1}{x+5}$
$$= \dfrac{3x+1}{x+5}$$

29. Harold: length $= x$, width $= x$

George: length $= 3x + x$, width $= x - 2$

$$A = LW$$
$$36 = (3+x)(x-2)$$
$$36 = x^2 + x - 6$$
$$0 = x^2 + x - 6$$
$$0 = (x+7)(x-6)$$

$x + 7 = 0 \qquad x - 6 = 0$
$\quad x = -7 \qquad\quad x = 6$

Not possible

Harold: 6 ft by 6 ft

George: 9 ft by 4 ft

5. $\dfrac{3x}{x+3} - \dfrac{x+5}{x+3} = \dfrac{3x-(x+5)}{x+3}$
$$= \dfrac{3x-x-5}{x+3}$$
$$= \dfrac{2x-5}{x+3}$$

7. $\dfrac{8x+3}{5x+7} - \dfrac{6x+10}{5x+7} = \dfrac{8x+3-(6x+10)}{5x+7}$
$$= \dfrac{8x+3-6x-10}{5x+7}$$
$$= \dfrac{2x-7}{5x+7}$$

9. $3ab$

a^2, b^2

LCD $= 3a^2b^2$

11. $18x^2 y^5 = 2 \cdot 3^2 x^2 y^5$

     $30x^3 y^3 = 2 \cdot 3 \cdot 5 x^3 y^3$

     $\text{LCD} = 2 \cdot 3^2 \cdot 5 x^3 y^5 = 90 x^3 y^5$

13. $5x - 15 = 5(x - 3)$

     $3x - 9 = 3(x - 3)$

     $\text{LCD} = 3 \cdot 5 (x - 3)$

15. $x + 3 = x + 3$

     $x^2 - 9 = (x + 3)(x - 3)$

     $\text{LCD} = (x + 3)(x - 3) = x^2 - 9$

17. $3x^2 + 14x - 5 = (3x - 1)(x + 5)$

     $9x^2 - 6x + 1 = (3x - 1)(3x - 1)$

     $\text{LCD} = (x + 5)(3x - 1)^2$

19. $\dfrac{7}{ab} + \dfrac{3}{b} = \dfrac{7}{ab} + \dfrac{3}{b} \cdot \dfrac{a}{a}$

     $= \dfrac{7}{ab} + \dfrac{3a}{ab}$

     $= \dfrac{7 + 3a}{ab}$

21. $\dfrac{3}{x + 7} + \dfrac{8}{x^2 - 49} = \dfrac{3}{x + 7} \cdot \dfrac{x - 7}{x - 7} + \dfrac{8}{(x + 7)(-7)}$

     $= \dfrac{3x - 21 + 8}{(x + 7)(x - 7)} = \dfrac{3x - 13}{(x + 7)(x - 7)}$

23. $\dfrac{3y}{y + 2} + \dfrac{y}{y - 2}$

     $= \dfrac{3y}{y + 2} \cdot \dfrac{y - 2}{y - 2} + \dfrac{y}{y - 2} \cdot \dfrac{y + 2}{y + 2}$

     $= \dfrac{3y^2 - 6y}{(y + 2)(y - 2)} + \dfrac{y^2 + 2y}{(y - 2)(y + 2)}$

     $= \dfrac{3y^2 - 6y + y^2 + 2y}{(y + 2)(y - 2)} = \dfrac{4y^2 - 4y}{(y + 2)(y - 2)}$

25. $\dfrac{6}{5a} + \dfrac{5}{3a + 2} = \dfrac{6}{5a} \cdot \dfrac{3a + 2}{3a + 2} + \dfrac{5}{3a + 2} \cdot \dfrac{5a}{5a}$

     $= \dfrac{6(3a + 2) + 5 \cdot 5a}{5a(3a + 2)}$

     $= \dfrac{18a + 12 + 25a}{5a(3a + 2)}$

     $= \dfrac{43a + 12}{5a(3a + 2)}$

27. $\dfrac{2}{3xy} + \dfrac{1}{6yz} = \dfrac{2}{3xy} \cdot \dfrac{2z}{2z} + \dfrac{1}{6yz} \cdot \dfrac{x}{x}$

     $= \dfrac{4z}{6xyz} + \dfrac{x}{6xyz} = \dfrac{4z + x}{6xyz}$

29. $\dfrac{5x + 6}{x - 3} - \dfrac{x - 2}{2x - 6} = \dfrac{5x + 6}{x - 3} \cdot \dfrac{2}{2} - \dfrac{x - 2}{2(x - 3)}$

     $= \dfrac{2(5x + 6) - (x - 2)}{2(x - 3)}$

     $= \dfrac{10x + 12 - x + 2}{2(x - 3)}$

     $= \dfrac{9x + 14}{2(x - 3)}$

185

31. $\dfrac{3x}{x^2-25}-\dfrac{2}{x+5}=\dfrac{3x}{(x+5)(x-5)}-\dfrac{2}{x+5}\cdot\dfrac{x-5}{x-5}$

$=\dfrac{3x-2(x-5)}{(x+5)(x-5)}$

$=\dfrac{3x-2x+10}{(x+5)(x-5)}$

$=\dfrac{x+10}{(x+5)(x-5)}$

33. $\dfrac{a+3b}{2}-\dfrac{a-b}{5}=\dfrac{a+3b}{2}\cdot\dfrac{5}{5}-\dfrac{a-b}{5}\cdot\dfrac{2}{2}$

$=\dfrac{5(a+3b)-2(a-b)}{2\cdot5}$

$=\dfrac{5a+15b-2a+2b}{10}$

$=\dfrac{3a+17b}{10}$

35. $\dfrac{8}{2x-3}-\dfrac{6}{x+2}$

$=\dfrac{8}{2x-3}\cdot\dfrac{x+2}{x+2}-\dfrac{6}{x+2}\cdot\dfrac{2x-3}{2x-3}$

$=\dfrac{8x+16}{(2x-3)(x+2)}-\dfrac{12x-18}{(2x-3)(x+2)}$

$=\dfrac{8x+16-(12x-18)}{(2x-3)(x+2)}=\dfrac{8x+16-12x+18}{(2x-3)(x+2)}$

$=\dfrac{-4x+34}{(2x-3)(x+2)}$

37. $\dfrac{x}{x^2+2x-3}-\dfrac{x}{x^2-5x+4}$

$=\dfrac{x}{(x+3)(x-1)}-\dfrac{x}{(x-4)(x-1)}$

$=\dfrac{x}{(x+3)(x-1)}\cdot\dfrac{x-4}{x-4}-\dfrac{x}{(x-4)(x-1)}\cdot\dfrac{x+3}{x+3}$

$=\dfrac{x^2-4x}{(x+3)(x-1)(x-4)}-\dfrac{x^2+3x}{(x+3)(x-1)(x-4)}$

$=\dfrac{x^2-4x-(x^2+3x)}{(x+3)(x-1)(x-4)}$

$=\dfrac{x^2-4x-x^2-3x}{(x+3)(x-1)(x-4)}$

$=\dfrac{-7x}{(x+3)(x-1)(x-4)}$

39. $\dfrac{2}{x^2+5x+6}+\dfrac{3}{x^2+7x+10}$

$=\dfrac{2}{(x+2)(x+3)}\cdot\dfrac{x+5}{x+5}+\dfrac{3}{(x+2)(x+5)}\cdot\dfrac{x+3}{x+3}$

$=\dfrac{2x+10+3x+9}{(x+2)(x+3)(x+5)}=\dfrac{5x+19}{(x+2)(x+3)(x+5)}$

41. $\dfrac{3x-8}{x^2-5x+6}+\dfrac{x+2}{x^2-6x+8}$

$=\dfrac{3x-8}{(x-2)(x-3)}+\dfrac{x+2}{(x-4)(x-2)}$

$=\dfrac{3x-8}{(x-2)(x-3)}\cdot\dfrac{x-4}{x-4}+\dfrac{x+2}{(x-4)(x-2)}\cdot\dfrac{x-3}{x-3}$

$=\dfrac{3x^2-20x+32}{(x-2)(x-3)(x-4)}+\dfrac{x^2-x-6}{(x-2)(x-3)(x-4)}$

$=\dfrac{3x^2-20x+32+x^2-x-6}{(x-2)(x-3)(x-4)}$

$=\dfrac{4x^2-21x+26}{(x-2)(x-3)(x-4)}$

$=\dfrac{(x-2)(4x-13)}{(x-2)(x-3)(x-4)}=\dfrac{4x-13}{(x-3)(x-4)}$

186

43. $\dfrac{6x}{y-2x} - \dfrac{5x}{2x-y} = \dfrac{6x}{-(2x-y)} - \dfrac{5x}{2x-y}$

$$= \dfrac{-6x-5x}{2x-y}$$

$$= \dfrac{-11x}{2x-y}$$

$$= \dfrac{11x}{y-2x}$$

45. $\dfrac{3y}{8y^2+2y-1} - \dfrac{5y}{2y^2-9y-5}$

$$= \dfrac{3y}{(4y-1)(2y+1)} - \dfrac{5y}{(2y+1)(y-5)}$$

$$= \dfrac{3y}{(4y-1)(2y+1)} \cdot \dfrac{y-5}{y-5} - \dfrac{5y}{(2y+1)(y-5)}$$

$$\cdot \dfrac{4y-1}{4y-1}$$

$$= \dfrac{3y^2-15y}{(4y-1)(2y+1)(y-5)} - \dfrac{20y^2-5y}{(4y-1)(2y+1)(y-5)}$$

$$= \dfrac{3y^2-15y-(20y^2-5y)}{(4y-1)(2y+1)(y-5)}$$

$$= \dfrac{3y^2-15y-20y^2+5y}{(4y-1)(2y+1)(y-5)}$$

$$= \dfrac{-17y^2-10y}{(4y-1)(2y+1)(y-5)}$$

47. $\dfrac{4y}{y^2+4y+3} + \dfrac{2}{y+1} = \dfrac{4y}{(y+3)(y+1)} + \dfrac{2}{y+1}$

$$= \dfrac{4y}{(y+3)(y+1)} + \dfrac{2}{y+1} \cdot \dfrac{y+3}{y+3}$$

$$= \dfrac{4y}{(y+3)(y+1)} + \dfrac{2y+6}{(y+3)(y+1)}$$

$$= \dfrac{4y+2y+6}{(y+3)(y+1)} = \dfrac{6y+6}{(y+3)(y+1)}$$

$$= \dfrac{6(y+1)}{(y+3)(y+1)} = \dfrac{6}{y+3}$$

49. $\dfrac{2x}{x-3} + \dfrac{3x}{x+2} + \dfrac{7}{x^2-x-6}$

$$= \dfrac{2x}{x-3} \cdot \dfrac{x+2}{x+2} + \dfrac{3x}{x+2} \cdot \dfrac{x-3}{x-3} + \dfrac{7}{(x+2)(x-3)}$$

$$= \dfrac{2x^2+4x+3x^2-9x+7}{(x+2)(x-3)}$$

$$= \dfrac{5x^2-5x+7}{(x+2)(x-3)}$$

Cumulative Review

51. $\dfrac{1}{3}(x-2) + \dfrac{1}{2}(x+3) = \dfrac{1}{4}(3x+1)$

$$12\left[\dfrac{1}{3}(x-2) + \dfrac{1}{2}(x+3)\right] = 12\left(\dfrac{1}{4}\right)(3x+1)$$

$$4(x-2) + 6(x+3) = 3(3x+1)$$

$$4x-8+6x+18 = 9x+3$$

$$10x+10 = 9x+3$$

$$x = -7$$

53. $\dfrac{1}{2}x < \dfrac{1}{3}x + \dfrac{1}{4}$

$12\left(\dfrac{1}{2}x\right) < 12\left(\dfrac{1}{3}x + \dfrac{1}{4}\right)$

$6x < 4x + 3$

$2x < 3$

$x < \dfrac{3}{2}$

55. Let x = number of days.

$1.50(2x) > 50$

$3x > 50$

$x > \dfrac{50}{3}$

$x > 16\dfrac{2}{3}$

At least 17 days per month

57. (a) Drop $20 - 18 = 18$ million

Rate $= \dfrac{18}{20} = 0.9$ million

$= 900,000$ fish/month

(b) x = number of months

$0.9x = 2$

$x \approx 2.2$

It would be destroyed after 3 months.

How Am I Doing? Sections 6.1-6.3

1. $\dfrac{8x - 48}{x^2 - 6x} = \dfrac{8(x-6)}{x(x-6)} = \dfrac{8}{x}$

2. $\dfrac{2x^2 - 7x - 15}{x^2 - 12x + 35} = \dfrac{(2x+3)(x-5)}{(x-5)(x-7)}$

$= \dfrac{2x+3}{x-7}$

3. $\dfrac{y^2 + 6y + 9}{27x^2 - 3x^2y^2} = \dfrac{(y+3)(y+3)}{3x^2(9 - y^2)}$

$= \dfrac{(y+3)(y+3)}{3x^2(3+y)(3-y)}$

$= \dfrac{y+3}{3x^2(3-y)}$

4. $\dfrac{5x^2 - 23x + 12}{5x^2 + 7x - 6} = \dfrac{(5x-3)(x-4)}{(5x-3)(x+2)}$

$= \dfrac{x-4}{x+2}$

5. $\dfrac{8x^3}{3x+12} \cdot \dfrac{9x+36}{16x^2} = \dfrac{8x^3}{3(x+4)} \cdot \dfrac{9(x+4)}{2 \cdot 8x^2}$

$= \dfrac{3x}{2}$

6. $\dfrac{x-5}{x^2+5x-14} \cdot \dfrac{x^2+12x+35}{15-3x}$

$= \dfrac{x-5}{(x+7)(x-2)} \cdot \dfrac{(x+7)(x+5)}{3(5-x)}$

$= -\dfrac{x+5}{3(x-2)}$

7. $\dfrac{x^2-9}{2x+6} \div \dfrac{2x^2-5x-3}{4x^2-1}$

$= \dfrac{x^2-9}{2x+6} \cdot \dfrac{4x^2-1}{2x^2-5x-3}$

$= \dfrac{(x+3)(x-3)}{2(x+3)} \cdot \dfrac{(2x+1)(2x-1)}{(2x+1)(x-3)}$

$= \dfrac{2x-1}{2}$

8. $\dfrac{3a^2+7a+2}{4a^2+11a+6} \div \dfrac{16a^2-9}{6a^2-9}$

$= \dfrac{3a^2+7a+2}{4a^2+11a+6} \cdot \dfrac{16a^2-9}{6a^2-13a-5}$

$= \dfrac{(3a+1)(a+2)}{(4a+3)(a+2)} \cdot \dfrac{(4a+3)(4a-3)}{(2a-5)(3a+1)}$

$= \dfrac{4a-3}{2a-5}$

9. $\dfrac{x-3y}{xy} - \dfrac{4a-y}{ay} = \dfrac{x-3y}{xy} \cdot \dfrac{a}{a} - \dfrac{4a-y}{ay} \cdot \dfrac{x}{x}$

$= \dfrac{a(x-3y)-x(4a-y)}{axy}$

$= \dfrac{ax-3ay-4ax+xy}{axy}$

$= \dfrac{xy-3ax-3ay}{axy}$

10. $\dfrac{7}{2x-4} + \dfrac{-14}{x^2-4} = \dfrac{7}{2(x-2)} \cdot \dfrac{x+2}{x+2}$

$\phantom{\dfrac{7}{2x-4}} + \dfrac{-14}{(x+2)(x-2)} \cdot \dfrac{2}{2}$

$= \dfrac{7(x+2)=14\cdot 2}{2(x+2)(x-2)}$

$= \dfrac{7x+14-28}{2(x+2)(x-2)}$

$= \dfrac{7x-14}{2(x+2)(x-2)}$

$= \dfrac{7(x-2)}{2(x+2)(x-2)}$

$= \dfrac{7}{2(x+2)}$

11. $\dfrac{2x}{x^2+10x+21} + \dfrac{x-3}{x+7}$

$= \dfrac{2x}{(x+3)(x+7)} + \dfrac{x-3}{x+7} \cdot \dfrac{x+3}{x+3}$

$= \dfrac{2x+(x-3)(x+3)}{(x+3)(x+7)}$

$= \dfrac{2x+x^2-9}{(x+3)(x+7)}$

$= \dfrac{x^2+2x-9}{(x+3)(x+7)}$

12. $\dfrac{2}{x^2+3x-10}-\dfrac{5x}{x^2-6x+8}$

$=\dfrac{2}{(x+5)(x-2)}\cdot\dfrac{x-4}{x-4}-\dfrac{5x}{(x-2)(x-4)}\cdot\dfrac{x+5}{x+5}$

$=\dfrac{2(x-4)-5(x+5)}{(x-2)(x-4)(x+5)}$

$=\dfrac{2x-8-5x^2-25x}{(x-2)(x-4)(x+5)}$

$=\dfrac{-5x^2-23x-8}{(x-2)(x-4)(x+5)}$

6.4 Exercises

1. $\dfrac{\frac{3}{x}}{\frac{2}{x^2}+\frac{5}{x}}=\dfrac{\frac{3}{x}}{\frac{2}{x^2}+\frac{5}{x}}\cdot\dfrac{x^2}{x^2}$

$=\dfrac{\frac{3x^2}{x}}{\frac{2x^2}{x^2}+\frac{5x^2}{x}}$

$=\dfrac{3x}{2+5x}$

3. $\dfrac{\frac{1}{x}+\frac{1}{y}}{\frac{1}{xy}}=\dfrac{\frac{1}{x}+\frac{1}{y}}{\frac{1}{xy}}\cdot\dfrac{(xy)}{(xy)}$

$=\dfrac{\frac{xy}{x}+\frac{xy}{x}}{\frac{xy}{xy}}=\dfrac{y+x}{1}=y+x$

5. $\dfrac{\frac{x}{6}-\frac{1}{3}}{\frac{2}{3x}+\frac{5}{6}}=\dfrac{\frac{x}{6}(6x)-\frac{1}{3}(6x)}{\frac{2}{3x}(6x)+\frac{5}{6}(6x)}$

$=\dfrac{x^2-2x}{4+5x}$

7. $\dfrac{\frac{7}{5x}-\frac{1}{x}}{\frac{3}{5}+\frac{2}{x}}=\dfrac{\frac{7}{5x}(5x)-\frac{1}{x}(5x)}{\frac{3}{5}(5x)+\frac{2}{x}(5x)}$

$=\dfrac{7-5}{3x+10}$

$=\dfrac{2}{3x+10}$

9. $\dfrac{\frac{5}{x}+\frac{3}{y}}{3x+5y}=\dfrac{\frac{5}{x}+\frac{3}{y}}{3x+5y}\cdot\dfrac{xy}{xy}$

$=\dfrac{\frac{5xy}{x}+\frac{3xy}{y}}{(3x+5y)xy}$

$=\dfrac{5y+3x}{(3x+5y)xy}$

$=\dfrac{1}{xy}$

11. $\dfrac{4-\frac{1}{x^2}}{2+\frac{1}{x}}=\dfrac{4-\frac{1}{x^2}}{2+\frac{1}{x}}\cdot\dfrac{x^2}{x^2}$

$=\dfrac{4x^2-\frac{x^2}{x^2}}{2x^2+\frac{x^2}{x}}$

$=\dfrac{4x^2-1}{2x^2+x}$

$=\dfrac{(2x+1)(2x-1)}{x(2x+1)}$

$=\dfrac{2x-1}{x}$

13. $\dfrac{\frac{10}{x^2-25}}{\frac{3}{x+5}+\frac{2}{x-5}} = \dfrac{\frac{10}{x^2-25}}{\frac{3}{x+5}+\frac{2}{x-5}} \cdot \dfrac{(x+5)(x-5)}{(x+5)(x-5)}$

$= \dfrac{\frac{10(x+5)(x-5)}{(x+5)(x-5)}}{\frac{(x+5)(x-5)}{(x+5)}+\frac{2(x+5)(x-5)}{(x-5)}}$

$= \dfrac{10}{3(x-5)+2(x+5)}$

$= \dfrac{10}{3x-15+2x+10}$

$= \dfrac{10}{5x-5}$

$= \dfrac{10}{5(x-1)}$

$= \dfrac{2}{x-1}$

15. $\dfrac{a+\frac{3}{a}}{\frac{a^2+2}{3a}} = \dfrac{a+\frac{3}{a}}{\frac{a^2+2}{3a}} \cdot \dfrac{3a}{3a}$

$= \dfrac{a(3a)+\left(\frac{3}{a}\right)(3a)}{\left(\frac{a^2+2}{3a}\right)(3a)}$

$= \dfrac{3a^2+9}{a^2+2}$

17. $\dfrac{\frac{3}{x-3}}{\frac{1}{x^2-9}+\frac{2}{x+3}}$

$= \dfrac{\frac{3}{x-3}}{\frac{1}{x^2-9}+\frac{2}{x+3}} \cdot \dfrac{(x+3)(x-3)}{(x+3)(x-3)}$

$= \dfrac{\left(\frac{3}{x-3}\right)\frac{(x+3)(x-3)}{1}}{\frac{1}{(x+3)(x-3)}\frac{(x+3)(x-3)}{1}+\left(\frac{2}{x+3}\right)\frac{(x+3)(x-3)}{1}}$

$= \dfrac{3(x+3)}{1+2(x-3)}$

$= \dfrac{3(x+3)}{1+2x-6}$

$= \dfrac{3x+9}{2x-5}$

19. $\dfrac{\frac{2}{y-1}+2}{\frac{2}{y+1}-2} = \dfrac{\frac{2}{y-1}+2}{\frac{2}{y+1}-2} \cdot \dfrac{(y-1)(y+1)}{(y-1)(y+1)}$

$= \dfrac{\frac{2(y-1)(y+1)}{y-1}+2(y-1)(y+1)}{\frac{2(y-1)(y+1)}{(y+1)}-2(y-1)(y+1)}$

$= \dfrac{2(y+1)[1+(y-1)]}{2(y-1)[1-(y+1)]} = \dfrac{(y+1)(y)}{(y-1)(1-y-1)}$

$= \dfrac{y(y+1)}{(y-1)(-y)} = \dfrac{y+1}{-y+1}$

21. No expression in any denominator can be allowed to be zero, since division by zero is undefined. So -3, 5, and 0 are not allowable replacements for the variable x.

Cumulative Review

23.
$$P = 2(\ell + w)$$
$$P = 2\ell + 2w$$
$$P - 2\ell = 2w$$
$$\frac{P - 2\ell}{2} = w$$

25. $4000 - 125(17) = 1875$

She has yet to pay \$1875.

6.5 Exercises

1.
$$\frac{7}{x} + \frac{3}{4} = \frac{-2}{x}$$
$$4x\left(\frac{7}{x}\right) + 4x\left(\frac{3}{4}\right) = 4x\left(-\frac{2}{x}\right)$$
$$28 + 3x = -8$$
$$3x = -36$$
$$x = -12$$

Check: $\dfrac{7}{-12} + \dfrac{3}{4} \overset{?}{=} \dfrac{-2}{-12}$

$$\frac{7}{-12} + \frac{9}{12} \overset{?}{=} \frac{1}{6}$$
$$\frac{2}{12} \overset{?}{=} \frac{1}{6}$$
$$\frac{1}{6} = \frac{1}{6}$$

3.
$$\frac{-1}{4x} + \frac{3}{2} = \frac{5}{x}$$
$$4x\left(-\frac{1}{4x}\right) + 4x\left(\frac{3}{2}\right) = 4x\left(\frac{5}{x}\right)$$
$$-1 + 6x = 20$$
$$6x = 21$$
$$x = \frac{21}{6}$$
$$x = \frac{7}{2} \text{ or } 3\frac{1}{2}$$

Check: $-\dfrac{1}{4(7/2)} + \dfrac{3}{2} \overset{?}{=} \dfrac{5}{7/2}$

$$-\frac{1}{14} + \frac{3}{2} \overset{?}{=} \frac{10}{7}$$
$$\frac{1}{14} + \frac{21}{14} \overset{?}{=} \frac{10}{7}$$
$$\frac{20}{14} \overset{?}{=} \frac{10}{7}$$
$$\frac{10}{7} = \frac{10}{7}$$

5.
$$\frac{5x+3}{3x} = \frac{7}{3} - \frac{9}{x}$$
$$3x\left(\frac{5x+3}{3x}\right) = 3x\left(\frac{7}{3}\right) - 3\left(\frac{9}{x}\right)$$
$$5x + 3 = 7x - 27$$
$$3 = 2x - 27$$
$$30 = 2x$$
$$15 = x$$

Check: $\dfrac{5(15)+3}{3(15)} \overset{?}{=} \dfrac{3}{\left(-\frac{3}{4}\right)-3}$

$$\dfrac{78}{45} \overset{?}{=} \dfrac{35}{15} - \dfrac{9}{15}$$

$$\dfrac{26}{15} = \dfrac{26}{15}$$

7. $\dfrac{x+1}{2x} = \dfrac{2}{3}$

$$6x\left(\dfrac{x+1}{2x}\right) = 6x\left(\dfrac{2}{3}\right)$$

$$3(x+1) = 4x$$

$$3x+3 = 4x$$

$$3 = x$$

Check: $\dfrac{3+1}{2(3)} \overset{?}{=} \dfrac{2}{3}$

$$\dfrac{4}{6} \overset{?}{=} \dfrac{2}{3}$$

$$\dfrac{2}{3} = \dfrac{2}{3}$$

9. $\dfrac{6}{3x-5} = \dfrac{3}{2x}$

$$2x(3x-5)\left(\dfrac{6}{3x-5}\right) = 2x(3x-5)\left(\dfrac{3}{2x}\right)$$

$$12x = 9x - 15$$

$$3x = -15$$

$$x = -5$$

Check: $\dfrac{6}{3(-5)-5} \overset{?}{=} \dfrac{3}{2(-5)}$

$$-\dfrac{6}{20} \overset{?}{=} -\dfrac{3}{10}$$

$$-\dfrac{3}{10} = -\dfrac{3}{10}$$

11. $\dfrac{2}{2x+5} = \dfrac{4}{x-4}$

$$(2x+5)(x-4)\left(\dfrac{2}{2x+5}\right) = (2x+5)(x-4)\left(\dfrac{4}{x-4}\right)$$

$$2(x-4) = 4(2x+5)$$

$$2x - 8 = 8x + 20$$

$$-8 = 6x + 20$$

$$-28 = 6x$$

$$-\dfrac{28}{6} = x$$

$$-\dfrac{14}{3} = x \ \text{ or } \ x = -4\dfrac{2}{3}$$

Check: $\dfrac{2}{2\left(-\frac{14}{3}\right)+5} \overset{?}{=} \dfrac{4}{-\frac{14}{3}-4}$

$$\dfrac{2}{-\frac{28}{3}+\frac{15}{3}} \overset{?}{=} \dfrac{4}{-\frac{14}{3}-\frac{12}{3}}$$

$$\dfrac{2}{-\frac{13}{3}} = \dfrac{4}{-\frac{26}{3}}$$

$$-\dfrac{6}{13} = -\dfrac{6}{13}$$

13. $\dfrac{2}{x} + \dfrac{x}{x+1} = 1$

$$x(x+1)\left(\dfrac{2}{x}\right) + x(x+1)\left(\dfrac{x}{x+1}\right) = x(x+1)(1)$$

$$(x+1)(2) + x^2 = x^2 + x$$

$$2x + 2 + x^2 = x^2 + x$$

$$2x + 2 = x$$

$$2 = -x$$

$$-2 = x$$

Check: $\dfrac{2}{-2} + \dfrac{-2}{-2+1} \overset{?}{=} 1$

$$-1 + 2 \overset{?}{=} 1$$

$$1 = 1$$

15. $\dfrac{85-4x}{x}=7-\dfrac{3}{x}$

$x\left(\dfrac{85-4x}{x}\right)=7x-x\left(\dfrac{3}{x}\right)$

$85-4x=7x-3$

$85=11x-3$

$88=11x$

$8=x$

Check: $\dfrac{85-4(8)}{8}\overset{?}{=}7-\dfrac{3}{9}$

$\dfrac{53}{8}\overset{?}{=}\dfrac{56}{8}-\dfrac{3}{8}$

$\dfrac{53}{8}=\dfrac{53}{8}$

17. $\dfrac{3}{x+2}-4=\dfrac{4x-1}{x+2}$

$(x+2)\left(\dfrac{3}{x+2}\right)-(x+2)(4)=(x+2)\left(\dfrac{4x-1}{x+2}\right)$

$3-4(x+2)=4x-1$

$3-4x-8=4x-1$

$-4x-5=4x-1$

$-5=8x-1$

$-4=8x$

$-\dfrac{4}{8}=x$

$-\dfrac{1}{2}=x$

Check: $\dfrac{3}{-\frac{1}{2}+2}-4\overset{?}{=}\dfrac{4\left(-\frac{1}{2}\right)-1}{-\frac{1}{2}+2}$

$2-4\overset{?}{=}-2$

$-2=-2$

19. $\dfrac{2}{x-6}-5=\dfrac{2(x-5)}{x-6}$

$(x-6)\left(\dfrac{2}{x-6}\right)-5(x-6)=(x-6)\left[\dfrac{2(x-5)}{x-6}\right]$

$2-5x+30=2x-10$

$-5x+32=2x-10$

$42=7x$

$6=x$

Check: $\dfrac{2}{6-6}-5\overset{?}{=}\dfrac{2(6-5)}{6-6}$

$\dfrac{2}{0}-5\overset{?}{=}\dfrac{2}{0}$

$x=6$ makes the denominators zero so it is an extraneous solution. There is no solution.

21. $\dfrac{2}{x+1}-\dfrac{1}{x-1}=\dfrac{2x}{x^2-1}$

$\dfrac{2}{x+1}-\dfrac{1}{x-1}=\dfrac{2x}{(x+1)(x-1)}$

$(x+1)(x-1)\left(\dfrac{2}{x+1}\right)-(x+1)(x-1)\left(\dfrac{1}{x-1}\right)$

$=(x+1)(x-1)\left(\dfrac{2x}{(x+1)(x-1)}\right)$

$(x-1)(2)-(x+1)=2x$

$2x-2-x-1=2x$

$x-3=2x$

$-3=x$

Check: $\dfrac{2}{-3+1}-\dfrac{1}{-3-1}\overset{?}{=}\dfrac{2(-3)}{(-3)^2-1}$

$-1+\dfrac{1}{4}\overset{?}{=}-\dfrac{6}{8}$

$-\dfrac{3}{4}=-\dfrac{3}{4}$

194

23. $\dfrac{y+1}{y^2+2y-3}=\dfrac{1}{y+3}-\dfrac{1}{y-1}$

$\dfrac{y+1}{(y+3)(y-1)}=\dfrac{1}{y+3}-\dfrac{1}{y-1}$

$(y+3)(y-1)\left(\dfrac{y+1}{(y+3)(y-1)}\right)$

$=(y+3)(y-1)\left(\dfrac{1}{y+3}\right)-(y+3)(y-1)\left(\dfrac{1}{y-1}\right)$

$y+1=y-1-y-3$

$y+1=-4$

$y=-5$

Check: $\dfrac{-5+1}{(-5)^2+2(-5)-3}\overset{?}{=}\dfrac{1}{-5+3}-\dfrac{1}{-5-1}$

$\dfrac{-4}{12}\overset{?}{=}-\dfrac{1}{2}+\dfrac{1}{6}$

$\dfrac{4}{12}=-\dfrac{4}{12}$

25. $\dfrac{2x}{x+4}-\dfrac{8}{x-4}=\dfrac{2x^2+32}{x^2-16}$

$\dfrac{2x}{x+4}-\dfrac{8}{x-4}=\dfrac{2x^2+32}{(x+4)(x-4)}$

$(x+4)(x-4)\left(\dfrac{2x}{x+4}\right)-(x+4)(x-4)\left(\dfrac{8}{x-4}\right)$

$=(x+4)(x-4)\left(\dfrac{2x^2+32}{(x+4)(x-4)}\right)$

$(x-4)(2x)-(x+4)(8)=2x^2+32$

$2x^2-8x-8x-32=2x^2+32$

$2x^2-16x-32=2x^2+32$

$-16x-32=32$

$-16x=64$

$x=-4\ \text{Extraneous}$

No solution.

27. $\dfrac{4}{x^2-1}+\dfrac{7}{x+1}=\dfrac{5}{x-1}$

$\dfrac{4}{(x+1)(x-1)}+\dfrac{7}{x+1}=\dfrac{5}{x-1}$

$(x+1)(x-1)\dfrac{4}{(x+1)(x-1)}+(x+1)(x-1)$

$\times\dfrac{7}{x+1}=(x+1)(x-1)\dfrac{5}{x-1}$

$4+(x-1)(7)=(x+1)(5)$

$4+7x-7=5x+5$

$2x-3=5$

$2x=8$

$x=4$

Check:

$\dfrac{4}{(4)^2-1}+\dfrac{7}{4+1}\overset{?}{=}\dfrac{5}{4-1}$

$\dfrac{4}{15}+\dfrac{7}{5}\overset{?}{=}\dfrac{5}{3}$

$\dfrac{25}{15}\overset{?}{=}\dfrac{5}{3}$

$\dfrac{5}{3}=\dfrac{5}{3}$

29. $\dfrac{x+11}{x^2-5x+4}+\dfrac{3}{x-1}=\dfrac{5}{x-4}$

$\dfrac{x+11}{(x-4)(x-1)}+\dfrac{3}{x-1}=\dfrac{5}{x-4}$

$(x-4)(x-1)\left(\dfrac{x+11}{(x-4)(x-1)}\right)$

$+(x-4)(x-1)\left(\dfrac{3}{x-1}\right)=(x-4)(x-1)\left(\dfrac{5}{x-4}\right)$

$x+11+(x-4)(3)=(x-1)(5)$

$x+11+3x-12=5x-5$

$4x-1=5x-5$

$-1=x-5$

$4=x$ Extraneous

No solution.

31. $x-2\neq0$, so $x\neq2$

$x-4\neq0$, so $x\neq4$

$x^2-6x+8\neq0$

$(x-2)(x-4)\neq0$

$x-2\neq0\qquad x-4\neq0$

$x\neq2\qquad\qquad x\neq4$

Extraneous solutions $x=2$, $x=4$

Cumulative Review

33. $6x^2-x-12=(3x+4)(2x-3)$

35. $x=$ width

$3x-1=$ length

$P=2L+2W$

$54=2(3x-1)+2x$

$54=6x-2+2x$

$56=8x$

$7=x$

$3x-1=3(7)-1-1=20$

Width = 7 meters and length = 20 meters

37. Decrease: $7.3-5.7=1.6$

$\dfrac{1.6}{7.3}=0.219=21.9\%$

39. Increase: $9.3-8.4=0.9$

$\dfrac{0.9}{8.4}=0.107$

For $2010-2020$ the increase is

$0.107(9.3)=0.995$

Expected number $=9.3+0.995$

≈10.3 million people

6.6 Exercises

1. $\dfrac{4}{9}=\dfrac{8}{x}$

$4x=72$

$x=18$

3. $\dfrac{x}{17}=\dfrac{12}{5}$

$5x=204$

$x=\dfrac{204}{5}$ or $40\dfrac{4}{5}$

5. $\dfrac{8}{5} = \dfrac{x}{7}$

$56 = 5x$

$\dfrac{56}{5} = x$ or $x = 11\dfrac{1}{5}$

7. $\dfrac{7}{x} = \dfrac{40}{130}$

$40x = 910$

$x = \dfrac{910}{40} = 22.75$

9. $d = $ distance apart

$\dfrac{d}{5.5} = \dfrac{15}{3/4}$

$\dfrac{3}{4}d = 82.5$

$d = 110$ miles

11. (a) $700 U.S. $\left(\dfrac{\$1.49 \text{ Australian}}{\$1 \text{ U.S.}}\right)$

$= \$1043$ Australian

(b) $700 U.S. $\left(\dfrac{\$1.68 \text{ Australian}}{\$1 \text{ U.S.}}\right)$

$= \$1176$ Australian

$1176 - 1043 = \$133$ more Australian

13. $x = $ speed limit in miles per hour

$\dfrac{x}{90} = \dfrac{62}{100}$

$100x = 5580$

$x = 55.8 \approx 56$

The limit is 56 miles per hour.

15. $x = $ miles from base of mountain

$\dfrac{x}{\frac{3}{4}} = \dfrac{136}{3\frac{1}{2}}$

$\dfrac{7}{2}x = \dfrac{3}{4}(136)$

$\dfrac{7}{2}x = 102$

$x = 29.1$

He is 29 miles away.

17. $x = 20, \ y = 29, \ m = 13$

$\dfrac{n}{m} = \dfrac{y}{x}$

$\dfrac{n}{13} = \dfrac{29}{20}$

$20n = 377$

$n = \dfrac{377}{20} = 18\dfrac{17}{20}$ inches

19. $\dfrac{y}{40} = \dfrac{175}{35}$

$35y = 7000$

$y = 200$ meters

21. $\dfrac{d}{k} = \dfrac{a}{g}$

$\dfrac{d}{12} = \dfrac{7}{9}$

$9d = 84$

$d = \dfrac{84}{9} = 9\dfrac{1}{3}$ in.

23. $\dfrac{k}{d} = \dfrac{h}{b}$

$\dfrac{k}{32} = \dfrac{24}{20}$

$k = \dfrac{768}{20} = 38\dfrac{2}{5}$ m

25. $x = \text{length}$

$\dfrac{30}{x} = \dfrac{5}{8}$

$5x = 8(30)$

$x = \dfrac{240}{5}$

$x = 48 \text{ inches}$

27. $x = \text{flower height}$

$\dfrac{x}{13} = \dfrac{5}{3}$

$3x = 65$

$x = \dfrac{65}{3} \approx 22 \text{ inches}$

Total height $= 13 + 22 = 35$ inches

29. $x = \text{amount of accceleration in 11 seconds}$

$\dfrac{x}{11} = \dfrac{3}{2}$

$2x = 33$

$x = 16.5$

$45 + 16.5 = 61.5$

61.5 miles per hour

31.

	D	R	$T = \dfrac{D}{R}$
Helicopter	1050	s	$\dfrac{1050}{s}$
Airline	1250	$s + 40$	$\dfrac{1250}{s + 40}$

$\dfrac{1250}{s + 40} = \dfrac{1050}{s}$

$1050s = 1050s + 42{,}000$

$200s = 42{,}000$

$s = 210$

$s + 40 = 250$

commuter airline, 250 kilometers/hr;

helicopter, 210 kilometers/hr

33. a. $\dfrac{\$0.79}{7.5 \text{ oz}} = \$0.11/\text{oz}$

b. $\dfrac{\$1.49}{16 \text{ oz}} = \$0.09$

c. $x = \text{price of 40 oz. bucket}$

$\dfrac{x}{40} = \dfrac{1.49}{16}$

$16x = 59.6$

$x = 3.73$

The price would be $3.73.

35. $x = \text{time to mow together}$

$\dfrac{1}{4} + \dfrac{1}{5} = \dfrac{1}{x}$

$5x + 4x = 20$

$9x = 20$

$x = \dfrac{20}{9} = 2\dfrac{2}{9} \text{ hours}$

$60\left(\dfrac{2}{9}\right) = 13.3$

It will take $2\frac{2}{9}$ hours or 2 hours

13 minutes.

37. x = time to rake together

$$\frac{1}{6}+\frac{1}{8}=\frac{1}{x}$$

$$24x\left(\frac{1}{6}\right)+24x\left(\frac{1}{8}\right)=24x\left(\frac{1}{x}\right)$$

$$4x+3x=24$$

$$7x=24$$

$$x=\frac{24}{7}=3\frac{3}{7}$$

It will take $3\frac{3}{7}$ hours or 3 hours

26 minutes.

Cumulative Review

39. $0.000892465 = 8.92465\times10^{-4}$

41. $\dfrac{x^{-3}y^{-2}}{z^{4}w^{-8}}=\dfrac{w^{8}}{x^{3}y^{2}z^{4}}$

Putting Your Skills to Work

1. $15-12=3$

    $3000

2. $18-16.8=1.2$

    $1200

3. $P=\dfrac{24x^{2}+120x}{x^{2}+8x+15}$

$$P=\dfrac{24x(x+5)}{(x+3)(x+5)}$$

$$P=\dfrac{24x}{x+3}$$

4. $P=\dfrac{24(11)}{11+3}$

$$P=\dfrac{264}{14}$$

$$P=\$18.857 \text{ thousand}$$

$$P=\$18,857$$

5. $20=\dfrac{24x}{x+3}$

$$20(x+3)=24x$$

$$20x+60=24x$$

$$60=4x$$

$$15=x$$

$15,000

6. $21=\dfrac{24x}{x+3}$

$$21(x+3)=24x$$

$$21x+63=24x$$

$$63=3x$$

$$21=x$$

$21,000

Chapter 6 Review Problems

1. $\dfrac{bx}{bx - by} = \dfrac{bx}{b(x - y)}$

$ = \dfrac{x}{x - y}$

2. $\dfrac{4x - 4y}{5y - 5x} = \dfrac{4(x - y)}{-5(x - y)} = -\dfrac{4}{5}$

3. $\dfrac{2x^2 + 5x - 3}{2x^2 - 9x + 4} = \dfrac{(2x - 1)(x + 3)}{(2x - 1)(x - 4)} = \dfrac{x + 3}{x - 4}$

4. $\dfrac{3x^2 + 7x + 2}{3x^2 + 13x + 4}$

$= \dfrac{(3x + 1)(x + 2)}{(3x + 1)(x + 4)}$

$= \dfrac{x + 2}{x + 4}$

5. $\dfrac{x^2 - 9}{x^2 - 10x + 21} = \dfrac{(x + 3)(x - 3)}{(x - 7)(x - 3)} = \dfrac{x + 3}{x - 7}$

6. $\dfrac{2x^2 + 18x + 40}{3x + 15}$

$= \dfrac{2(x + 5)(x + 4)}{3(x + 5)}$

$= \dfrac{2(x + 4)}{3}$

7. $\dfrac{x^3 + 3x^2}{x^3 - 2x^2 - 15x}$

$= \dfrac{x^2(x + 3)}{x(x - 5)(x + 3)}$

$= \dfrac{x}{x - 5}$

8. $\dfrac{4x^2 + 4x - 3}{4x^2 - 2x} = \dfrac{(2x + 3)(2x - 1)}{2x(2x - 1)} = \dfrac{2x + 3}{2x}$

9. $\dfrac{2x^2 - 2xy - 24y^2}{2x^2 + 5xy - 3y^2}$

$= \dfrac{2(x - 4y)(x + 3y)}{(2x - y)(x + 3y)}$

$= \dfrac{2(x - 4y)}{2x - y}$

10. $\dfrac{4 - y^2}{3y^2 + 5y - 2}$

$= \dfrac{(2 + y)(2 - y)}{(3y - 1)(y + 2)}$

$= \dfrac{2 - y}{3y - 1}$

11. $\dfrac{5x^3 - 10x^2}{25x^4 + 5x^3 - 30x^2}$

$= \dfrac{5x^2(x - 2)}{5x^2(5x + 6)(x - 1)}$

$= \dfrac{x - 2}{(5x + 6)(x - 1)}$

200

12. $\dfrac{16x^2 - 4y^2}{4x - 2y}$

$= \dfrac{4(2x+y)(2x-y)}{2(2x-y)}$

$= 2(2x+y)$

$= 4x + 2y$

13. $\dfrac{3x^2 - 13x - 10}{3x^2 + 2x} \cdot \dfrac{x^2 - 25x}{x^2 - 25}$

$= \dfrac{(3x+2)(x-5)}{x(3x+2)} \cdot \dfrac{x(x-25)}{(x+5)(x-5)}$

$= \dfrac{x - 25}{x + 5}$

14. $\dfrac{2y^2 - 18}{3y^2 + 3y} \div \dfrac{y^2 + 6y + 9}{y^2 + 4y + 3}$

$= \dfrac{2y^2 - 18}{3y^2 + 3y} \cdot \dfrac{y^2 + 4y + 3}{y^2 + 6y + 9}$

$= \dfrac{2(y+3)(y-3)}{3y(y+1)} \cdot \dfrac{(y+3)(y+1)}{(y+3)(y+3)}$

$= \dfrac{2(y-3)}{3y}$

15. $\dfrac{2y^2 + 3y - 2}{2y^2 + y - 1} \div \dfrac{2y^2 + y - 1}{2y^2 - 3y - 2}$

$= \dfrac{2y^2 + 3y - 2}{2y^2 + y - 1} \cdot \dfrac{2y^2 - 3y - 2}{2y^2 + y - 1}$

$= \dfrac{(2y-1)(y+2)}{(2y-1)(y+1)} \cdot \dfrac{(2y+1)(y-2)}{(2y-1)(y+1)}$

$= \dfrac{(y+2)(2y+1)(y-2)}{(y+1)^2 (2y-1)}$

16. $\dfrac{6y^2 + 13y - 5}{9y^2 + 3y} \div \dfrac{4y^2 + 20y + 25}{12y^2}$

$= \dfrac{6y^2 + 13y - 5}{9y^2 + 3y} \cdot \dfrac{12y^2}{4y^2 + 20y + 25}$

$= \dfrac{(3y-1)(2y+5)}{3y(3y+1)} \cdot \dfrac{12y^2}{(2y+5)(2y+5)}$

$= \dfrac{4y(3y-1)}{(3y+1)(2y+5)}$

17. $\dfrac{3xy^2 + 12y^2}{2x^2 - 11x + 5} \div \dfrac{2xy + 8y}{8x^2 + 2x - 3}$

$= \dfrac{3xy^2 + 12y^2}{2x^2 - 11x + 5} \cdot \dfrac{8x^2 + 2x - 3}{2xy + 8y}$

$= \dfrac{3y^2(x+4)}{(2x-1)(x-5)} \cdot \dfrac{(2x-1)(4x+3)}{2y(x+4)}$

$= \dfrac{3y(4x+3)}{2(x-5)}$

18. $\dfrac{11}{x-2} \cdot \dfrac{2x^2 - 8}{44} = \dfrac{11}{x-2} \cdot \dfrac{2(x+2)(x-2)}{44}$

$= \dfrac{x+2}{2}$

19. $\dfrac{x^2 - 5xy - 24y^2}{2x^2 - 2xy - 24y^2} \cdot \dfrac{4x^2 + 4xy - 24y^2}{x^2 - 10xy + 16y^2}$

$= \dfrac{(x-8y)(x+3y)}{2(x-4y)(x+3y)} \cdot \dfrac{4(x+3y)(x-2y)}{(x-8y)(x-2y)}$

$= \dfrac{2(x+3y)}{x - 4y}$

20. $\dfrac{2x^2+10x+2}{8x-8}\cdot\dfrac{3x-3}{4x^2+20x+4}$

$=\dfrac{2(x^2+5x+1)}{8(x-1)}\cdot\dfrac{3(x-1)}{4(x^2+5x+1)}$

$=\dfrac{3}{16}$

21. $\dfrac{7}{x+1}+\dfrac{4}{2x}=\dfrac{7}{x+1}\cdot\dfrac{2x}{2x}+\dfrac{4}{2x}\cdot\dfrac{x+1}{x+1}$

$=\dfrac{14x+4x+4}{2x(x+1)}$

$=\dfrac{18x+4}{2x(x+1)}$

$=\dfrac{9x+2}{x(x+1)}$

22. $5+\dfrac{1}{x}+\dfrac{1}{x+1}$

$=\dfrac{5}{1}\cdot\dfrac{x(x+1)}{x(x+1)}+\dfrac{1}{x}\cdot\dfrac{x+1}{x+1}+\dfrac{1}{x+1}\cdot\dfrac{x}{x}$

$=\dfrac{5x^2+5x}{x(x+1)}+\dfrac{x+1}{x(x+1)}+\dfrac{x}{x(x+1)}$

$=\dfrac{5x^2+5x+x+1+x}{x(x+1)}$

$=\dfrac{5x^2+7x+1}{x(x+1)}$

23. $\dfrac{7}{x+2}+\dfrac{3}{x-4}$

$=\dfrac{7}{x+2}\cdot\dfrac{x-4}{x-4}+\dfrac{3}{x-4}\cdot\dfrac{x+2}{x+2}$

$=\dfrac{7x-28}{(x+2)(x-4)}+\dfrac{3x+6}{(x+2)(x-4)}$

$=\dfrac{7x-28+3x+6}{(x+2)(x-4)}$

$=\dfrac{10x-22}{(x+2)(x-4)}$

24. $\dfrac{2}{x^2-9}+\dfrac{x}{x+3}$

$=\dfrac{2}{(x+3)(x-3)}+\dfrac{x}{x+3}\cdot\dfrac{x-3}{x-3}$

$=\dfrac{2+x^2-3x}{(x+3)(x-3)}$

$=\dfrac{(x-2)(x-1)}{(x+3)(x-3)}$

25. $\dfrac{x}{y}+\dfrac{3}{2y}+\dfrac{1}{y+2}$

$=\dfrac{x}{y}\cdot\dfrac{2(y+2)}{2(y+2)}+\dfrac{3}{2y}\cdot\dfrac{y+2}{y+2}+\dfrac{1}{y+2}\cdot\dfrac{2y}{2y}$

$=\dfrac{2x(y+2)+3y+6+2y}{2y(y+2)}$

$=\dfrac{2xy+4x+5y+6}{2y(y+2)}$

26. $\dfrac{4}{a}+\dfrac{2}{b}+\dfrac{3}{a+b}$

$=\dfrac{4}{a}\cdot\dfrac{b(a+b)}{b(a+b)}+\dfrac{2}{b}\cdot\dfrac{a(a+b)}{a(a+b)}+\dfrac{3}{a+b}\cdot\dfrac{ab}{ab}$

$=\dfrac{4ab+4b^2}{ab(a+b)}+\dfrac{2a^2+2ab}{ab(a+b)}+\dfrac{3ab}{ab(a+b)}$

$=\dfrac{4ab+4b^2+2a^2+2ab+3ab}{ab(a+b)}$

$=\dfrac{2a^2+9ab+4b^2}{ab(a+b)}$

$=\dfrac{(2a+b)(a+4b)}{ab(a+b)}$

27. $\dfrac{3x+1}{3x}-\dfrac{1}{r}=\dfrac{3x+1}{3x}-\dfrac{1}{x}\cdot\dfrac{3}{3}$

$=\dfrac{3x+1-3}{3x}$

$=\dfrac{3x-2}{3x}$

28. $\dfrac{x+4}{x+2}-\dfrac{1}{2x}$

$=\dfrac{x+4}{x+2}\cdot\dfrac{2x}{2x}-\dfrac{1}{2x}\cdot\dfrac{x+2}{x+2}$

$=\dfrac{2x^2+8x}{2x(x+2)}-\dfrac{x+2}{2x(x+2)}$

$=\dfrac{2x^2+8x-(x+2)}{2x(x+2)}$

$=\dfrac{2x^2+8x-x-2}{2x(x+2)}$

$=\dfrac{2x^2+7x-2}{2x(x+2)}$

29. $\dfrac{27}{x^2-81}+\dfrac{3}{2(x+9)}$

$=\dfrac{27}{(x+9)(x-9)}\cdot\dfrac{2}{2}+\dfrac{3}{2(x+9)}\cdot\dfrac{x-9}{x-9}$

$=\dfrac{54+3x-27}{2(x+9)(x-9)}$

$=\dfrac{3x+27}{2(x+9)(x-9)}$

$=\dfrac{3(x+9)}{2(x+9)(x-9)}$

$=\dfrac{3}{2(x-9)}$

30. $\dfrac{1}{x^2+7x+10}-\dfrac{x}{x+5}$

$=\dfrac{1}{(x+2)(x+5)}-\dfrac{x}{x+5}\cdot\dfrac{x+2}{x+2}$

$=\dfrac{1-x^2-2x}{(x+2)(x+5)}$

31. $\dfrac{\frac{3}{2y}-\frac{1}{y}}{\frac{4}{y}+\frac{3}{2y}}=\dfrac{\frac{3}{2y}-\frac{1}{y}}{\frac{4}{y}+\frac{3}{2y}}\cdot\dfrac{2y}{2y}$

$=\dfrac{3-2}{8+3}=\dfrac{1}{11}$

32. $\dfrac{\frac{2}{x}+\frac{1}{2x}}{x+\frac{x}{2}}$

$=\dfrac{\frac{2}{x}+\frac{1}{2x}}{x+\frac{x}{2}}\cdot\dfrac{2x}{2x}$

$=\dfrac{4+1}{2x^2+x^2}=\dfrac{5}{3x^2}$

33.

$$\frac{w - \frac{4}{w}}{1 + \frac{2}{w}} = \frac{w - \frac{4}{w}}{1 + \frac{2}{w}} \cdot \frac{w}{w}$$

$$= \frac{w^2 - 4}{w + 2}$$

$$= \frac{(w + 2)(w - 2)}{w + 2}$$

$$= w - 2$$

34.

$$\frac{1 - \frac{w}{w-1}}{1 + \frac{w}{1-w}}$$

$$= \frac{1 - \frac{w}{x-1}}{1 + \frac{w}{-(w-1)}}$$

$$= \frac{1 - \frac{w}{w-1}}{1 - \frac{w}{w-1}} = 1$$

35.

$$\frac{1 + \frac{1}{y^2-1}}{\frac{1}{y+1} - \frac{1}{y-1}} = \frac{1 + \frac{1}{(y+1)(y-1)}}{\frac{1}{y+1} - \frac{1}{y-1}} \cdot \frac{(y+1)(y-1)}{(y+1)(y-1)}$$

$$= \frac{(y+1)(y-1) + 1}{y - 1 - (y+1)}$$

$$= \frac{y^2}{-2} = -\frac{y^2}{2}$$

36.

$$\frac{\frac{1}{y} + \frac{1}{x+y}}{1 + \frac{2}{x+y}}$$

$$= \frac{\frac{1}{y} + \frac{1}{x+y}}{1 + \frac{2}{x+y}} \cdot \frac{y(x+y)}{y(x+y)}$$

$$= \frac{x + y + y}{y(x+y) + 2y}$$

$$= \frac{x + 2y}{xy + y^2 + 2y}$$

$$= \frac{x + 2y}{y(x + y + 2)}$$

37.

$$\frac{\frac{1}{a+b} - \frac{1}{a}}{b} = \frac{\frac{a-(a+b)}{a(a+b)}}{b}$$

$$= -\frac{1}{a(a+b)}$$

38.

$$\frac{\frac{2}{a+b} - \frac{3}{b}}{\frac{1}{a+b}}$$

$$= \frac{\frac{2}{a+b} - \frac{3}{b}}{\frac{1}{a+b}} \cdot \frac{b(a+b)}{b(a+b)}$$

$$= \frac{2b - 3(a+b)}{b}$$

$$= \frac{2b - 3a - 3b}{b} = \frac{-3a - b}{b}$$

39.

$$\frac{x+5y}{x-6y} \div \left(\frac{1}{5y} - \frac{1}{x+5y} \right)$$

$$= \frac{x+5y}{x-6y} \div \left(\frac{1}{5y} \cdot \frac{x+5y}{x+5y} - \frac{1}{x+5y} \cdot \frac{5y}{5y} \right)$$

$$= \frac{x+5y}{x-6y} \div \left[\frac{x+5y}{5y(x+5y)} - \frac{5y}{5y(x+5y)} \right]$$

$$= \frac{x+5y}{x-6y} \div \frac{x+5y - 5y}{5y(x+5y)}$$

$$= \frac{x+5y}{x-6y} \div \frac{x}{5y(x+5y)}$$

$$= \frac{x+5y}{x-6y} \cdot \frac{5y(x+5y)}{x}$$

$$= \frac{5y(x+5y)^2}{x(x-6y)}$$

40. $\left(\dfrac{1}{x+2y}-\dfrac{1}{x-y}\right)\div\dfrac{2x-4y}{x^2-3xy+2y^2}$

$$=\left(\dfrac{1}{x+2y}-\dfrac{1}{x-y}\right)\cdot\dfrac{x^2-3xy+2y^2}{2x-4y}$$

$$=\dfrac{x-y-(x+2y)}{(x+2y)(x-y)}\cdot\dfrac{(x-y)(x-2y)}{2(x-2y)}$$

$$=\dfrac{-3y}{2(x+2y)}$$

41. $\qquad\qquad\dfrac{8a-1}{6a+8}=\dfrac{3}{4}$

$$\dfrac{8a-1}{2(3a+4)}=\dfrac{3}{4}$$

$$4(3a+4)\left[\dfrac{8a-1}{2(3a+4)}\right]=4(3a+4)\left(\dfrac{3}{4}\right)$$

$$2(8a-1)=3(3a+4)$$

$$16a-2=9a+12$$

$$7a-2=12$$

42. $\qquad\qquad\dfrac{8}{a-3}=\dfrac{12}{a+3}$

$$(a-3)(a+3)\dfrac{8}{a-3}=(a-3)(a+3)\dfrac{12}{a+3}$$

$$8a+24=12a-36$$

$$60=4a$$

$$15=a$$

43. $\qquad\qquad\dfrac{2x-1}{x}-\dfrac{1}{2}=-2$

$$2x\left(\dfrac{2x-1}{x}\right)-2x\left(\dfrac{1}{2}\right)=-2(2x)$$

$$4x-2-x=-4x$$

$$7x=2$$

$$x=\dfrac{2}{7}$$

44. $\qquad\qquad\dfrac{5-x}{x}-\dfrac{7}{x}=-\dfrac{3}{4}$

$$4x\left(\dfrac{5-x}{x}\right)-4x\left(\dfrac{7}{x}\right)=4x\left(-\dfrac{3}{4}\right)$$

$$4(5-x)-28=3x$$

$$20-4x-28=-3x$$

$$-4x-8=-3x$$

$$-8=x$$

45. $\qquad\qquad\dfrac{5}{2}-\dfrac{2y+7}{y+6}=3$

$$2(y+6)\left(\dfrac{5}{2}\right)-2(y+6)\left(\dfrac{2y+7}{y+6}\right)=2(y+6)(3)$$

$$5y+30-4y-14=6y+36$$

$$-20=5y$$

$$-4=y$$

46. $\qquad\qquad\dfrac{5}{4}-\dfrac{1}{2x}=\dfrac{1}{x}+2$

$$4x\left(\dfrac{5}{4}\right)-4x\left(\dfrac{1}{2x}\right)=4x\left(\dfrac{1}{x}\right)+4x(2)$$

$$5x - 2 = 4 + 8x$$
$$-2 = 4 + 3x$$
$$-6 = 3x$$
$$-2 = x$$

$$15 = 5y$$
$$3 = y$$

Since $y = 3$ causes a denominator in the original equation to equal 0, there is no solution.

47.
$$\frac{7}{8x} - \frac{3}{4} = \frac{1}{4x} + \frac{1}{2}$$
$$8x\left(\frac{7}{8x}\right) - 8x\left(\frac{3}{4}\right) = 8x\left(\frac{1}{4x}\right) + 8x\left(\frac{1}{2}\right)$$
$$7 - 6x = 2 + 4x$$
$$7 = 2 + 10x$$
$$5 = 10x$$
$$\frac{1}{2} = x$$

48.
$$\frac{1}{3x} + 2 = \frac{5}{6x} - \frac{1}{2}$$
$$6x\left(\frac{1}{3x}\right) + 6x(2) = 6x\left(\frac{5}{6x}\right) - 6x\left(\frac{1}{2}\right)$$
$$2 + 12x = 5 - 3x$$
$$15x = 3$$
$$x = \frac{1}{5}$$

49.
$$\frac{3}{y-3} = \frac{3}{2} + \frac{y}{y-3}$$
$$2(y-3)\left(\frac{3}{y-3}\right)$$
$$= 2(y-3)\left(\frac{3}{2}\right) + 2(y-3)\left(\frac{y}{y-3}\right)$$
$$6 = 3(y-3) + 2y$$
$$6 = 3y - 9 + 2y$$
$$6 = 5y - 9$$

50.
$$\frac{x-8}{x-2} = \frac{2x}{x+2} - 2$$
$$(x+2)(x-2)\left(\frac{x-8}{x-2}\right)$$
$$= (x+2)(x-2)\left(\frac{2x}{x+2}\right) - (x+2)(x-2)(2)$$
$$x^2 - 6x - 16 = 2x^2 - 4x - 2x^2 + 8$$
$$x^2 - 2x - 24 = 0$$
$$(x-6)(x+4) = 0$$
$$x - 6 = 0 \qquad x + 4 = 0$$
$$x = 6 \qquad\quad x = -4$$

51.
$$\frac{9}{2} - \frac{7y-4}{y+2} = -\frac{1}{4}$$
$$4(y+2)\left(\frac{9}{2}\right) - 4(y+2)\left(\frac{7y-4}{y+2}\right)$$
$$= 4(y+2)\left(-\frac{1}{4}\right)$$
$$18(y+2) - 4(7y-4) = -(y+2)$$
$$18y + 36 - 28y + 16 = -y - 2$$
$$-10y + 52 = -y - 2$$
$$52 = 9y - 2$$
$$54 = 9y$$
$$6 = y$$

206

52. $\dfrac{3y-1}{3y} - \dfrac{6}{5y} = \dfrac{1}{y} - \dfrac{4}{15}$

$$15y\left(\dfrac{3y-1}{3y}\right) - 15y\left(\dfrac{6}{5y}\right)$$

$$= 15y\left(\dfrac{1}{y}\right) - 15y\left(\dfrac{4}{15}\right)$$

$$15y - 5 - 18 = 15 - 4y$$

$$19y = 38$$

$$y = 2$$

53. $\dfrac{y+18}{y^2 - 16} = \dfrac{y}{y+4} - \dfrac{y}{y-4}$

$$\dfrac{y+18}{(y+4)(y-4)} = \dfrac{y}{y+4} - \dfrac{y}{y-4}$$

$$y+18 = (y-4)(y) - (y+4)(y)$$

$$y+18 = y^2 - 4y - y^2 - 4y$$

$$y+18 = -8y$$

$$18 = -9y$$

$$-2 = y$$

54. $\dfrac{4}{x^2 - 1} = \dfrac{2}{x-1} + \dfrac{2}{x+1}$

$$4 = (x+1)(2) + (x-1)(2)$$

$$4 = 2x + 2 + 2x - 2$$

$$4 = 4x$$

$$1 = x$$

$x = 1$ is not an allowed solution.

There is no solution.

55. $\dfrac{9y-3}{y^2 + 2y} - \dfrac{5}{y+2} = \dfrac{3}{y}$

$$y(y+2)\left[\dfrac{9y-3}{y(y+2)}\right] - y(y+2)\left(\dfrac{5}{y+2}\right)$$

$$= y(y+2)\left(\dfrac{3}{y}\right)$$

$$9y - 3 - 5y = 3y + 6$$

$$y = 9$$

56. $\dfrac{2}{3-3y} + \dfrac{2}{2y-1} = \dfrac{4}{3y-3}$

$$\dfrac{2}{-3(y-1)} + \dfrac{2}{2y-1} - \dfrac{4}{3(y-1)}$$

$$\dfrac{-2}{3(y-1)} + \dfrac{2}{2y-1} = \dfrac{4}{3(y-1)}$$

$$(2y-1)(-2) + 3(y-1)(2) = (2y-1)(4)$$

$$-2(2y-1) + 6(y-1) = 4(2y-1)$$

$$-4y + 2 + 6y - 6 = 8y - 4$$

$$2y - 4 = 8y - 4$$

$$-4 = 6y - 4$$

$$0 = 6y$$

$$0 = y$$

57. $\dfrac{x}{4} = \dfrac{12}{17}$

$$17x = (4)(12)$$

$$17x = 48$$

$$\dfrac{17x}{17} = \dfrac{48}{17}$$

$$x = 2.8$$

58. $\dfrac{8}{5} = \dfrac{2}{x}$

$8x = 10$

$x = \dfrac{5}{4} = 1.25 = 1.3$

59. $\dfrac{33}{10} = \dfrac{x}{8}$

$264 = 10x$

$26.4 = x$

60. $\dfrac{5}{x} = \dfrac{22}{9}$

$22x = (5)(9)$

$22x = 45$

$\dfrac{22x}{22} = \dfrac{45}{22}$

$x = 2.0$

61. $\dfrac{13.5}{0.6} = \dfrac{360}{x}$

$13.5x = 216$

$x = 16$

62. $\dfrac{2\frac{1}{2}}{3\frac{1}{4}} = \dfrac{7}{x}$

$\dfrac{\frac{5}{2}}{\frac{13}{4}} = \dfrac{7}{x}$

$\dfrac{5}{2}x = \dfrac{91}{4}$

$x = 9.1$

63. x = gallons to cover 400 square feet

$\dfrac{x}{400} = \dfrac{5}{240}$

$240x = 2000$

$x = \dfrac{2000}{240} = 8\dfrac{1}{3}$

8.3 gallons of paint are needed.

64. $\dfrac{3}{100} = \dfrac{5}{x}$

$3x = 5(100)$

$3x = 500$

$\dfrac{3x}{3} = \dfrac{500}{3}$

$x = \dfrac{500}{3} = 166\dfrac{2}{3}$

167 cookies

65. x = gallons to get to Denver

$\dfrac{x}{1300} = \dfrac{7}{200}$

$200x = 9100$

$x = \dfrac{91}{2} = 45\dfrac{1}{2}$

He will use 46 gallons of gas.

66. $\dfrac{4}{122} = \dfrac{3}{x}$

$4x = (122)(3)$

$4x = 366$

$\dfrac{4x}{4} = \dfrac{366}{4}$

$x = 91.5$ miles

208

67.

	D	R	$T = \dfrac{D}{R}$
Train	180	$s + 20$	$\dfrac{180}{s + 20}$
Car	120	s	$\dfrac{120}{s}$

$$\frac{180}{s + 20} = \frac{120}{s}$$
$$180s = 120s + 2400$$
$$60s = 2400$$
$$s = 40$$
$$s + 20 = 60$$

Car's speed is 40 mph.

Trains speed is 60 mph.

68.

	Time for whole job	Part of job done in 1 hr
Professional	5	1 / 5
John	8	1 / 8
Together	x	1 / x

$$\frac{1}{5} + \frac{1}{8} = \frac{1}{x}$$
$$40x\left(\frac{1}{5}\right) + 40x\left(\frac{1}{8}\right) = 40x\left(\frac{1}{x}\right)$$
$$8x + 5x = 40$$
$$13x = 40$$
$$\frac{13x}{13} = \frac{40}{13}$$
$$x = 3\frac{1}{13}$$
$$\frac{1}{13} \times \frac{60}{1} = 5$$

3 hours, 5 minutes

69.
$$\frac{5.75}{3} = \frac{x}{95}$$
$$(5.75)(95) = 3x$$
$$546.25 = 3x$$
$$\frac{546.25}{3} = \frac{3x}{3}$$
$$182.1 = x$$

182 feet tall

70. x = height of building
$$\frac{x}{450} = \frac{8}{3}$$
$$3x = 3600$$
$$x = 1200$$

Office building is 1200 feet tall.

71. x = time to paint together
$$\frac{1}{5} + \frac{1}{10} = \frac{1}{x}$$
$$10x\left(\frac{1}{5}\right) + 10x\left(\frac{1}{10}\right) = 10x\left(\frac{1}{x}\right)$$
$$2x + x = 10$$
$$3x = 10$$
$$x = 3\frac{1}{3}$$

$3\frac{1}{3}$ hours or 3 hours, 20 minutes

72. x = time to plow together

$$\frac{1}{20} + \frac{1}{30} = \frac{1}{x}$$

$$60x\left(\frac{1}{20}\right) + 60x\left(\frac{1}{30}\right) = 60x\left(\frac{1}{x}\right)$$

$$3x + 2x = 60$$

$$5x = 60$$

$$x = 12 \text{ hours}$$

73. $\dfrac{a^2 + a - 12}{48a^2 - 16a^3} = \dfrac{(a+4)(a-3)}{16a^2(3-a)}$

$$= \frac{(a+4)(a-3)}{-16a^2(a-3)}$$

$$= -\frac{a+4}{16a^2}$$

74. $\dfrac{6b^3 - 24b^2}{b^2 + b - 20} = \dfrac{6b^2(b-4)}{(b+5)(b-4)}$

$$= \frac{6b^2}{b+5}$$

75. $\dfrac{x^2 - y^2}{x^2 + 4xy + 3y^2} \cdot \dfrac{x^2 + xy - 6y^2}{x^2 + xy - 2y^2}$

$$= \frac{(x+y)(x-y)}{(x+y)(x+3y)} \cdot \frac{(x+3y)(x-2y)}{(x+2y)(x-y)}$$

$$= \frac{x-2y}{x+2y}$$

76. $\dfrac{x^2 - 6xy - 16y^2}{x^2 + 4xy - 21y^2} \cdot \dfrac{x^2 - 8xy + 15y^2}{x^2 = 3xy - 10y^2}$

$$= \frac{(x-8y)(x+2y)}{(x+7y)(x-3y)} \cdot \frac{(x-3y)(x-5y)}{(x-5y)(x+2y)}$$

$$= \frac{x-8y}{x+7y}$$

77. $\dfrac{x}{x+3} + \dfrac{9x+18}{x^2 + 3x} = \dfrac{x}{x+3} \cdot \dfrac{x}{x} + \dfrac{9x+18}{x(x+3)}$

$$= \frac{x^2 + 9x + 18}{x(x+3)}$$

$$= \frac{(x+6)(x+3)}{x(x+3)}$$

$$= \frac{x+6}{x}$$

78. $\dfrac{x-30}{x^2 - 5x} + \dfrac{x}{x-5} = \dfrac{x-30}{x(x-5)} + \dfrac{x}{x-5} \cdot \dfrac{x}{x}$

$$= \frac{x-30 + x^2}{x(x-5)}$$

$$= \frac{x^2 + x - 30}{x(x-5)}$$

$$= \frac{(x+6)(x-5)}{x(x-5)}$$

$$= \frac{x+6}{x}$$

79. $\dfrac{a+b}{ax+ay} - \dfrac{a+b}{bx+by}$

$= \dfrac{a+b}{a(x+y)} \cdot \dfrac{b}{b} - \dfrac{a+b}{b(x+y)} \cdot \dfrac{a}{a}$

$= \dfrac{b(a+b) - a(a+b)}{ab(x+y)}$

$= \dfrac{ab+b^2-a^2-ab}{ab(x+y)}$

$= \dfrac{b^2-a^2}{ab(x+y)}$

80. $\dfrac{\frac{5}{3x}+\frac{2}{9x}}{\frac{3}{x}+\frac{8}{3x}} = \dfrac{\frac{5}{3x}+\frac{2}{9x}}{\frac{3}{x}+\frac{8}{3x}} \cdot \dfrac{9x}{9x}$

$= \dfrac{\frac{5(9x)}{3x}+\frac{2(9x)}{9x}}{\frac{3(9x)}{x}+\frac{8(9x)}{3x}}$

$= \dfrac{15+2}{27+24}$

$= \dfrac{17}{51}$

$= \dfrac{1}{3}$

81. $\dfrac{\frac{4}{5y}-\frac{8}{xy}}{y+\frac{y}{5}} = \dfrac{\frac{4}{5y}-\frac{8}{y}}{y+\frac{y}{5}} \cdot \dfrac{5y}{5y}$

$= \dfrac{\frac{4(5y)}{5y}-\frac{8(5y)}{y}}{y(5y)+\frac{y(5y)}{5}}$

$= \dfrac{4-40}{5y^2+y^2}$

$= \dfrac{-36}{6y^2}$

$= -\dfrac{6}{y^2}$

82. $\dfrac{x-3y}{x+2y} \div \dfrac{2}{y} - \dfrac{12}{x+3y}$

$= \dfrac{\frac{x-3y}{x+2y}}{\frac{2}{y}-\frac{12}{x+3y}}$

$= \dfrac{\frac{x-3y}{x+2y}}{\frac{2}{y}-\frac{12}{x+3y}} \cdot \dfrac{y(x+2y)(x+3y)}{y(x+2y)(x+3y)}$

$= \dfrac{y(x-3y)(x+3y)}{2(x+2y)(x+3y)-12y(x+2y)}$

$= \dfrac{y(x-3y)(x+3y)}{2(x+2y)[x+3y-6y]}$

$= \dfrac{y(-3y)(x+3y)}{2(x+2y)(x-3y)}$

$= \dfrac{y(x+3y)}{2(x+2y)}$

83. $\dfrac{10}{x-3} = \dfrac{9}{x-5}$

$10(x-5) = 9(x-3)$

$10x - 50 = 9x - 27$

$x = 23$

84. $\dfrac{7x-4}{6x-5} = \dfrac{8}{7}$

$7(7x-4) = 8(6x-5)$

$49x - 28 = 48x - 40$

$x - 28 = -40$

$x = -12$

85. $2 + \dfrac{4}{b-1} = \dfrac{4}{b^2 - b}$

$2b(b-1) + b(b-1)\left(\dfrac{4}{b-1}\right) = b(b-1)\left(\dfrac{4}{b(b-1)}\right)$

$2b^2 - 2b + 4b = 4$

$2b^2 + 2b = 4$

$2b^2 + 2b - 4 = 0$

$2(b^2 + b - 2) = 0$

$b^2 + b - 2 = 0$

$b + 2 = 0 \qquad b - 1 = 0$

$b = -2 \qquad\quad b = 1$

Check: $2 + \dfrac{4}{1-1} \overset{?}{=} \dfrac{4}{1^2 - 1}$

$2 + \dfrac{4}{0} \overset{?}{=} \dfrac{4}{0}$

$b = 1$ does not check

Solution: $b = -2$

86. x = weight of 40 m of wire

$\dfrac{x}{40} = \dfrac{8}{30}$

$30x = 8(40)$

$30x = 320$

$x = 10.7$

It weighs 10.7 kg

87. x = distance driven in 7 hours

$\dfrac{x}{7} = \dfrac{270}{4.5}$

$4.5x = 7(270)$

$4.5x = 1890$

$x = 420$

She drove 420 miles

How Am I Doing? Chapter 6 Test

1. $\dfrac{2ac + 2ad}{3a^2 c + 3a^2 d} = \dfrac{2a(c+d)}{3a^2(c+d)} = \dfrac{2}{3a}$

2. $\dfrac{8x^2 - 2x^2 y^2}{y^2 + 4y + 4}$

$= \dfrac{2x^2(2-y)(2+y)}{(y+2)^2}$

$= \dfrac{2x^2(2-y)}{y+2}$

3. $\dfrac{x^2 + 2x}{2x - 1} \cdot \dfrac{10x^2 - 5x}{12x^3 + 24x^2}$

$= \dfrac{x(x+2)}{2x-1} \cdot \dfrac{5x(2x-1)}{12x^2(x+2)}$

$= \dfrac{5}{12}$

4. $\dfrac{x+2y}{12y^2} \cdot \dfrac{4y}{x^2 + xy - 2y^2}$

$= \dfrac{x+2y}{12y^2} \cdot \dfrac{4y}{(x+2y)(x-y)}$

$= \dfrac{1}{3y(x-y)}$

5. $\dfrac{2a^2 - 3a - 2}{a^2 + 5a + 6} \div \dfrac{a^2 - 5a + 6}{a^2 - 9}$

$= \dfrac{2a^2 - 3a - 2}{a^2 + 5a + 6} \cdot \dfrac{a^2 - 9}{a^2 - 5a + 6}$

$= \dfrac{(2a+1)(a-2)}{(a+2)(a+3)} \cdot \dfrac{(a+3)(a-3)}{(a-2)(a-3)}$

$= \dfrac{2a+1}{a+2}$

6. $\dfrac{1}{a^2-a-2}+\dfrac{3}{a-2}$

$=\dfrac{1}{(a-2)(a+1)}+\dfrac{3}{a-2}\cdot\dfrac{a+1}{a+1}$

$=\dfrac{1+3(a+1)}{(a-2)(a+1)}$

$=\dfrac{1+3a+3}{(a-2)(a+1)}$

$=\dfrac{3a+4}{(a-2)(a+1)}$

7. $\dfrac{x-y}{xy}-\dfrac{a-y}{ay}=\dfrac{x-y}{xy}\cdot\dfrac{a}{a}-\dfrac{a-y}{ay}\cdot\dfrac{x}{x}$

$=\dfrac{ax-ay-ax+xy}{axy}$

$=\dfrac{xy-ay}{axy}$

$=\dfrac{y(x-a)}{axy}$

$=\dfrac{x-a}{ax}$

8. $\dfrac{3x}{x^2-3x-18}-\dfrac{x-4}{x-6}$

$=\dfrac{3x}{(x-6)(x+3)}-\dfrac{x-4}{x-6}$

$=\dfrac{3x}{(x-6)(x+3)}-\dfrac{x-4}{x-6}\cdot\dfrac{x+3}{x+3}$

$=\dfrac{3x}{(x-6)(x+3)}-\dfrac{x^2-x-12}{(x-6)(x+3)}$

$=\dfrac{3x-(x^2-x-12)}{(x-6)(x+3)}$

$=\dfrac{3x-x^2+x+12}{(x-6)(x+3)}$

$=\dfrac{-x^2+4x+12}{(x-6)(x+3)}$

$=\dfrac{-(x-6)(x+2)}{(x-6)(x+3)}$

$=-\dfrac{x+2}{x+3}$

9. $\dfrac{\frac{x}{3y}-\frac{1}{2}}{\frac{4}{3y}-\frac{2}{x}}=\dfrac{\frac{x}{3y}-\frac{1}{2}}{\frac{4}{3y}-\frac{2}{x}}\cdot\dfrac{6xy}{6xy}$

$=\dfrac{2x^2-3xy}{8x-12y}$

$=\dfrac{x(2x-3y)}{4(2x-3y)}$

$=\dfrac{x}{4}$

10. $\dfrac{\frac{6}{b}-4}{\frac{5}{bx}-\frac{10}{3x}}=\dfrac{\frac{6}{b}-4}{\frac{5}{bx}-\frac{10}{3x}}\cdot\dfrac{3bx}{3bx}$

$=\dfrac{\frac{6(3bx)}{b}-4(3bx)}{\frac{5(3bx)}{bx}-\frac{10(3bx)}{3x}}$

$=\dfrac{18x-12bx}{15-10b}$

$=\dfrac{6x(3-2b)}{5(3-2b)}$

$=\dfrac{6x}{5}$

11. $\dfrac{2x^2 + 3xy - 9y^2}{4x^2 + 13xy + 3y^2}$

$= \dfrac{(2x - 3y)(x + 3y)}{(4x + y)(x + 3y)}$

$= \dfrac{2x - 3y}{4x + y}$

12. $\dfrac{1}{x + 4} - \dfrac{2}{x^2 + 6x + 8}$

$= \dfrac{1}{x + 4} - \dfrac{2}{(x + 4)(x + 2)}$

$= \dfrac{1}{x + 4} \cdot \dfrac{x + 2}{x + 2} - \dfrac{2}{(x + 4)(x + 2)}$

$= \dfrac{x + 2}{(x + 4)(x + 2)} - \dfrac{2}{(x + 4)(x + 2)}$

$= \dfrac{x + 2 - 2}{(x + 4)(x + 2)}$

$= \dfrac{x}{(x + 4)(x + 2)}$

13. $\dfrac{4}{3x} - \dfrac{5}{2x} = 5 - \dfrac{1}{6x}$

$6x\left(\dfrac{4}{3x}\right) - 6x\left(\dfrac{5}{2x}\right) = 6x(5) - 6x\left(\dfrac{1}{6x}\right)$

$8 - 15 = 30x - 1$

$-7 = 30x - 1$

$-6 = 30x$

$\dfrac{-6}{30} = x$

$-\dfrac{1}{5} = x$

14. $\dfrac{x - 3}{x - 2} = \dfrac{2x^2 - 15}{x^2 + x - 6} - \dfrac{x + 1}{x + 3}$

$\dfrac{x - 3}{x - 2} = \dfrac{2x^2 - 15}{(x + 3)} - \dfrac{x + 1}{x + 3}$

$(x - 2)(x + 3)\left(\dfrac{x - 3}{x - 2}\right)$

$= (x - 2)(x + 3)\left[\dfrac{2x^2 - 15}{(x + 3)(x - 2)}\right]$

$\quad - (x - 2)(x + 3)\left(\dfrac{x + 1}{x + 3}\right)$

$(x + 3)(x - 3) = 2x^2 - 15 - (x - 2)(x + 1)$

$x^2 - 9 = 2x^2 - 15 - (x^2 - x - 2)$

$x^2 - 9 = 2x^2 - 15 - x^2 + x + 2$

$x^2 - 9 = x^2 + x - 13$

$-9 = x - 13$

$4 = x$

Check: $\dfrac{4 - 3}{4 - 2} \stackrel{?}{=} \dfrac{2(4)^2 - 15}{4^2 + 4 - 6} - \dfrac{4 + 1}{4 + 3}$

$\dfrac{1}{2} \stackrel{?}{=} \dfrac{17}{14} - \dfrac{5}{7}$

$\dfrac{7}{14} \stackrel{?}{=} \dfrac{17}{14} - \dfrac{10}{14}$

$\dfrac{7}{14} = \dfrac{7}{14}$

15. $3 - \dfrac{7}{x + 3} = \dfrac{x - 4}{x + 3}$

$(x + 3)(3) - (x + 3)\left(\dfrac{7}{x + 3}\right) = (x + 3)\left(\dfrac{x - 4}{x + 3}\right)$

$3x + 9 - 7 = x - 4$

$2x = -6$

$x = -3$

$x = -3$ is not allowed.

There is no solution.

16. $\dfrac{3}{3x-5} = \dfrac{7}{5x+4}$

$3(5x+4) = 7(3x-5)$

$15x + 12 = 21x - 35$

$12 = 6x - 35$

$47 = 6x$

$\dfrac{47}{6} = x$

Check:

$$\dfrac{3}{3\left(\frac{47}{6}\right) - 5} \overset{?}{=} \dfrac{7}{5\left(\frac{47}{6}\right) + 4}$$

$$\dfrac{3}{\frac{111}{6}} \overset{?}{=} \dfrac{7}{\frac{259}{6}}$$

$$\dfrac{18}{111} \overset{?}{=} \dfrac{42}{259}$$

$$\dfrac{6}{37} = \dfrac{6}{37}$$

17. $\dfrac{9}{x} = \dfrac{13}{5}$

$45 = 13x$

$\dfrac{45}{13} = x$

18. $\dfrac{9.3}{2.5} = \dfrac{x}{10}$

$\dfrac{10(9.3)}{2.5} = x$

$37.2 = x$

19. $x =$ on time flights

$\dfrac{x}{200} = \dfrac{113}{150}$

$150x = 113(200)$

$150x = 22,600$

$x = 151$ flights

20. $x =$ Cost of wood for 92 days

$\dfrac{x}{92} = \dfrac{100}{25}$

$25x = 9200$

$x = 368$

It will cost $368.

21. $\dfrac{\text{height}}{\text{shadow}}: \dfrac{6}{7} = \dfrac{87}{x}$

$6x = 609$

$x = 101.5$

102 feet

Cumulative Test for Chapters 0 - 6

1. 0.25% of $2.57 = (0.0025)(2.57)$

$= 0.006$ centimeters

2. Percent $= \dfrac{252}{720} = 0.35 = 35\%$

3. Difference $= 6\% - 5.5\% = 0.5\%$

Savings $= 0.005(18,500) = \$92.50$

4. $5(x-3)-2(4-2x)=7(x-1)-(x-2)$

$$5x-15-8+4x=7x-7-x+2$$
$$9x-23=6x-5$$
$$3x-23=-5$$
$$3x=18$$
$$x=6$$

5. $A=\pi r^2 h$

$$\frac{A}{\pi r^2}=\frac{\pi r^2 h}{\pi r^2}$$
$$\frac{A}{\pi r^2}=h$$

6. $4(2-x)<3$

$$8-4x<3$$
$$-4x<-5$$
$$x>\frac{5}{4}$$

7. $\dfrac{3}{5}x-2\le\dfrac{1}{2}x+\dfrac{3}{5}$

$$10\left(\frac{3}{5}x\right)-10(2)\le 10\left(\frac{1}{2}x\right)+10\left(\frac{3}{5}\right)$$
$$6x-20\le 5x+6$$
$$x-20\le 6$$
$$x\le 26$$

8. $3ax+3bx-2ay-2by$

$$=3x(a+b)-2y(a+b)$$
$$=(a+b)(3x-2y)$$

9. $8a^3-38a^2b-10ab^2$

$$=2a(4a^2-19ab-5b^2)$$
$$=2a(4a+b)(a-5b)$$

10. $\dfrac{-12x^{-2}y^4}{3x^{-5}y^{-8}}=-4x^3y^{12}$

11. $\dfrac{4x^2-25}{2x^2+9x-35}=\dfrac{(2x+5)(2x-5)}{(2x-5)(x+7)}$

$$=\frac{2x+5}{x+7}$$

12. $\dfrac{x^2-4}{x^2-25}\cdot\dfrac{3x^2-14x-5}{3x^2+6x}$

$$=\frac{(x+2)(x-2)}{(x+5)(x-5)}\cdot\frac{(3x+1)(x-5)}{3x(x+2)}$$
$$=\frac{(x-2)(3x+1)}{3x(x+5)}$$

13. $\dfrac{2x^2-9x+9}{8x-12}\div\dfrac{x^2-3x}{2x}$

$$=\frac{2x^2-9x+9}{8x-12}\cdot\frac{2x}{x^2-3x}$$
$$=\frac{(2x-3)(x-3)}{4(2x-3)}\cdot\frac{2x}{x(x-3)}$$
$$=\frac{1}{2}$$

216

14. $\dfrac{5}{2x+4}+\dfrac{3}{x-3}$

$=\dfrac{5}{2(x+2)}\cdot\dfrac{x-3}{x-3}+\dfrac{3}{x-3}\cdot\dfrac{2(x+2)}{2(x+2)}$

$=\dfrac{5x-15+6x+12}{2(x+2)(x-3)}$

$=\dfrac{11x-3}{2(x+2)(x-3)}$

15. $\dfrac{8}{c^2-4}-\dfrac{2}{c^2-5c+6}$

$=\dfrac{8}{(c+2)(c-2)}\cdot\dfrac{c-3}{c-3}-\dfrac{2}{(c-2)(c-3)}\cdot\dfrac{c+2}{c+2}$

$=\dfrac{8(c-3)}{(c+2)(c-2)(c-3)}-\dfrac{2(c+2)}{(c-2)(c-3)(c+2)}$

$=\dfrac{8c-24-(2c+4)}{(c+2)(c-2)(c-3)}$

$=\dfrac{6c-28}{(c+2)(c-2)(c-3)}$

16. $\dfrac{3x-2}{3x+2}=2$

$(3x+2)\left(\dfrac{3x-2}{3x+2}\right)=(3x+2)(2)$

$3x-2=6x+4$

$-6=3x$

$-2=x$

17. $\dfrac{x-3}{x}=\dfrac{x+2}{x+3}$

$x(x+2)=(x-3)(x+3)$

$x^2+2x=x^2-9$

$2x=-9$

$x=-\dfrac{9}{2}$

18. $\dfrac{\frac{1}{x-3}+\frac{5}{x^2-9}}{\frac{6x}{x+3}}=\dfrac{\frac{1}{x-3}+\frac{5}{(x+3)(x-3)}}{\frac{6x}{x+3}}\cdot\dfrac{(x+3)(x-3)}{(x+3)(x-3)}$

$=\dfrac{x+3+5}{6x(x-3)}$

$=\dfrac{x+8}{6x(x-3)}$

19. $\dfrac{\frac{3}{a}+\frac{2}{b}}{\frac{5}{a^2}-\frac{2}{b^2}}=\dfrac{\frac{3}{a}+\frac{2}{b}}{\frac{5}{a^2}-\frac{2}{b^2}}\cdot\dfrac{a^2b^2}{a^2b^2}$

$=\dfrac{3ab^2+2a^2b}{5b^2-2a^2}$

20. $\dfrac{2x+1}{3}=\dfrac{4}{5}$

$5(2x+1)=3(4)$

$10x+5=12$

$10x=7$

$x=\dfrac{7}{10}$

21. $\dfrac{\text{mi}}{\text{in.}}:\dfrac{130}{2\frac{1}{2}}=\dfrac{x}{4}$

$\left(2\dfrac{1}{2}\right)x=520$

$\dfrac{5}{2}x=520$

$x=208$

22. $x=$ phone calls to make 110 sales

$\dfrac{x}{110}=\dfrac{22}{5}$

$5x=2420$

$x=484$

He must make 484 calls.

Chapter 7

7.1 Exercises

1. The x – coordinate of the origin is 0.

3. $(5, 1)$ is an ordered pair because the order is important. The graphs of $(5, 1)$ and $(1, 5)$ are different.

5.

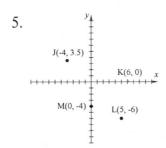

7. R: $(-3, -5)$

S: $\left(-4\frac{1}{2}, 0\right)$

X: $(3, -5)$

Y: $\left(2\frac{1}{2}, 6\right)$

9. $(-4, -1), (-3, -2), (-2, -3)$
$(-1, -5), (0, -3), (2, -1)$

11. $y = 4x + 7$

(a) $(0,)$, $y = 4(0) + 7 = 7$
$(0, 7)$

(b) $(2,)$, $y = 4(2) + 7 = 15$
$(2, 15)$

13. $y = -4x + 2$

(a) $(-5,)$, $y = -4(-5) + 2 = 22$
$(5, 22)$

(b) $(4,)$, $y = -4(4) + 2 = -14$
$(4, -14)$

15. $3x - 4y = 11$

(a) $3(-3) - 4y = 11$
$-9 - 4y = 11$
$-4y = 20$
$y = -5$
$(-3, -5)$

(b) $3x - 4(1) = 11$
$3x - 4 = 11$
$3x = 15$
$x = 5$
$(5, 1)$

17. $2y + 3x = -6$

   (a) $2y + 3(-2) = -6$

          $2y - 6 = -6$

             $2y = 0$

               $y = 0$

      $(-2, 0)$

   (b) $2(3) + 3x = -6$

          $6 + 3x = -6$

            $3x = -12$

              $x = -4$

      $(-4, 3)$

19. $2x + \dfrac{1}{5}y = 6$

   (a) $2x + \dfrac{1}{5}(20) = 6$

          $2x + 4 = 6$

            $2x = 2$

              $x = 1$

      $(1, 20)$

19. (b) $2\left(\dfrac{9}{5}\right) + \dfrac{1}{5}y = 6$

         $\dfrac{18}{5} + \dfrac{1}{5}y = 6$

           $18 + y = 30$

              $y = 12$

      $\left(\dfrac{9}{5}, 12\right)$

21. B5

23. E1

25. D3

27. (a)

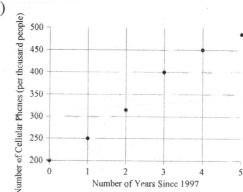

   (b)   The number of cellular users has increased significantly in the 5 year period. The rate of increase is smaller as time goes on.

29. (a)

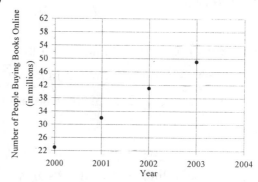

   (b)   An estimated 57 to 58 million people would buy books online in 2004.

Cumulative Review

31. $\dfrac{8x}{x+y} + \dfrac{8y}{x+y} = \dfrac{8x+8y}{x+y} = \dfrac{8(x+y)}{x+y} = 8$

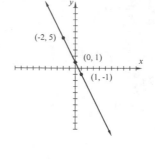

33. $A = \pi r^2$, $r = 19$

    $A = 3.14(19)^2$

      $= 1133.54$ square yards

35. Decrease $= 6,109,005 - 358,205$

           $= 5,750,800$

   % Decrease $= \dfrac{5,750,800}{6,109,005} \times 100\%$

            $= 94.1\%$

  There was a 94.1% decrease in readership.

7. $y = x - 4$

   $(0, -4), (2, -2), (4, 0)$

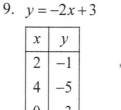

9. $y = -2x + 3$

x	y
2	-1
4	-5
0	3

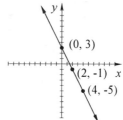

7.2 Exercises

1. Replacing x by -2 and y by 5 in $2x + 5y = 0$ does not result in a true statement so $(-2, 5)$ is not a solution.

11. $y = 3x + 2$

x	y
-1	-1
0	2
1	5

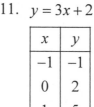

3. The x – intercept of a line is the point where the line crosses the _x - axis_.

5. $y = -2x + 1$

   $(0, 1), (-2, 5), (1, -1)$

13. $3x - 2y = 0$

x	y
-2	-3
0	0
2	3

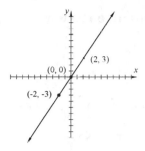

21. $x + 3 = 6y$

x	y
-3	0
0	$\dfrac{1}{2}$
3	1

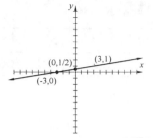

15. $y = -\dfrac{3}{4}x + 3$

x	y
-4	6
0	3
4	0

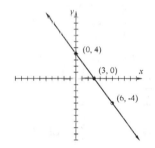

23. $y - 2 = 3y$

$$-2 = 2y$$
$$-1 = y$$

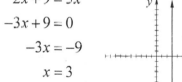

17. $4x + 3y = 12$

x	y
0	4
3	0
6	-4

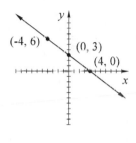

25. $2x + 9 = 5x$

$$-3x + 9 = 0$$
$$-3x = -9$$
$$x = 3$$

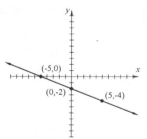

19. $y = 6 - 2x$

x	y
0	6
1	4
3	0

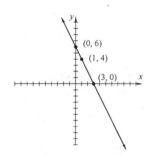

27. $2x + 5y - 2 = -12$

$$2x + 5y = -10$$

x	y
-5	0
0	-2
5	-4

29. $C = 8m$

m	0	15	30	45	60	75
C	0	120	240	360	480	600

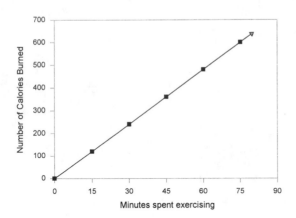

31. $S = 12t + 280$

t	s
0	280
6	352
15	460
21	532

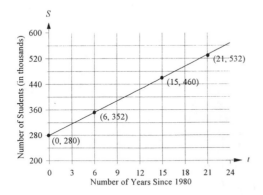

Cumulative Review

33. $$\frac{x}{x+4} + \frac{x-1}{x-4} = 2$$
$$(x-4)(x) + (x+4)(x-1) = 2(x+4)(x-4)$$
$$x^2 - 4x + x^2 + 3x - 4 = 2x^2 - 32$$
$$-x = -28$$
$$x = 28$$

35. $x = \text{length}$
$$\frac{x}{2} + 1 = \text{width}$$
$$p = 2L + 2w$$
$$53 = 2x + 2\left(\frac{x}{2} + 1\right)$$
$$53 = 2x + x + 2$$
$$51 = 3x$$
$$17 = x$$
$$\frac{17}{2} + 1 = 9\frac{1}{2}$$

$\text{width} = 9\dfrac{1}{2}$ meters

Length = 17 meters

37. $x = \text{cost of mailing from Japan}$
$$\frac{1}{2}x - 2 = \text{cost of mailing from U.S.}$$
$$x + \frac{1}{2}x - 2 = 184$$
$$2x + x - 4 = 368$$
$$3x - 4 = 368$$
$$3x = 372$$
$$x = 124$$

The cost is $1.24

39. x = length of one base

     $2x - 3$ = length of other base

$$A = \frac{1}{2}(B + b)h$$

$$63 = \frac{1}{2}(2x - 2 + x)(14)$$

$$126 = (3x - 3)(14)$$

$$126 = 42x - 42$$

$$168 = 42x$$

$$4 = x$$

$$2x - 3 = 2(4) - 3 = 5$$

7.3 Exercises

Use $m = \dfrac{y_2 - y_1}{x_2 - x_1}$ in Exercises 1-11.

1.   You cannot find the slope of the line passing through $(5, -12)$ and $(5, -6)$ because division by zero is impossible.

3. $(4, 1)$ and $(6, 7)$

$$m = \frac{7 - 1}{6 - 4} = \frac{6}{2} = 3$$

5. $(6, 6)$ and $(9, 3)$

$$m = \frac{3 - 6}{9 - 6} = \frac{-3}{3} = -1$$

7. $(-2, 1)$ and $(3, 4)$

$$m = \frac{4 - 1}{3 - (-2)} = \frac{3}{5}$$

9. $(-6, -5)$ and $(2, -7)$

$$m = \frac{-7 - (-5)}{2 - (-6)} = \frac{-2}{8} = -\frac{1}{4}$$

11. $(-3, 0)$ and $(0, -4)$

$$m = \frac{-4 - 0}{0 - (-3)} = \frac{-4}{3} = -\frac{4}{3}$$

Use $y = mx + b$ in Exercises 13-41.

13. $\left(\dfrac{3}{4}, -4\right)$ and $(2, -8)$

$$m = \frac{8 - (-4)}{2 - \frac{3}{4}} = \frac{-4}{\frac{5}{4}} = -\frac{16}{5}$$

15. $y = 8x + 9; \quad m = 8, \quad b = 9$

17. $y = -3x + 4, \quad m = -3, \quad b = 4$

19. $y = -\dfrac{8}{7}x + \dfrac{3}{4}; \quad m = -\dfrac{8}{7}, \quad b = -\dfrac{3}{4}$

21. $y = -6x; \quad m = -6, \quad b = 0$

23. $6x + y = \dfrac{4}{5}$

$$y = -6x + \frac{4}{5}; \quad m = -6, \quad b = \frac{4}{5}$$

25. $5x + 2y = 3$

$$y = -\frac{5}{2}x + \frac{3}{2}; \quad m = -\frac{5}{2}, \quad b = \frac{3}{2}$$

27. $7x - 3y = 4$

$$y = \frac{7}{3}x - \frac{4}{3}; \quad m = \frac{7}{3}, \quad b = -\frac{4}{3}$$

29. $m = \frac{3}{5}, \quad y\text{-intercept } (0, 3)$

$$y = \frac{3}{5}x + 3$$

31. $m = 6, \quad y\text{-intercept } (0, -3)$

$$y = 6x - 3$$

33. $m = -\frac{5}{4}, \quad y\text{-intercept } \left(0, -\frac{3}{4}\right)$

$$y = -\frac{5}{4}x - \frac{3}{4}$$

35. $m = \frac{3}{4}, \quad b = -4$

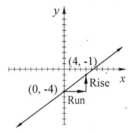

37. $m = -\frac{5}{3}, \quad b = 2$

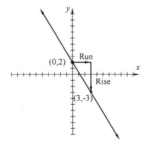

39. $y = \frac{2}{3}x + 2$

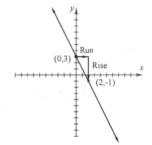

41. $y + 2x = 3$

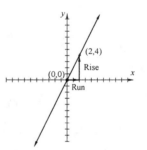

43. $y = 2x$

45. $\qquad m = \frac{5}{6}$

    (a) $m_{11} = m = \frac{5}{6}$

    (b) $m_\perp = -\frac{1}{m} = -\frac{6}{5}$

47. $\qquad m_1 = 6$

    (a) $m_2 = m_2 = 6$

    (b) $m_2 = -\frac{1}{m_1} = -\frac{1}{6}$

49. $y = \dfrac{1}{3}x + 2$

$m = \dfrac{1}{3}$

(a) $m_{11} = m = \dfrac{1}{3}$

(b) $m_\perp = -\dfrac{1}{m} = -3$

51.

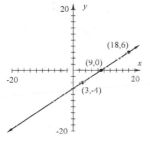

Yes

$m = \dfrac{0 - (-4)}{9 - 3} = \dfrac{4}{6} = \dfrac{2}{3}$

From the graph, $b = -6$

$y = \dfrac{2}{3}x - 6$

53. $y = 14(4x + 35)$

(a) $y = 562x + 490$

(b) $m = 56, \ b = 490$

(c) The slope is the increase in the
United States Federal Budget in
billions of dollars per year.

Cumulative Review

55. $3x + 8 > 2x + 12$

$3x - 2x + 8 > 2x - 2x + 12$

$x + 8 > 12$

$x > 4$

57. $\dfrac{1}{2}(x + 2) \le \dfrac{1}{3}x + 5$

$3(x + 2) \le 2x + 30$

$3x + 6 \le 2x + 30$

$x \le 24$

59. Decrease in range $= 0.62 \times$ cruising range
$= 0.62(390) = 241.8$

$390 - 241.8 = 148.2$

Range at maximum speed $= 148$ miles

61. 1990-1999: $\dfrac{240 - 206}{206} = 0.165 = 16.5\%$

1999-2008: $\dfrac{288 - 240}{240} = 0.20 = 20\%$

Difference $= 20.0\% - 16.5\% = 3.5\%$

How Am I Doing? Sections 7.1-7.3

1.

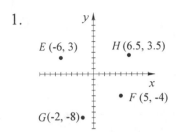

$E\,(-6, 3)$ $H\,(6.5, 3.5)$

$F\,(5, -4)$

$G(-2, -8)$

2. $A\,(3, 9)$

$B\,(7, -7)$

$C\,(-7, -8)$

$D\,(-4, 3)$

3. $y = -7x + 3$

$y = -7(4) + 3 = -25,\ (4, -25)$

$y = -7(0) + 3 = 3,\ (0, 3)$

$y = -7(-2) + 3 = 17,\ (-2, 17)$

4. $6x - 5y = -30$

x	y
0	6
-5	0
-10	-6

$0 - 5y = -30 \Rightarrow y = 6$

$6x - 5(0) - 30 \Rightarrow x = -5$

$6x - 5(-6) = -30 \Rightarrow x = -10$

5. $y = -4x - 3$

x	y
-2	5
-1	1
0	-3

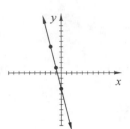

6. $y = \dfrac{3}{4}x - 1$

x	y
-4	-4
0	-1
4	2

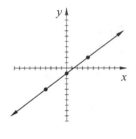

7. $y = \dfrac{3}{5}x$

x	y
-5	-3
0	0
5	3

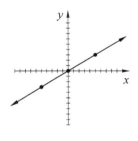

8. $-5x + 2 = y + 3$

$-5x - 1 = y$

x	y
-1	4
0	-1
1	-6

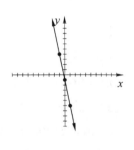

9. $(-6, -8)$ and $(2, -3)$

$$y = \frac{-3 - (-8)}{2 - (-6)} = \frac{5}{8}$$

10. $9x - 3y - 5 = 0$

$$-3y - 5 = -9x$$
$$-3y = -9x + 5$$
$$y = 3x - \frac{5}{3}$$

$m = 3$, y-intercept $\left(0, -\frac{5}{3}\right)$

11. $m = \frac{3}{4}$

$$m_\perp = -\frac{1}{m} = -\frac{4}{3}$$

12. $3y + 11x + 7 = 0$

$$3y = -11x - 7$$
$$y = -\frac{11}{3}x - \frac{7}{3}$$

$$m = -\frac{11}{3}$$
$$m_{11} = -\frac{11}{3}$$

7.4 Exercises

Use $m = \dfrac{y_2 - y_1}{x_2 - x_1}$ and $y = mx + b$

as needed in Exercises 1-31.

1. $m = 4$, $(-3, 0)$

$$0 = 4(-3) + b \Rightarrow b = 12$$
$$y = 4x + 12$$

3. $m = -3$, $(2, 5)$

$$5 = -3(2) + b \Rightarrow b = 11$$
$$y = -3x + 11$$

5. $m = -3$, $\left(\frac{1}{2}, 2\right)$

$$2 = -3\left(\frac{1}{2}\right) + b \Rightarrow b = \frac{7}{2}$$
$$y = -3x + \frac{7}{2}$$

7. $m = -\frac{2}{5}$, $(5, -3)$

$$-3 = -\frac{2}{5}(5) + b \Rightarrow b = -1$$
$$y = -\frac{2}{5}x - 1$$

9. $(3, -12)$ and $(-4, 2)$

$$m = \frac{2 - (-12)}{-4 - 3} = \frac{14}{-7} = -2$$
$$2 = -2(-4) + b \Rightarrow b = -6$$
$$y = -2x - 6$$

11. $(2, -6)$ and $(-1, 6)$

$$m = \frac{6 - (-6)}{-1 - 2} = \frac{12}{-3} = -4$$
$$-6 = -4(-1) + b \Rightarrow b = 2$$
$$y = -4x + 2$$

227

13. $(3, 5)$ and $(-1, -15)$

$$m = \frac{-15 - 5}{-1 - 3} = \frac{-20}{-4} = 5$$

$$5 = 5(3) + b \Rightarrow b = -10$$

$$y = 5x - 10$$

15. $\left(1, \frac{5}{6}\right)$ and $\left(3, \frac{3}{2}\right)$

$$m = \frac{\frac{3}{2} - \frac{5}{6}}{3 - 1} = \frac{\frac{4}{6}}{2} = \frac{1}{3}$$

$$\frac{5}{6} = \frac{1}{3}(1) + b \Rightarrow b = \frac{1}{2}$$

$$y = \frac{1}{3}x + \frac{1}{2}$$

17. $m = -2$, $(4, 3)$

$$3 = -2(4) + b \Rightarrow b = 11$$

$$y = -2x + 11$$

19. $(2, -3)$ and $(-1, 6)$

$$m = \frac{6 - (-3)}{-1 - 2} = \frac{9}{-3} = -3$$

$$-3 = -3(2) + b \Rightarrow b = 3$$

$$y = -3x + 3$$

21. $b = 1$, $m = -\frac{2}{3}$

$$y = -\frac{2}{3}x + 1$$

23. $b = -4$, $m = \frac{2}{3}$

$$y = \frac{2}{3}x - 4$$

25. $b = 0$, $m = -\frac{2}{3}$

$$y = -\frac{2}{3}x$$

27. $b = -2$, $m = 0$

$$y = -2$$

29. $m = 0$, $(7, -2)$

The line is horizontal so

$$y = -2$$

31. $(4, -6)$ perpendicular to x – axis

so m is undefined.

$x = 4$ for all values of y.

$x = 4$

33. $(0, -4) \Rightarrow b = -4$

Parallel to $y = \frac{3}{4}x + 2 \Rightarrow m_1 = \frac{3}{4}$

$$m_2 = m_1 = \frac{3}{4}$$

$$y = \frac{3}{4}x - 4$$

35. Perpendicular to $y = 2x - 9 \Rightarrow m_1 = 2$

$$m_2 = -\frac{1}{m_1} = -\frac{1}{2}$$

$$y = mx + b, \ (2, 3)$$

$$3 = -\frac{1}{2}(2) + b \Rightarrow b = 4$$

$$y = -\frac{1}{2}x + 4$$

37. $(0, 227)$ and $(10, 251)$

$$m = \frac{251 - 227}{10 - 0} = \frac{24}{10} = 2.4, \ b = 227$$

$$y = 2.4x + 227$$

Cumulative Review

39.

$$\frac{3}{t} - \frac{2}{t-1} = \frac{4}{t}$$

$$t(t-1)\left(\frac{3}{t}\right) - t(t-1)\left(\frac{2}{t-1}\right) = t(t-1)\left(\frac{4}{t}\right)$$

$$3(t-1) - 2t = 4(t-1)$$

$$3t - 3 - 2t = 4t - 4$$

$$t - 3 = 4t - 4$$

$$1 = 3t$$

$$\frac{1}{3} = t$$

41. 2nd week:

Price $= 80 - 0.15(80) = \$68$

3rd week:

Price $= 68 - 0.1(68) = \$61.20$

43. Number shipped $= 35(60) = 2100$

Percent defective $= \frac{104}{2100} \cdot 100\% \approx 4.95\%$

45. $x = $ width

$2x + 70 = $ length

$P = 2L + 2W$

$3440 = 2(2x + 70) + 2x$

$3440 = 4x + 140 + 2x$

$3440 = 6x + 140$

$3300 = 6x$

$550 = x$

$2x + 70 = 2(550) + 70 = 1170$

width $= 550$ feet

length $= 1170$ feet

7.5 Exercises

1. Any convenient point not on the boundary line may be used as a test point.

3. $y > 2 - 3x$

Test point: $(0, 0)$

$0 > 2 - 3(0)$

$0 > 2$ False

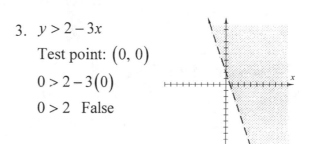

5. $2x - 3y < 6$

   Test point: $(0, 0)$

   $2(0) - 3(0) < 6$

   $0 < 6$ True

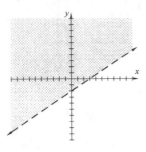

13. $x \geq 2$

   Test point: $(0, 0)$

   $0 \geq 2$ False

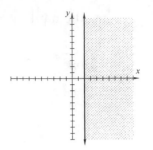

7. $2x - y \geq 3$

   Test point: $(0, 0)$

   $2(0) - (0) \geq 3$

   $0 \geq 3$ False

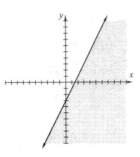

15. $2x - 3y + 6 \geq 0$

   Test point: $(0, 0)$

   $2(0) - 3(0) + 6 \geq 0$

   $6 \geq 0$ True

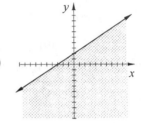

9. $y \geq 4x$

   Test point: $(1, 0)$

   $0 \geq 4(1)$

   $0 \geq 4$ False

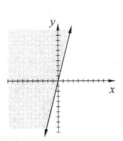

17. $2x > -3y$

   Test point: $(1, 1)$

   $2(1) > -3(1)$

   $2 > -3$ True

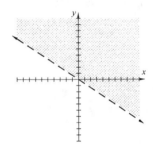

11. $y < -\dfrac{1}{2}x$

   Test point: $(1, 0)$

   $0 < -\dfrac{1}{2}(1)$

   $0 < -\dfrac{1}{2}$ False

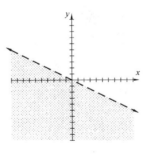

19. $2x > 3 - y$

   Test point: $(0, 0)$

   $2(0) > 3 - (0)$

   $0 > 3$ False

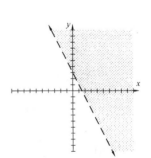

21. $x > -2y$

Test point: $(1, 0)$

$(1) > -2(0)$

$1 > 0$ True

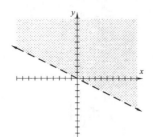

23. $3x + 3 > 5x - 3$

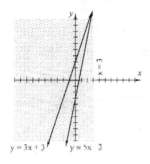

(a) $x < 3$

(b) $3x + 3 > 5x - 3$

    $-2x > -6$

     $x < 3$

(c) $3x + 3$ will be greater than $5x - 3$ for those values of x where the graph of $y = 3x + 3$ lies above the graph of $y = 5x - 3$.

Cumulative Review

25. $5x^2 + 12x - 9 = 0$

   $(6x - 3)(x + 3) = 0$

   $5x - 3 = 0$ $x + 3 = 0$

      $5x = 3$ $x = -3$

       $x = \dfrac{3}{5}$

27. $x =$ the number of miles over 36,000

Total cost = cost for months + cost for excess miles.

$195(36) + 0.15x \le 8400$

$7020 + 0.15x \le 8400$

$0.15x \le 1380$

$x \le 9200$

She may drive 9200 miles above the limit.

29. x – amount of zinc

$\dfrac{4}{3}x$ – amount of copper

$x + \dfrac{4}{3}x = 210$

$3x + 4x = 630$

$7x = 630$

$x = 90$ ounces of zinc

7.6 Exercises

1. You can describe a function using a table of values, an algebraic equation, or a graph.

3. The domain of a function is the set of possible values of the independent variable.

5. If a vertical line can intersect the graph more than once, the relation is not a function.

231

7. $\left\{\left(\frac{2}{5}, 4\right), \left(3, \frac{2}{5}\right), \left(-3, \frac{2}{5}\right), \left(\frac{2}{5}, -1\right)\right\}$

Domain $= \left\{-3, \frac{2}{5}, 3\right\}$

Range $= \left\{-1, \frac{2}{5}, 4\right\}$

Not a function

9. $\left\{(7, 3.1), (5, 0), (7, 2.3)\right\}$

Domain $= \{5, 7\}$

Range $= \{0, 2.3, 3.1\}$

Not a function

11. $\left\{(12, 1), (14, 3), (1, 12), (9, 12)\right\}$

Domain $= \{1, 9, 12, 14\}$

Range $= \{1, 3, 12\}$

Function

13. $\left\{(3, 75), (5, 95), (3, 85), (7, 100)\right\}$

Domain $= \{3, 5, 7\}$

Range $= \{75, 85, 95, 100\}$

Not a function

15. $y = x^2 + 3$

x	y
-2	7
-1	4
0	3
1	4
2	7

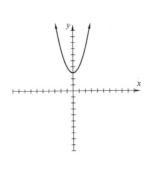

17. $y = 2x^2$

x	y
-2	8
-1	2
0	0
1	2
2	8

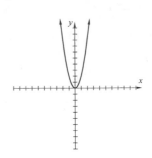

19. $x = -2y^2$

x	y
-8	-2
-2	-1
0	0
-2	1
-8	2

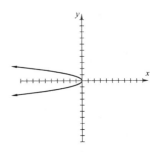

21. $x = y^2 - 4$

x	y
0	-2
-3	-1
-4	0
-3	1
0	2

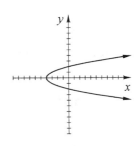

23. $y = \dfrac{2}{x}$

x	y
-4	$-\frac{1}{2}$
-2	-1
-1	-2
1	2
2	1
4	$\frac{1}{2}$

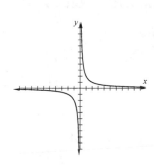

25. $y = \dfrac{4}{x^2}$

x	y
-4	$\frac{1}{4}$
-2	1
-1	4
1	4
2	1
4	$\frac{1}{4}$

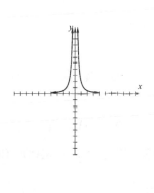

27. $x = (y+1)^2$

x	y
4	-3
1	-2
0	-1
1	0
4	1

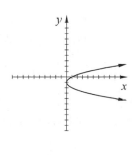

29. $y = \dfrac{4}{x-2}$

x	y
0	-2
1	-4
$\frac{3}{2}$	-8
$\frac{5}{2}$	8
3	4
4	2

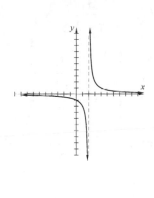

31. Function, passes the vertical line test

33. Not a function, fails the vertical line test

35. Function, passes the vertical line test

37. Not a function, fails the vertical line test

39. $f(x) = 2 - 3x$
   (a) $f(-8) = 2 - 3(-8) = 26$
   (b) $f(0) = 2 - 3(0) = 2$
   (c) $f(2) = 2 - 3(2) = -4$

41. $f(x) = 2x^2 - x + 3$
   (a) $f(0) = 2(0)^2 - 0 + 3 = 3$
   (b) $f(-3) = 2(-3)^2 - (-3) + 3 = 24$
   (c) $f(2) = 2(2)^2 - (2) + 3 = 9$

43. $f(x) = \dfrac{3}{x+2}$

    (a) $f(3) = \dfrac{3}{3+2} = \dfrac{3}{5}$

    (b) $f(0) = \dfrac{3}{0+2} = \dfrac{3}{2}$

    (c) $f(-5) = \dfrac{3}{-5+2} = -1$

45. Yes

47. $f(1980) = 45\%$

    $x = 1980$

49. $f(x) = 2x^2 + 20x + 800$

    $f(0) = 2(0)^2 + 20(0) + 800 = 800$

    $f(3) = 2(3)^2 + 20(3) + 800 = 878$

    $f(6) = 2(6)^2 + 20(6) + 800 = 992$

    $f(10) = 2(10)^2 + 20(10) + 800 = 1200$

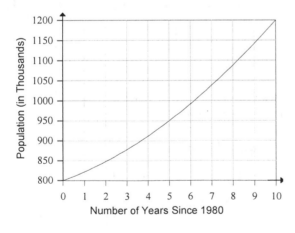

The curve slopes upward more steeply for larger values of x. The growth rate is increasing as x gets larger.

Cumulative Review

51. $(5x^2 - 6x + 2) + (-7x^2 - 8x + 4)$

    $= 5x^2 - 6x + 2 - 7x^2 - 8x + 4$

    $= (5-7)x^2 + (-6-8)x + 2 + 4$

    $= -2x^2 - 14 + 6$

53. $(4x^2 - 2x + 3)(x + 2)$

    $= 4x^3 - 2x^2 + 3x + 8x^2 - 4x + 6$

    $= 4x^3 + (-2+8)x^2 + (3-4)x + 6$

    $= 4x^3 + 6x^2 - x + 6$

Putting Your Skills to Work

1. $2.47(60)(60)(24) = 213{,}408$ acres/day

    $213{,}408(365) \approx 78{,}000{,}000$ acres/year

2. $1756(2.47) = 4337$ million acres

             $= 4{,}337{,}000{,}000$ acres

3. $1992: 4337 - 2(78) = 4181$ million acres

    $1995: 4337 - 5(78) = 3947$ million acres

4. $t =$ number of years after 1990

    $(0,\, 4337)$ and $(5,\, 3947)$

    $m = \dfrac{3947 - 4337}{5 - 0} = -78,\ b = 4337$

    $r(t) = -78t + 4337$

5.

t	0	5	10	15	20
r	4337	3947	3557	3167	2777

2. $E: (4, 4), \quad F: (0, 3),$
$\quad G: (1, -4), \quad H: (-4, -1)$

6.

Acres Remaining (in Millions) vs Number of Years Since 1990

3. $y = 7 - 3x$

  (a) $y = 7 - 3x$

  (b) $10 = 7 - 3x \Rightarrow x = -1, \ (-1, 10)$

4. $2x + 5y = 12$

  (a) $(1, \ ): \ 2(1) + 5y = 12$
$$5y = 10$$
$$y = 2: \ (1, 2)$$

  (b) $(\ , 4): \ 2x + 5(4) = 12$
$$2x = -8$$
$$x = -4: \ (-4, 4)$$

7. $t - 2035 - 1990 = 45$

$r(45) \approx 827$ million acres

8. $r(55) = 0$

There will be no rainforests
after $1990 + 55 = 2045$.

5. $x = 6$

  (a) $(\ , -1): \ x = 6: \ (6, -1)$
  (b) $(\ , 3): \ x = 6: \ (6, 3)$

Chapter 7 Review Problems

6. $3y = 2x + 6$

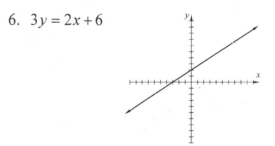

1. A: $(2, -3), \quad$ B: $(-1, 0),$
   C: $(3, 2), \quad$ D: $(-2, -3)$

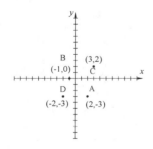

7. $5y + x = -15$

235

8. $2y + 4x = -8 + 2y$

       $4x = -8$

        $x = -2$

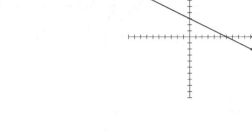

13. $y = -\dfrac{1}{2}x + 3$

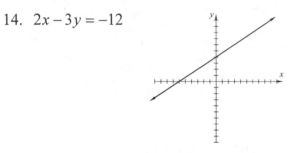

9. $(5, -3)$ and $\left(2, -\dfrac{1}{2}\right)$

$$m = \frac{y_2 - y_1}{x_2 - x_1} = \frac{-\frac{1}{2} - (-3)}{2 - 5} = -\frac{5}{6}$$

14. $2x - 3y = -12$

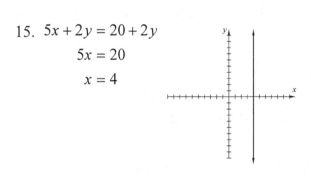

10. $9x - 11y + 15 = 0$

      $9x + 15 = 11y$

      $\dfrac{9}{11}x + \dfrac{15}{11} = y$

      $m = \dfrac{9}{11}, \quad b = \dfrac{15}{11}$

15. $5x + 2y = 20 + 2y$

       $5x = 20$

        $x = 4$

11. $m = -\dfrac{1}{2}, \quad b = 3$

     $y = mx + b$

     $y = -\dfrac{1}{2}x + 3$

16. $(5, 6), \quad m = 2$

     $y = mx + b$

     $6 = 2(5) + b \Rightarrow b = -4$

     $y = 2x - 4$

12. $y = \dfrac{3}{5}x - 2, \; m = \dfrac{3}{5}$

     $m_\perp = -\dfrac{1}{m} = -\dfrac{5}{3}$

17. $(3, -4), \ m = -6$

$$y = mx + b$$
$$-4 = -6(3) + b \Rightarrow b = 14$$
$$y = -6x + 14$$

18. $(-4, 3), \ m = -\dfrac{3}{2}$

$$y = mx + b$$
$$3 = -\dfrac{3}{2}(-4) + b \Rightarrow b = -3$$
$$y = -\dfrac{3}{2}x - 3$$

19. $(3, 7)$ and $(-6, 7)$

$$m = \dfrac{y_2 - y_1}{x_2 - x_1} = \dfrac{7 - 7}{-6 - 3} = 0$$

Horizontal line with $y - 7$

$$y = 7$$

20. $\quad y = -\dfrac{2}{3}x + 4, \ m = -\dfrac{2}{3}$

$$m_{11} = m = -\dfrac{2}{3}$$

21. $-3x + 4y = 8$

$$4y = 3x + 8$$
$$y = \dfrac{3}{4}x + 1$$
$$m = \dfrac{3}{4}, \ m_\perp = -\dfrac{1}{m} = -\dfrac{4}{3}$$

22. $(0, -3)$ and $(3, -1)$

$$m = \dfrac{-3 - (-1)}{0 - 3} = \dfrac{2}{3}, \ b = -3$$
$$y = \dfrac{2}{3}x - 3$$

23. $(0, 1)$ and $(1, -2)$

$$m = \dfrac{-2 - 1}{1 - 0} = -3, \ b = 1$$
$$y = -3x + 1$$

24. $x = 5$

25. $y < \dfrac{1}{3}x + 2$

Test point: $(0, 0)$

$$0 < \dfrac{1}{3}(0) + 2$$
$$0 < 2 \quad \text{True}$$

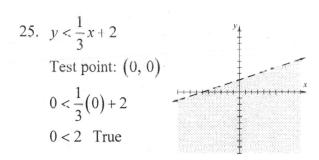

26. $3y + 2x \geq 12$

Test point: $(0, 0)$

$$3(0) + 2(0) \geq 12$$
$$0 \geq 12 \quad \text{False}$$

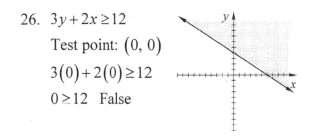

27. $x \leq 2$

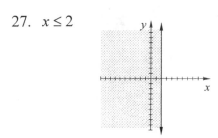

28. $\{(5, -6), (-6, 5), (-5, 5), (-6, -6)\}$

    Domain $\{-6, -5, 5\}$

    Range $\{-6, 5\}$

    Not a function

29. $\{(2, -3), (5, -3), (6, 4), (-2, 4)\}$

    Domain $\{-2, 2, 5, 6\}$

    Range $\{-3, 4\}$

    Function

30. Function, passes the vertical line test

31. Not a function, fails the vertical line test

32. Function, passes the vertical line test

33. $y = x^2 - 5$

x	y
-2	-1
-1	-4
0	-5
1	-4
2	-1

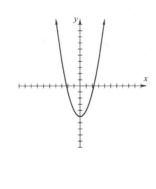

34. $x = y^2 + 3$

x	y
7	-2
4	-1
3	0
4	1
7	2

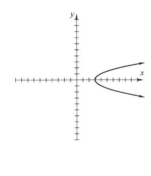

35. $y = (x - 3)^2$

x	y
1	4
2	1
3	0
4	1
5	4

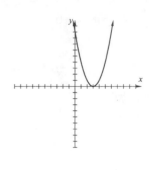

36. $f(x) = 7 - 6x$

    (a) $f(0) = 7 - 6(0) = 7$

    (b) $f(-4) = 7 - 6(-4) = 31$

37. $g(x) = -2x^2 + 3x + 4$

    (a) $g(-1) = -2(-1)^2 + 3(-1) + 4 = -1$

    (b) $g(3) = -2(3)^2 + 3(3) + 4 = -5$

38. $f(x) = 8x - 3$

    (a) $f(-1) = 8(-1) - 3 = -11$

    (b) $f\left(\dfrac{1}{2}\right) = 8\left(\dfrac{1}{2}\right) - 3 = 1$

39. $f(x) = \dfrac{2}{x + 4}$

    (a) $f(-2) = \dfrac{2}{-2 + 4} = 1$

    (b) $f(6) = \dfrac{2}{6 + 4} = \dfrac{1}{5}$

238

40. $f(x) = x^2 - 2x + \dfrac{3}{x}$

    (a) $f(-1) = (-1)^2 - 2(-1) + \dfrac{3}{(-1)} = 0$

    (b) $f(3) = (3)^2 - 2(3) + \dfrac{3}{3} = 4$

Use $y = 30 + 0.09x$ in Exercises 41-46.

41. $y = 30 + 0.09(2000) = \$210$

42. $y = 30 + 0.09(1600) = \$174$

43. $y = 0.09x + 30$
    $y = mx + b, \ b = 30$
    It tells us that if no electricity is used, the cost is a minimum of $30.

44. $y = 0.09x + 30$
    $y = mx + b, \ m = 0.09$
    It tells us that the bill increases $0.09 for each kilowatt-hour of use.

45. $147 = 0.09x + 30$
    $117 = 0.09x$
    $x = 1300$ kilowatt-hours

46. $246 = 0.09x + 30$
    $216 = 0.09x$
    $x = 2400$ kilowatt-hours

Use $y = 0.4x + 23.6$ in Exercises 47-52.

47. $x = 2008 - 1960 = 48$
    $y = 0.4(48) + 23.6$
    $y = 42.8$ quadrillion Btu

48. $x = 2010 - 1960 = 50$
    $y = 0.4(50) + 23.6$
    $y = 43.6$ quadrillion Btu

49. The slope is 0.4. The significance of the slope is that it tells us the rate of change per year. In this case it tells us that for each additional year the U.S. consumes 0.4 quadrillion Btu of petroleum.

50. The y-intercept is $(0, 23.6)$. This tells us that when $x = 0$, which is the year 1960, a total of 23.6 quadrillion Btu of petroleum were used.

51. $y = 47.6$
    $47.6 = 0.4x + 23.6$
    $24 = 0.4x$
    $60 = x$
    Year $= 1960 + 60 = 2020$

52. $y = 51.6$
    $51.6 = 0.4x + 23.6$
    $28 = 0.4x$
    $70 = x$
    Year $= 1960 + 70 = 2030$

53. $5x + 3y = -15$

x	y
0	-5
-3	0

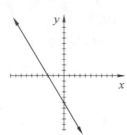

54.

$y = \dfrac{3}{4}x - 3$

x	y
0	-3
4	0

55. $(2, -7)$ and $(-3, -5)$

$$y = \frac{-5 - (-7)}{-3 - 2} = \frac{2}{-5} = -\frac{2}{5}$$

56. $7x + 6y - 10 = 0$

$$6y - 10 = -7x$$
$$6y = -7x + 10$$
$$y = -\frac{7}{6}x + \frac{5}{3}$$

57. $m = \dfrac{2}{3}, \; (3, -5)$

$$-5 = \frac{2}{3}(3) + b \Rightarrow b = -7$$

$$y = \frac{2}{3}x - 7$$

58. $y < -2x + 1$

Test point: $(0, 0)$

$$0 < -2(0) + 1$$

$0 < 1$ True

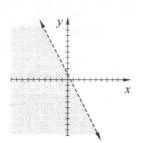

Use $y = -130x + 22,000$ in Exercises 59-64.

59. 1980:

$$x = 1980 - 1980 = 0$$
$$y = -130(0) + 22,000$$
$$y = 22,000$$

$22,000,000$ people

1990:

$$x = 1990 - 1980 = 10$$
$$y = -130(10) + 22,000$$
$$y = 20,700$$

$20,700,000$ people

2000:

$$x = 2000 - 1980 = 20$$
$$y = -130(20) + 22,000$$
$$y = 19,400$$

$19,400,000$ people

60.

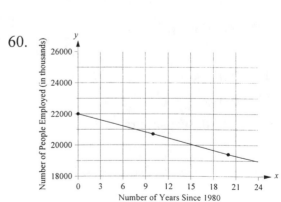

240

61. The slope is -130. The slope tells us that the number of people employed in manufacturing decreases each year by 130 thousand.

62. The y-intercept is $(0, 22,000)$. This tells us that in the year 1980 the number of manufacturing jobs was 22,000,000.

63. $y = 18,100$
$$18,100 = -130x + 22,000$$
$$-3900 = -130x$$
$$30 = x$$
$$\text{Year} - 1980 + 30 = 2010$$

64. $y = 16,800$
$$16,800 = -130x + 22,000$$
$$-5200 = -130x$$
$$40 = x$$
$$\text{Year} = 1980 + 40 = 2020$$

How Am I Doing? Chapter 7 Test

1. $B = (6, 1)$ $C = (-4, -3)$
$D = (-3, 0)$ $E = (5, -2)$

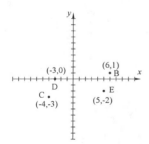

2. $6x - 3 = 5x - 2y$
$$x + 2y = 3$$

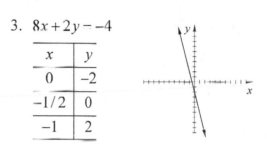

3. $8x + 2y = -4$

x	y
0	-2
$-1/2$	0
-1	2

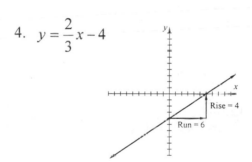

4. $y = \dfrac{2}{3}x - 4$

5. $3x + 2y - 5 = 0$
$$2y = -3x + 5$$
$$y = -\frac{3}{2}x + \frac{5}{2}$$
$$m = -\frac{3}{2}, \ b = \frac{5}{2}$$

6. $(8, 6)$ and $(-3, -5)$
$$m = \frac{-5 - 6}{-3 - 8} = \frac{-11}{-11} = 1$$

7. $(4, -2)$, $m = \dfrac{1}{2}$

$y = mx + b$

$-2 = \dfrac{1}{2}(4) + b \Rightarrow b = -4$

$y = \dfrac{1}{2}x - 4$ or $x - 2y = 8$

8. $(-3, 11)$ and $(-6, 11)$

$m = \dfrac{11 - 11}{-6 - (-3)} = 0$

9. $(5, -4)$ and $(-3, 8)$

$m = \dfrac{y_2 - y_1}{x_2 - x_1} = \dfrac{8 - (-4)}{-3 - 5} = -\dfrac{3}{2}$

$y = mx + b$

$-4 = \left(-\dfrac{3}{2}\right)(5) + b$

$-8 = -15 + 2b$

$\dfrac{7}{2} = b$

$y = -\dfrac{3}{2}x + \dfrac{7}{2}$

10. $(2, 7)$ and $(2, -2)$

$m = \dfrac{y_2 - y_1}{x_2 - x_1} = \dfrac{-2 - 7}{2 - 2} = \dfrac{-9}{0}$ undefined

Vertical line: $x = 2$

11. $4y \le 3x$

Test point: $(1, 1)$

$4(1) \le 3(1)$

$4 \le 3$ False

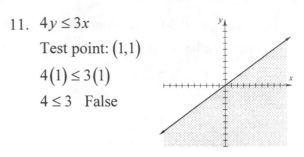

12. $-3x - 2y > 10$.

Test point: $(0, 0)$

$-3(0) - 2(0) > 10$

$0 > 10$ False

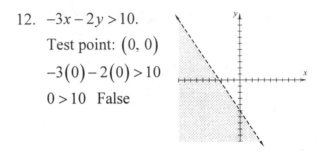

13. $\{(2, -8), (3, -7), (2, 5)\}$

no; two different ordered pairs have the same first coordinate.

14. Function, passes the vertical line test

15. $y = 2x^2 - 3$

x	y
-2	5
-1	-1
0	-3
1	-1
2	5

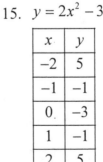

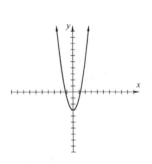

16. $f(x) = -x^2 - 2x - 3$

(a) $f(0) = -(0)^2 - 2(0) - 3 = -3$

(b) $f(-2) = -(-2)^2 - 2(-2) - 3 = -3$

17. $g(x) = \dfrac{3}{x-4}$

    (a) $g(3) = \dfrac{3}{3-4} = -3$

    (b) $g(-11) = \dfrac{3}{-11-4} = \dfrac{3}{-15} = -\dfrac{1}{5}$

Cumulative Test for Chapters 0-7

1. $\left(-3x^3 y^4 z\right)^3 = -27 x^9 y^{12} z^3$

2. $\dfrac{-16x^3 y^4}{24 x^5 y^{-6}} = \dfrac{-2y^{10}}{3x^8}$

3. $2 - 3(4-x) = x - (3-x)$

    $2 - 12 + 3x = x - 3 + x$

              $x = 7$

4. $\dfrac{600}{R} = \dfrac{600}{R+50} + \dfrac{500(R+20)}{R^2 + 50R}$

  $R(R+50)\left(\dfrac{600}{R}\right)$

      $= R(R+50)\left[\dfrac{600}{R+50} + \dfrac{500(R+20)}{R^2 + 50R}\right]$

    $600(R+50) = 600R + 500(R+20)$

  $600R + 30{,}000 = 600R + 500R + 10{,}000$

         $20{,}000 = 500R$

             $40 = R$

5. $x = 2^3 - 6 \div 3 - 1$

    $= 8 - 6 \div 3 - 1$

    $= 8 - 2 - 1$

    $= 5$

6. $A = lw + lh$

    $A - lh = lw$

    $\dfrac{A - lh}{l} = w$

7. $50a^2 - 98b^2$

    $= 2\left(25a^2 - 49b^2\right)$

    $= 2(5a + 7b)(5a - 7b)$

8. $4x^2 + 4x - 15 = (2x - 3)(2x + 5)$

9. $\dfrac{x - \frac{1}{x}}{\frac{1}{2} + \frac{1}{2x}} = \dfrac{x - \frac{1}{x}}{\frac{1}{2} + \frac{1}{2x}} \cdot \dfrac{2x}{2x}$

    $= \dfrac{2x^2 - 2}{x + 1}$

    $= \dfrac{2(x+1)(x-1)}{x+1}$

    $= 2(x - 1)$

10. $(6, 8)$ and $(7, 11)$

    $m = \dfrac{y_2 - y_1}{x_2 - x_1} = \dfrac{11 - 8}{7 - 6} = \dfrac{3}{1} = 3$

    $y = mx + b$

    $8 = 3(6) + b \Rightarrow b = -10$

    $y = 3x - 10$

11. $(7, -4)$ and slope is undefined

    $x = 7$

12. $(3, -5)$, $m = -\dfrac{2}{3}$

$y = mx + b$

$-5 = \left(-\dfrac{2}{3}\right)(3) + b$

$-5 = -2 + b$

$-3 = b$

$y = -\dfrac{2}{3}x - 3$

13. $(-8, -3)$ and $(11, -3)$

$m = \dfrac{y_2 - y_1}{x_2 - x_1} = \dfrac{-3 - (-3)}{11 - (-8)} = 0$

14. $3x - 7y = -2$

$-7y = -3x - 2$

$y = \dfrac{3}{7}x + \dfrac{2}{7}$

$y = mx + b$

$m = \dfrac{3}{7}$

15. $y = \dfrac{2}{3}x - 4$

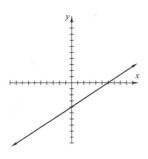

16. $3x + 8 = 5x$

$8 = 2x$

$4 = x$

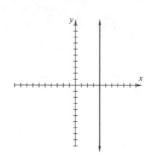

17. $2x + 5y \leq -10$

Test point: $(0, 0)$

$2(0) + 5(0) \leq -10$

$0 \leq -10$ False

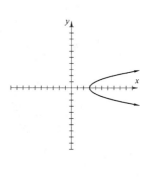

18. $x = y^2 + 3$

x	y
7	-2
4	-1
3	0
4	1
7	2

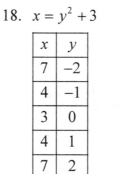

Not a Function

19. $\{(3, 10), (10, -3), (0, -3), (5, 10)\}$

This is a function

20. $f(x) = 3x^2 - 2x + \dfrac{4}{x}$

(a) $f(-1) = 3(-1)^2 - 2(-1) + \dfrac{4}{-1} = 1$

(b) $f(2) = 3(2)^2 - 2(2) + \dfrac{4}{2} = 10$

Chapter 8

8.1 Exercises

1. The lines $y = 2x - 5$ and $y = 2x + 6$ are parallel with y – intercepts at -5 and 6 respectively. There is no solution. The system is inconsistent.

3. If two lines have different slopes you can conclude they <u>intersect</u> and the system has <u>one</u> solution.

5. If two lines have different slopes but the same y – intercept, the lines intersect at the y – intercept which is the solution to the system.

7. $x - y = 3$
$x + y = 5$
$(4,1)$

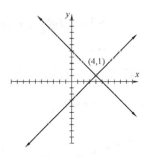

9. $2x + y = 0$
$-3x + y = 5$
$(-1, 2)$

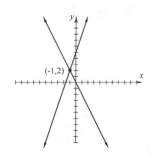

11. $4x + y = 5$
$3x - 2y = 12$
$(2, -3)$

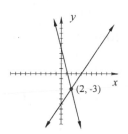

13. $-2x + y - 3 = 0$
$4x + y + 3 = 0$
$(-1, 1)$

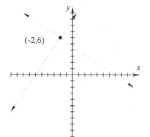

15. $3x - 2y = -18$
$2x + 3y = 14$
$(-2, 6)$

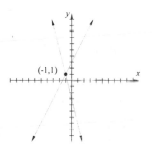

17. $y = \frac{3}{4}x + 7$
$y = -\frac{1}{2}x + 2$
$(-4, 4)$

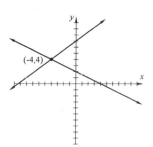

245

19. $3x - 2y = -4$

     $-9x + 6y = -9$

     No solution

     Inconsistent system.

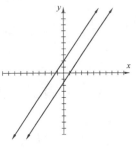

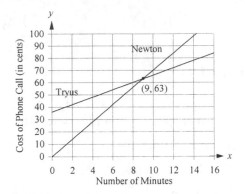

21. $y - 2x - 6 = 0$

     $\dfrac{1}{2}y - 3 = x$

     Infinite number

     of solutions,

     dependent

     equations

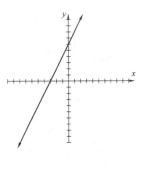

(c)   9 minutes

(b)   Tyrus Telephone Company

23. $y = \dfrac{1}{2}x - 2$

     $y = \dfrac{2}{3}x - 1$

     $(-6, -5)$

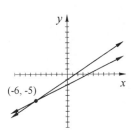

(-6, -5)

27. $y = \;\; 56x + 1808$

     $y = -62x - 2086$

     $(-33, \; -40)$

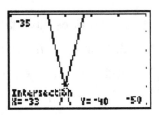

29. $88x + 57y = 683.10$

     $95x - 48y = 7460.64$

     $(47.52, \; -61.38)$

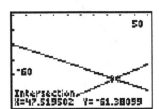

25.   (a)   Newtown: $y = 7x$

         Tryus: $y = 3x + 36$

     (b) $y = 7x$ $y = 3x + 36$

x	y	x	y
1	7	1	39
4	28	4	48
8	56	8	60
12	84	12	72

Cumulative Review

31. $7 - 3(4 - x) \leq 11x - 6$

$$7 - 12 + 3x \leq 11x - 6$$
$$-5 + 3x \leq 11x - 6$$
$$-5 - 8x \leq -6$$
$$-8x \leq -1$$
$$x \geq \frac{1}{8}$$

33. $(3x - 7)^2 = (3x - 7)(3x - 7)$

$$= 9x^2 - 21x - 21x + 49$$
$$- 9x^2 - 42x + 49$$

35. $x =$ the number of people in 1991

$$4x = 360,000$$
$$x = 90,000 \text{ people}$$

37. $1500(365) = 547,500$ people

8.2 Exercises

1. $4x + 3y = 9$ (1)

$x - 3y = 6$ (2)

Solve (2) for x

$x = 3y + 6$ (3)

Substitute $3y + 6$ for x in (1)

$$4(3y + 6) + 3y = 9$$
$$12y + 24 + 3y = 9$$
$$15y + 24 = 9$$
$$15y = -15$$
$$y = -1$$

Substitute -1 for y in (3)

$$x = 3(-1) + 6 = 3$$
$$(3, -1)$$

Check: $4(3) + 3(-1) \overset{?}{=} 9$

$$9 = 9$$

3. $2x + y = 4$ (1)

$2x - y = 0$ (2)

Solve (1) for y

$y = -2x + 4$ (3)

Substitute $-2x + 4$ for y in (2)

$$2x - (-2x + 4) = 0$$
$$2x + 2x - 4 = 0$$
$$4x - 4 = 0$$
$$4x = 4$$
$$x = 1$$

Substitute 1 for x in (3)

$$y = -2(1) + 4 = 2$$
$$(1, 2)$$

Check: $2(1) - 2 \overset{?}{=} 0$

$$0 = 0$$

5. $5x + 2y = 5$ (1)

   $3x + y = 4$ (2)

Solve (2) for y

$y = -3x + 4$ (3)

Substitute $-3x + 4$ for y in (1)

$5x + 2(-3x + 4) = 5$

$5x - 6x + 8 = 5$

$-x = -3$

$x = 3$

Substitute 3 for x in (3)

$y = -3(3) + 4 = -5$

$(3, -5)$

Check: $5(3) + 2(-5) \overset{?}{=} 5$

$5 = 5$

7. $3x - 2y = -8$ (1)

   $x + y = 4$ (2)

Solve (2) for y

$y = -x + 4$ (3)

Substitute $-x + 4$ for y in (1)

$3x - 2(-x + 4) = -8$

$3x + 2x - 8 = -8$

$5x = 0$

$x = 0$

Substitute 0 for x in (3)

$y = -0 + 4 = 4$

$(0, 4)$

Check: $3(0) - 2(4) \overset{?}{=} -8$

$-8 = -8$

9. $3a - 5b = 2$ (1)

   $3a + b = 32$ (2)

Solve (2) for b

$b = -3a + 32$ (3)

Substitute $-3a + 32$ for b in (1)

$3a - 5(-3a + 32) = 2$

$3a + 15a - 160 = 2$

$18a - 160 = 2$

$18a = 162$

$a = 9$

11. $3x - y = 3$ (1)

     $x + 3y = 11$ (2)

Solve (2) for x

$x = -3y + 11$ (3)

Substitute $-3y + 11$ for x in (1)

$3(-3y + 11) - y = 3$

$-9y + 33 - y = 3$

$-10y + 33 = 3$

$-10y = -30$

$y = 3$

Substitute 3 for y in (3)

$x = -3(3) + 11$

$x = 2$

$(2, 3)$

Check: $3(2) - 3 \overset{?}{=} 6$

$3 = 3$

13. $p + 2q - 4 = 0$　　　(1)

$7p - q - 3 = 0$　　　(2)

Solve (1) for p

$p = 4 - 2q$　　　(3)

Substitute $4 - 2q$ for p in (2)

$7(4 - 2q) - q - 3 = 0$

$28 - 14q - q - 3 = 0$

$-15q = -25$

$q = \dfrac{5}{3}$

Substitute $\dfrac{5}{3}$ for q in (3)

$p = 4 - 2\left(\dfrac{5}{3}\right) = \dfrac{12}{3} - \dfrac{10}{3} = \dfrac{2}{3}$

$\left(\dfrac{2}{3}, \dfrac{5}{3}\right)$

Check: $\dfrac{2}{3} + 2\left(\dfrac{5}{3}\right) - 4 \overset{?}{=} 0$

$\dfrac{2}{3} + \dfrac{10}{3} - \dfrac{12}{3} \overset{?}{=} 0$

$0 = 0$

15. $3x - y - 9 = 0$　　　(1)

$8x + 5y - 1 = 0$　　　(2)

Solve (1) for y

$3x - 9 = y$　　　(3)

Substitute $3x - 9$ for y in (2)

$8x + 5(3x - 9) - 1 = 0$

$8x + 15x - 45 - 1 = 0$

$23x - 46 = 0$

$x = 2$

Substitute 2 for x in (3)

$y = 3(2) - 9 = -3$

$(2, -3)$

Check: $8(2) + 5(-3) - 1 \overset{?}{=} 0$

$0 = 0$

17. $\dfrac{5}{3}x + \dfrac{1}{3}y = -3$　　　(1)

$-2x + 3y = 24$　　　(2)

Multiply (1) by 3

$5x + y = -9$　　　(3)

Solve (3) for y

$y = -5x - 9$　　　(4)

Substitute $-5x - 9$ for y in (2)

$-2x + 3(-5x - 9) = 24$

$-2x - 15x - 27 = 24$

$-17x = 51$

$x = -3$

Substitute -3 for x in (4)

$y = -5(-3) - 9 = 6$

$(-3, 6)$

19. $4x + 5y = 2$ (1)

$\dfrac{1}{5}x + y = \dfrac{-7}{5}$ (2)

Multiply (2) by 5

$x + 5y = -7$

Solve for x

$x = -5y - 7$ (3)

Substitute $-5y - 7$ for x in (1)

$4(-5y - 7) + 5y = 2$

$-20y - 28 + 5y = 2$

$-15y = 30$

$y = -2$

Substitute -2 for y in (3)

$x = -5(-2) - 7 = 3$

$(3, -2)$

21. $\dfrac{4}{7}x - \dfrac{2}{7}y = 2$

$4x + 2y = 14$ (1)

$3x + y = 13$ (2)

Solve (2) for y

$y = -3x + 13$ (3)

Substitute $-3x + 13$ for y in (1)

$4x + 2(-3x + 13) = 14$

$4x - 6x + 26 = 14$

$-2x + 26 = 14$

$-2x = -12$

$x = 6$

Substitute 6 for x in (3)

$y = -3(6) + 13$

$y = -5$

$(6, -5)$

23. $3x + y = 6$ (1)

$3x - 2y = -3$ (2)

Solve (1) for y

$y = -3x + 6$ (3)

Substitute $-3x + 6$ for y in (2)

$3x - 2(-3x + 6) = -3$

$3x + 6x - 12 = -3$

$9x - 12 = -3$

$9x = 9$

$x = 1$

Substitute 1 for x in (3)

$y = -3(1) + 6$

$y = 3$

$(1, 3)$

25. $3x - 4y = 36$ (1)

$y + 3 = 3(x + 1)$

$y + 3 = 3x + 3$

$y = 3x$ (2)

Substitute $3x$ for y in (1)

$3x - 4(3x) = 36$

$3x - 12x = 36$

$-9x = 36$

$x = -4$

Substitute -4 for x in (2)

$y = 3(-4) = -12$

$(-4, -12)$

27. $2x = 4(2y + 2)$

$3(x - 3y) + 2 = 17$

$2x = 8y + 8$

$3x - 9y + 2 = 17$

$x = 4y + 4$ (1)

$3x - 9y = 15$ (2)

Substitute $4y + 4$ for x in (2)

$3(4y + 4) - 9y = 15$

$12y + 12 - 9y = 15$

$3y = 3$

$y = 1$

Substitute 1 for y in (1)

$x = 4(1) + 4 = 8$

$(8, 1)$

Check: $3[8 - 3(1)] + 2 \overset{?}{=} 17$

$17 = 17$

29. You would need 3 (7) equations to solve for 3(7) unknowns. Substitution can reduce the system to one equation with one unknown. Then substituting back successively gives another unknown, thus requiring one equation for each unknown.

31. The solution to a system must satisfy <u>both</u> equations.

33. If the graphs are parallel, the system has no solutions because there are no points in common.

35. (a) LEP: $y = 90x + 50$

AP: $y = 80x + 100$

(b) $90x + 50 = 80x + 100$

$10x = 50$

$x = 5$

$y = 90(5) + 50 = 500$

It would take 5 times and cost $500

(c) $90x + 50 - (80x + 100) = 80$

$10x - 50 = 80$

$10x = 130$

$x = 13$

They expect plowing 13 times and he should hire Adirondack Plowing.

Cumulative Review Problems

37. $6x + 3y \geq 9$

Test point: $(0, 0)$

$6(0) + 3(0) \geq 9$

$0 \geq 9$ False

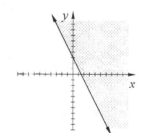

39. total cost = basic contract + bonus

bonus $= 0.03 \times$ basic contract

total cost $= 3.8 + 0.03(3.8)$

$= 3.914$

$= \$3,914,000$

41. $\dfrac{(5\text{trips})(360 \text{ miles/trip})(\$1.80/\text{gal})}{20 \text{ miles/gal}}$

$= \dfrac{5(360)(1.8)}{20}$

$= 162$

The cost of gasoline for family trips for one year is $162.

8.3 Exercises

1. $3x + 2y = 5$ (1)

  $5x - \ y = 3$ (2)

Multiply (2) by 2 to eliminate y

3. $4x - 3y = 10$ (1)

  $5x + 4y = 0$ (2)

Multiply (1) by 4 and (2) by 3 to eliminate y

5. $-x + y = -3$ (1)

  $\dfrac{-2x - y = 6}{}$ (2)

    $-3x = 3$

      $x = -1$

Substitute -1 for x in (1)

$-(-1) + y = -3$

      $y = -4$

$(-1, -4)$

  Check: $-2(-1) - (-4) \overset{?}{=} 6$

             $6 = 6$

7. $2x + 3y = 1$ (1)

  $x - 2y = 4$ (2)

Multiply (2) by -2

  $2x + 3y = 1$

  $\dfrac{-2x + 4y = -8}{}$

    $7y = -7$

     $y = -1$

Substitute -1 for y in (2)

$x - 2(-1) = 4$

    $x = 2$

$(2, -1)$

9. $4x + -2y = -2$ (1)

  $4x + 3y = -12$ (2)

Multiply (2) by -1

  $4x - 2y = -2$

  $\dfrac{-4x - 3y = 12}{}$

    $-5y = 10$

     $y = -2$

Substitute -2 for y in (1)

$4x - 2(-2) = -2$

  $4x + 4 = -2$

    $4x = -6$

     $x = -\dfrac{3}{2}$

$\left(-\dfrac{3}{2}, -2\right)$

Check: $4\left(-\dfrac{3}{2}\right) + 3(-2) \overset{?}{=} -12$

            $-12 = -12$

11. $5x - 15y = 9$ (1)

$-x + 10y = 1$ (2)

Multiply (2) by 5

$5x - 15y = 9$

$\underline{-5x + 50y = 5}$

$35y = 14$

$$y = \frac{2}{5}$$

Substitute $\frac{2}{5}$ for y in (2)

$$-x + 10\left(\frac{2}{5}\right) = 1$$

$-x = -3$

$x = 3$

$$\left(3, \frac{2}{5}\right)$$

Check: $5(3) - 15\left(\frac{2}{5}\right) \overset{?}{=} 9$

$9 = 9$

13. $2x + 5y = 2$ (1)

$3x + y = 3$ (2)

Multiply (2) by -5

$2x + 5y = 2$

$\underline{-15x - 5y = -15}$

$-13x = -13$

$x = 1$

Substitute 1 for x in (2)

$3(1) + y = 3$

$y = 0$

$(1, 0)$

Check: $2(1) + 5(0) \overset{?}{=} 2$

$2 = 2$

Substitute 4 for x in (2)

$2(4) - y = 6$

$-y = -2$

$y = 2$

$(4, 2)$

Check: $5(4) - 3(2) \overset{?}{=} 14$

$14 = 14$

15. $8x + 6y = -2$ (1)

$10x - 9y = -8$ (2)

Multiply (1) by 3 and (2) by 2

$24x + 18y = -6$

$\underline{20x - 18y = -16}$

$44x = -22$

$$x = -\frac{1}{2}$$

Substitute $-\frac{1}{2}$ for x in (1)

$$8\left(-\frac{1}{2}\right) + 6y = -2$$

$6y = 2$

$$y = \frac{1}{3}$$

$$\left(-\frac{1}{2}, \frac{1}{3}\right)$$

253

Check: $10\left(-\dfrac{1}{2}\right)-9\left(\dfrac{1}{3}\right)\overset{?}{=}-8$

$$-8=-8$$

17. $2x+3y=-8$ (1)

$5x+4y=-34$ (2)

Multiply (1) by -5 and (2) by 2

$-10x-15y=40$

$\underline{10x+\ 8y=-68}$

$-7y=-28$

$y=4$

Substitute 4 for y in (1)

$2x+3(4)=-8$

$2x=-20$

$x=-10$

$(-10,\ 4)$

Check: $5(-10)+4(4)\overset{?}{=}-34$

$$-34=-34$$

19. $2x-7y=8$ (1)

$3x-4y=-1$ (2)

Multiply (1) by 3 and (2) by -2

$6x-21y=24$

$\underline{-6x+8y=\ 2}$

$-13y=26$

$y=-2$

Substitute -2 for y in (2)

$3x-4(-2)=-1$

$3x+8=-1$

$3x=-9$

$x=-3$

$(-3,\ -2)$

Check: $2(-3)-7(-2)\overset{?}{=}8$

$$8=8$$

21. $12x-6y=-2$ (1)

$9x-7y=-10$ (2)

Multiply (1) by 3 and (2) by 4

$36x-18y=-6$

$\underline{-36x-28y=-40}$

$-46y=-46$

$y=1$

Substitute 1 for y in (1)

$12x-6(1)=-2$

$12x=4$

$x=\dfrac{1}{3}$

$\left(\dfrac{1}{3},1\right)$

Check: $-9\left(\dfrac{1}{3}\right)-7(1)\overset{?}{=}-10$

$$-10=-10$$

23. $\dfrac{1}{4}x-\dfrac{3}{4}y=2$ (1)

$2x+3y=1$ (2)

Multiply equation (1) by 4

25. $\dfrac{1}{2}x+\dfrac{2}{3}y=\dfrac{1}{3}$ (1)

$\dfrac{3}{4}x-\dfrac{4}{5}y=2$ (2)

Multiply (1) by 6 and (2) by 20.

254

27. $x + \dfrac{5}{4}y = \dfrac{9}{4}$ (1)

$\dfrac{2}{5}x - y = \dfrac{3}{5}$ (2)

Multiply (1) by 4 and (2) by 5

$4x + 5y = 9$

$\underline{2x - 5y = 3}$

$6x \quad\quad = 12$

$\quad\quad x = 2$

Substitute 2 for x in (1)

$2 + \dfrac{5}{4}y = \dfrac{9}{4}$

$\dfrac{5}{4}y = \dfrac{1}{4}$

$y = \dfrac{1}{5}$

$\left(2, \dfrac{1}{5}\right)$

Check: $\dfrac{2}{5}(2) - \dfrac{1}{5} \overset{?}{=} \dfrac{3}{5}$

$\dfrac{3}{5} = \dfrac{3}{5}$

29. $\dfrac{x}{6} + \dfrac{y}{2} = -\dfrac{1}{2}$ (1)

$x - 9y = 21$ (2)

Multiply (1) by -6

$-x - 3y = 3$

$\underline{x - 9y = 21}$

$-12y = 24$

$y = -2$

Substitute -2 for y in (2)

$x - 9(-2) = 21$

$x = 3$

$(3, -2)$

Check: $\dfrac{3}{6} + \dfrac{-2}{2} \overset{?}{=} -\dfrac{1}{2}$

$\dfrac{1}{2} - \dfrac{2}{2} \overset{?}{=} -\dfrac{1}{2}$

$-\dfrac{1}{2} = -\dfrac{1}{2}$

31. $\dfrac{5}{6}x + y = -\dfrac{1}{3}$ (1)

$-8x + 9y = 28$ (2)

Multiply (1) by 18 and (2) by -2

$15x + 18y = -6$

$\underline{16x - 18y = -56}$

$31x \quad\quad = -62$

$\quad\quad x = -2$

Substitute -2 for x in (2)

$-8(-2) + 9y = 28$

$9y = 12$

$y = \dfrac{4}{3}$

$\left(-2, \dfrac{4}{3}\right)$

Check: $\dfrac{5}{6}(-2) + \dfrac{4}{3} \overset{?}{=} -\dfrac{1}{3}$

$-\dfrac{1}{3} = -\dfrac{1}{3}$

33. $\dfrac{2}{3}x + \dfrac{3}{5}y = -\dfrac{1}{5}$ (1)

$\dfrac{1}{4}x + \dfrac{1}{3}y = \dfrac{1}{4}$ (2)

Multiply (1) by 15 and (2) by 12

$10x + 9y = -3$ (3)

$\underline{3x + 4y = 3}$ (4)

Multiply (3) by 3 and (4) by -10

$30x + 27y = -9$

$\underline{-30x - 40y = -30}$

$-13y = -39$

$y = 3$

Substitute 3 for y in (2)

$\dfrac{1}{4}x + \dfrac{1}{3}(3) = \dfrac{1}{4}$

$\dfrac{1}{4}x + 1 = \dfrac{1}{4}$

$x + 4 = 1$

$x = -3$

$(-3, 3)$

Check: $\dfrac{2}{3}(-3) + \dfrac{3}{5}(3) \overset{?}{=} -\dfrac{1}{5}$

$-2 + \dfrac{9}{5} \overset{?}{=} -\dfrac{1}{5}$

$-\dfrac{1}{5} = -\dfrac{1}{5}$

35. $0.5x - 0.3y = 0.1$ (1)

$5x + 3y = 6$ (2)

Multiply (1) by 10

$5x - 3y = 1$

$5x + 3y = 6$

37. $4x + 0.5y = 9$ (1)

$0.2x - 0.05y = 1$ (2)

Multiply (1) by 10 and (2) by 100

$40x + 5y = 90$

$20x - 5y = 100$

39. $0.5x - 0.2y = 0.4$ (1)

$-0.3x + 0.4y = 0.6$ (2)

Multiply (1) and (2) by 10

$5x - 2y = 4$ (3)

$-3x + 4y = 6$ (4)

Multiply (3) by 2

$10x - 4y = 8$

$\underline{-3x + 4y = 6}$

$7x = 14$

$x = 2$

Substitute 2 for x (1)

$0.5(2) - 0.2y = 0.4$

$-0.2y + 1 = 0.4$

$-0.2y = -0.6$

$y = 3$

$(2, 3)$

41. $0.02x - 0.04y = 0.26$ (1)

$0.07x - 0.09y = 0.66$ (2)

Multiply (1) and (2) by 100

$2x - 4y = 26$ (3)

$7x - 9y = 66$ (4)

Multiply (3) by 7 and (4) by -2

$14x - 28y = 182$

$\underline{-14x + 18y = -132}$

$-10y = 50$

$y = -5$

Substitute -5 for y in (3)

$$2x - 4(-5) = 26$$
$$2x = 6$$
$$x = 3$$

$(3, -5)$

43. $0.4x - 5y = -1.2$ (1)

     $-0.03x + 0.5y = 0.14$ (2)

Multiply (1) by 10 and (2) by 100

$$4x - 50y = -12$$
$$\underline{-3x + 50y = 14}$$
$$x = 2$$

Substitute 2 for x in (1)

$$0.4(2) - 5y = -1.2$$
$$-5y = -2$$
$$y = \frac{2}{5}$$

$\left(2, \dfrac{2}{5}\right)$

45. $2x + y = 11$ (1)

    $x + 3y = 18$ (2)

Multiply (1) by -3

$$-6x - 3y = -33$$
$$\underline{x + 3y = 18}$$
$$-5x = -15$$
$$x = 3$$

Substitute 3 for x in (1)

$$2(3) + y = 11$$
$$6 + y = 11$$
$$y = 5$$

$(3, 5)$

47. $\dfrac{5}{4}x + y = 16$ (1)

    $x - \dfrac{5}{3}y = -2$ (2)

Multiply (1) by 4 and (2) by 3

$$5x + 4y = 64 \quad (3)$$
$$3x - 5y = -6 \quad (4)$$

Multiply (3) by 5 and (4) by 4

$$25x + 20y = 320$$
$$\underline{12x - 20y = -24}$$
$$37x = 296$$
$$x = 8$$

Substitute 8 for x in (1)

$$\frac{5}{4}(8) + y = 16$$
$$10 + y = 16$$
$$y = 6$$

$(8, 6)$

49. $0.2x + 0.1y = 1.1$ (1)

    $0.01x + 0.03y = 0.18$ (2)

Multiply (1) by 10 and (2) by 100

$$2x + y = 11 \quad (3)$$
$$x + 3y = 18 \quad (4)$$

Multiply (4) by -2

$$2x + y = 11$$
$$\underline{-2x - 6y = -36}$$
$$-5y = -25$$
$$y = 5$$

Substitute 5 for y in (4)

$x + 3(5) = 18$

$x + 15 = 18$

$x = 3$

$(3, 5)$

51. $5(3x - y) = 2 - (y - x)$

$9(2x - 2) = y - 3x$

Expand both equations

$15x - 5y = 2 - y + x$

$18x - 18 = y - 3x$

Rearrange

$14x - 4y = 2$ (1)

$21x - y = 18$ (2)

Multiply (2) by -4

$14x - 4y = 2$

$-84x + 4y = -72$

$\overline{}$

$-70x = -70$

$x = 1$

Substitute 1 for x in (2)

$21(1) - y = 18$

$-y = -3$

$y = 3$

$(1, 3)$

Cumulative Review

53. $100\% - 89\% = 11\%$

$0.11(5000) = 550$

$0.11(7000) = 770$

Between 550 and 770 airplanes

55. $d = rt \Rightarrow t = \dfrac{d}{r}$

Bobby's time for 100 laps

         $<$ Carlos' time for 96 laps

$\dfrac{100 \times 4.75}{r} < \dfrac{96 \times 4.75}{95}$

$\dfrac{475}{r} < 4.8$

$475 < 4.8r$

$98.96 < r$

Bobby will have to average more than 99mph.

57. $75x^2 - 3 = 3(25x^2 - 1)$

$= 3\left[(5x)^2 - (1)^2 \right]$

$= 3(5x + 1)(5x - 1)$

How Am I Doing? Sections 8.1-8.3

1. $2x - y = -8$

$-x + 2y = 10$

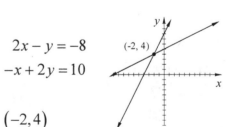

$(-2, 4)$

2. $-2x + y = 4$

$x - 3y = 3$

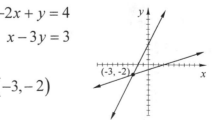

$(-3, -2)$

3. $5x + y = 26$ (1)

     $3x + 2y = 10$ (2)

     Solve (1) for y

     $y = -5x + 26$ (3)

     Substitute $-5x + 26$ for y in (2)

     $3x + 2(-5x + 26) = 10$

        $3x - 10x + 52 = 10$

          $-7x + 52 = 10$

             $-7x = -42$

                $x = 6$

     Substitute 6 for x in (3)

     $y = -5(6) + 26 = -4$

     $(6, -4)$

4. $4x - 3y = 18$ (1)

     $5x - \ y = 17$ (2)

     Solve (2) for y

     $y = 5x - 17$ (3)

     Substitute $5x - 17$ for y in (1)

     $4x - 3(5x - 17) = 18$

       $4x - 15x + 51 = 18$

         $-11x + 51 = 18$

            $-11x = -33$

               $x = 3$

     Substitute 3 for x in (3)

     $y = 5(3) - 17$

     $y = -2$

     $(3, -2)$

5. $2x + 3y = 5$ (1)

     $\dfrac{1}{2}x + \dfrac{1}{6}y = -\dfrac{1}{2}$ (2)

     Multiply (2) by 6

     $3x + y = -3$

     Solve for y

     $y = -3x - 3$ (3)

     Substitute $-3x - 3$ for y in (1)

     $2x + 3(-3x - 3) = 5$

       $2x - 9x - 9 = 5$

         $-7x - 9 = 5$

            $-7x = 14$

              $x = -2$

     Substitute -2 for x in (3)

     $y = -3(-2) - 3$

     $y = 3$

     $(-2, 3)$

6. $7x - 5y - 17 = 0$ (1)

     $x + 8y + 15 = 0$ (2)

     Solve (2) for x

     $x = -8y - 15$ (3)

     Substitute $-8y - 15$ for x in (1)

     $7(-8y - 15) - 5y - 17 = 0$

     $-56y - 105 - 5y - 17 = 0$

            $-61y - 122 = 0$

               $-61y = 122$

                 $y = -2$

     Substitute -2 for y in (3)

     $x = -8(-2) - 15 = 1$

     $(1, -2)$

7. $3x - 2y = 19$ (1)

     $x + y = 8$ (2)

Multiply (2) by 2

$3x - 2y = 19$

$\underline{2x + 2y = 16}$

$5x \quad\quad = 35$

     $x = -7$

Substitute 7 for x in (2)

$7 + y = 8$

   $y = 1$

$(7, 1)$

8. $9x - 8y = 3$ (1)

   $6x + 3y = 27$ (2)

Multiply (1) by 2 and (2) by -3

  $18x - 16y = 6$ (3)

  $\underline{-18x - 9y = -81}$ (4)

   $-25y = -75$

     $y = 3$

Substitute 3 for y in (2)

$6x + 3(3) = 27$

   $6x + 9 = 27$

     $6x = 18$

      $x = 3$

$(3, 3)$

9. $\dfrac{2}{3}x - \dfrac{3}{4}y = 3$ (1)

   $\dfrac{1}{9}x + \dfrac{1}{12}y = -2$ (2)

Multiply (1) by 12 and (2) by 36

$8x - 9y = 36$ (3)

$4x + 3y = -72$ (4)

Multiply (4) by 3

  $8x - 9y = \quad 36$

$\underline{12x + 9y = -216}$

$20x \quad\quad = -180$

     $x = -9$

Substitute -9 for x in (1)

$\dfrac{2}{3}(-9) - \dfrac{3}{4}y = 3$

   $-6 - \dfrac{3}{4}y = 3$

     $-\dfrac{3}{4}y = 9$

       $y = -12$

$(-9, -12)$

10. $0.6x - 0.5y = 2.1$ (1)

    $0.4x - 0.3y = 1.3$ (2)

Multiply (1) and (2) by 10

$6x - 5y = 21$ (3)

$4x - 3y = 13$ (4)

Multiply (3) by 2 and (4) by -3

  $12x - 10y = \quad 42$

$\underline{-12x + 9y = -39}$

     $-y = 3$

      $y = -3$

Substitute -3 for y in (1)

$0.5x - 0.5(-3) = 2.1$

$0.6x + 1.5 = 2.1$

$0.6x = 0.6$

$x = 1$

$(1, -3)$

8.4 Exercises

1. If there is no solution to a system of linear equations, the graphs of the equations are parallel lines. Solving the system algebraically, you will obtain an equation that is inconsistent with known facts.

3. If there is exactly one solution, the graphs of the equations intersect. This system is said to be independent and consistent.

5. $-2x - 3y = 15$ (1)

    $5x + 2y = 1$ (2)

Multiply (1) by 2 and (2) by 3

$-4x - 6y = 30$

$\underline{15x + 6y = 3}$

$11x \quad\quad = 33$

     $x = 3$

Substitute 3 for x in (2)

$5(3) + 2y = 1$

    $2y = -14$

     $y = -7$

$(3, -7)$

7. $4x - 5y = 1$ (1)

    $-3x + 4y = 4$ (2)

Multiply (1) by 3 and (2) by 4

$12x - 15y = 3$

$\underline{-12x + 16y = 16}$

      $y = 19$

Substitute 19 for y in (2)

$-3x + 4(19) = 4$

$-3x + 76 = 4$

    $x = 24$

$(24, 19)$

9. $2x - 4y = 5$ (1)

    $-4x + 8y = 9$ (2)

Multiply (1) by 2

$4x - 8y = 10$

$\underline{-4x + 8y = 9}$

     $0 = 19$

There is no solution.

11. $-5x + 2y = 2$ (1)

   $15x - 6y = -6$ (2)

Multiply (1) by 3

$-15x + 6y = 6$

$\underline{15x - 6y = -6}$

     $0 = 0$

There is an infinite number of solutions.

13. $5x - 3y = 13$ (1)

    $7x + 2y = 43$ (2)

    Multiply (1) by 2 and (2) by 3

$$10x - 6y = 26$$
$$\underline{21x + 6y = 129}$$
$$31x = 155$$
$$x = 5$$

    Substitute 5 for x in (1)

$$5(5) - 3y = 13$$
$$25 - 3y = 13$$
$$-3y = -12$$
$$y = 4$$

    $(5, 4)$

15. $3x - 2y = 70$ (1)

    $0.6x + 0.5y = 50$ (2)

    Multiply (1) by -2 and (2) by 10

$$-6x + 4y = -140$$
$$\underline{6x + 5y = 500}$$
$$9y = 360$$
$$y = 40$$

    Substitute 40 for y in (1)

$$3x - 2(40) = 70$$
$$3x = 150$$
$$x = 50$$

    $(50, 40)$

17. $0.3x - 0.5y = 0.4$ (1)

    $0.6x + 1.0y = 2.8$ (2)

    Multiply (1) by 20 and (2) by -10

$$6x - 10y = 8$$
$$\underline{-6x - 10y = -28}$$
$$-20y = -20$$
$$y = 1$$

    Substitute 1 for y in (1)

$$0.3x - 0.5(1) = 0.4$$
$$0.3x = 0.9$$
$$x = 3$$

    $(3, 1)$

19. $\dfrac{4}{3}x + \dfrac{1}{2}y = 1$ (1)

    $\dfrac{1}{3}x - \phantom{\dfrac{1}{2}} y = -\dfrac{1}{2}$ (2)

    Multiply (1) by 6 and (2) by -24

$$8x + 3y = 6$$
$$\underline{-8x + 24y = 12}$$
$$27y = 18$$
$$y = \dfrac{2}{3}$$

    Substitute $\dfrac{2}{3}$ for y in (2)

$$\dfrac{1}{3}x - \dfrac{2}{3} = -\dfrac{1}{2}$$
$$\dfrac{1}{3}x = \dfrac{1}{6}$$
$$x = \dfrac{1}{2}$$

    $\left(\dfrac{1}{2}, \dfrac{2}{3}\right)$

21. $\dfrac{2}{3}x + \dfrac{1}{6}y = 2$ (1)

$\dfrac{1}{4}x - \dfrac{1}{2}y = -\dfrac{3}{4}$ (2)

Multiply (1) by 12 and (2) by 4

$8x + 2y = 24$

$\underline{x - 2y = -3}$

$9x \qquad = 21$

$x = \dfrac{7}{3}$

Substitute $\dfrac{7}{3}$ for x in (1)

$\dfrac{2}{3}\left(\dfrac{7}{3}\right) + \dfrac{1}{6}y = 2$

$\dfrac{1}{6}y = \dfrac{4}{9}$

$y = \dfrac{8}{3}$

$\left(\dfrac{7}{3}, \dfrac{8}{3}\right)$

23. $4x + 3y = -2$ (1)

$5x - 2y = 49$ (2)

Multiply (1) by 2 and (2) by 3

$8x + 6y = -4$

$\underline{15x - 6y = 27}$

$23x \qquad = 23$

$x = 1$

Substitute 1 for x in (1)

$4(1) + 3y = -2$

$3y = -6$

$y = -2$

$(1, -2)$

25. $\dfrac{2}{3}x + y = 1$ (1)

$\dfrac{3}{4}x + \dfrac{1}{2}y = \dfrac{3}{4}$ (2)

Multiply (1) by 3 and (2) by 4

$2x + 3y = 3$ (3)

$\underline{3x + 2y = 3}$ (4)

Multiply (3) by 3 and (2) by -2

$6x + 9y = 9$

$\underline{-6x - 4y = -6}$

$5y = 3$

$y = \dfrac{3}{5}$

Substitute $\dfrac{3}{5}$ for y in (1)

$\dfrac{2}{3}x + \dfrac{3}{5} = 1$

$10x + 9 = 15$

$10x = 6$

$x = \dfrac{3}{5}$

$\left(\dfrac{3}{5}, \dfrac{3}{5}\right)$

27. $x - 2y + 2 = 0$ (1)

$3(x - 2y + 1) = 15$

$3x - 6y + 3 = 15$ (2)

Multiply (1) by -3

$-3x + 6y - 6 = 0$

$\underline{3x - 6y + 3 = 15}$

$-3 = 15$

No solution. The system is inconsistent.

29. $2(a+3) = b+1$

    $3(a-b) = a+1$

    Expand

    $2a+6 = b+1$

    $3a-3b = a+1$

    Rearrange

    $2a - b = -5$ (1)

    $\underline{-2a + 3b = -1}$ (2)

        $2b = -6$

         $b = -3$

    Substitute -3 for b in (1)

    $2a - (-3) = -5$

       $2a = -8$

        $a = -4$

    $(-4, -3)$

Cumulative Review

31. $20x + 12\left(\dfrac{9}{2} - x\right) = 70$

    $20x + 54 - 12x = 70$

          $8x = 16$

          $x = 2$

33. $x =$ Robert's taxable income

    $0.15x = 3225$

      $x = 21,500$

    Robert's taxable income was \$21,500

35. $100\% - 40\% = 60\%$

    $\dfrac{0.60(92,500)}{44} \approx 1261$ tickets

8.5 Exercises

1. $x =$ number of first class tickets

    $y =$ number of coach tickets

    $x + y = 14$ (1)

    $1150x + 250y = 10,700$ (2)

    Solve (1) for x

    $x = 14 - y$ (3)

    Substitute $14 - y$ for x in (2)

    $1150(14 - y) + 250y = 10,700$

    $16,100 - 1150y + 250y = 10,700$

        $16,100 - 900y = 10,700$

            $-900y = -5400$

                $y = 6$

    Substitute 6 for y in (3)

    $x = 14 - 6$

    $x = 8$

    8 first class tickets

    6 coach tickets

264

3. x = number of etchings sold at $35.

y = number of etchings sold at $40

$35x + 40y = 455 \qquad (1)$

$x + \quad y = 12 \qquad (2)$

Solve (2) for y

$y = -x + 12 \qquad (3)$

Substitute $-x + 12$ for y in (1)

$35x + 40(-x + 12) = 455$

$35x - 40x + 480 = 455$

$-5x = -25$

$x = 5$

Substitute 5 for x in (3)

$y = -5 + 12 = 7$

Sold 5 etchings at $35.

Sold 7 etchings at $40.

5. x = hours on day shift

y = hours on night shift

$x + \quad y = 23 \qquad (1)$

$13.50x + 16.50y = 352.50 (2) \qquad (2)$

Solve for x

$x = 23 - y \qquad (3)$

Substitute $23 - y$ for x in (2)

$13.50(23 - y) + 16.50y = 352.50$

$310.50 - 13.50y + 16.50y = 352.50$

$310.50 + 3y = 352.50$

$3y = 42$

$y = 14$

Substitute 14 for y in (3)

$x = 23 - 14$

$x = 9$

9 hours on day shift

14 hours on night shift

7. L = original length

W = original width

$2L + 2W = 38 \qquad\qquad (1)$

$2(2L - 6) + 2(W + 5) = 56$

$4L - 12 + 2W + 10 = 56$

$4L + 2W = 58 \qquad (2)$

Multiply (1) by -1

$-2L - 2W = -38$

$\underline{4L + 2W = 58}$

$2L \qquad = 20$

$L = 10$

Substitute 10 for L in (1)

$2(10) + 2W = 38$

$2W = 18$

$W = 9$

original length $= 10$ feet

original width $= 9$ feet

New length $= 2(10) - 6 = 14$ feet

New width $= 9 + 5 = 14$ feet

9. x = quarts before

y = quarts added

$$x + \quad y = 16 \qquad (1)$$
$$0.50x + 0.80y = 0.65(16) \qquad (2)$$

Multiply (1) by -5 and (2) by 10

$$-5x - 5y = -80$$
$$\underline{5x + 8y = 104}$$
$$3y = 24$$
$$y = 8$$

Substitute 8 for y in (1)

$$x + 8 = 16$$
$$x = 8$$

8 quarts before

8 quarts added

11. x = weight of nuts

y = weight of raisins

$$x + \quad y = 50 \qquad (1)$$
$$2.00x + 1.50y = 50(1.80) \qquad (2)$$

Multiply (1) by -2

$$-2x - 2y = -100$$
$$\underline{2x + 1.5y = 90}$$
$$-0.5y = -10$$
$$y = 20$$

Substitute 20 for y in (1)

$$x + 20 = 50$$
$$x = 30$$

30 lbs of nuts

20 lbs of raisins

13. w = speed of wind

r = airspeed of airplane

$$\text{speed} = \frac{\text{distance}}{\text{time}}$$

$$r + w = \frac{3000}{5} = 600 \qquad (1)$$
$$r - w = \frac{3000}{6} = 500 \qquad (2)$$
$$\overline{2r \qquad\qquad = 1100}$$
$$r = 550$$

Substitute 550 for r in (1)

$$550 + w = 600$$
$$w = 50$$

Airspeed $= 550$ kilometers per hour

Windspeed $= 50$ kilometers per hour

13. $$x - \quad y = -65 \qquad (1)$$
$$3x + 5y = 725 \qquad (2)$$

Multiply (1) by -3

$$-3x + 3y = 195$$
$$\underline{3x + 5y = 725}$$
$$8y = 920$$
$$y = 115$$

Substitute 115 for y in (1)

$$x - 115 = -65$$
$$x = 50$$

There will be 115,000 employees in 2040.

15. x = number of \$10 bills for Jewelry

 y = number of \$20 bills for Jewelry

 Total amount in \$10 and \$20 bills

 $= 320 - 25 - 55 = 240$

$$10x + 20y = 240 \qquad (1)$$

$$10(2x - 2) + 20(y - 4) = 240$$

$$20x - 20 + 20y - 80 = 240$$

$$20x + 20y = 340 \qquad (2)$$

 Multiply (1) by -1

$$-10x - 20y = -240$$

$$\underline{20x + 20y = 340}$$

$$10x \qquad\quad = 100$$

$$x = 10$$

 Substitute 10 for x in (1)

$$10(10) + 20y = 240$$

$$100 + 20y = 240$$

$$20y = 140$$

$$y = 7$$

 Jewelry: 10 - \$10 bills and 7 - \$20 bills

 Cosmetics: $2(10) - 2 = 18$ \$10 bills

$$7 - 4 = 3 \text{ \$20 bills}$$

17. x = price of oranges

 y = price of apples

$$7x + 5y = 8.78 \qquad (1)$$

$$3x + 8y = 8.39 \qquad (2)$$

 Multiply (1) by 3 and (2) by -7

$$21x + 15y = 26.34$$

$$\underline{-21x - 56y = -58.73}$$

$$-41y = -32.39$$

$$y = 0.79$$

 Substitute 0.79 for y in (1)

$$7x + 5(0.79) = 8.78$$

$$7x + 3.95 = 8.78$$

$$7x = 4.83$$

$$x = 0.69$$

 Oranges are \$0.69 per pound.

 Apples are \$0.79 per pound.

19. x = number of general admission tickets

 y = number of student admission tickets

$$4.5x + 3y = 1110 \qquad (1)$$

$$x + y = 290 \qquad (2)$$

 Solve (2) for x

$$x = 290 - y$$

 Substitute $290 - y$ for x in (1)

$$4.5(290 - y) + 3y = 1110$$

$$1305 - 4.5y + 3y = 1110$$

$$1305 - 1.5y = 1110$$

$$-1.5y = -195$$

$$y = 130$$

 Substitute 130 for y in (3)

$$x = 290 - 130$$

$$x = 160$$

 160 general admission tickets

 130 student admission tickets

21. $40x - y = -5275$ (1)

    $28x - 2y = -11,078$ (2)

    Multiply (1) by -2

$$-80x + 2y = 10,550$$
$$\underline{28x - 2y = -11,078}$$
$$-52x = -528$$
$$x \approx 10.154$$

    Substitute 10.154 for x in (2)

$$28(10.154) - 2y = -11,078$$
$$284.312 - 2y = -11,078$$
$$-2y = -11362.312$$
$$y \approx 5680$$

    The population will be 5,680,000 employees in 2013.

23. $x = $ cost of a kidney kit

    $y = $ cost of a heart kit

    $0.06x + 0.08y = 4480$ (1)

    $0.08x + 0.10y = 5780$ (2)

    Multiply (1) by 400 and (2) by -300

$$24x + 32y = 1,792,000$$
$$\underline{-24x - 30y = -1,734,000}$$
$$2y = 58,000$$
$$y = 29,000$$

    Substitute 29,000 for y in (2)

$$0.08x + 0.10(29,000) = 5780$$
$$0.08x = 2880$$
$$x = 36,000$$

    $36,000 for a kidney kit

    $29,000 for a heart kit

Cumulative Review

25.
$$\frac{1}{x-3} - \frac{1}{x+3} + 2$$
$$= \frac{1(x+3)}{(x-3)(x+3)} - \frac{1(x-3)}{(x+3)(x-3)}$$
$$+ \frac{2(x+3)(x-3)}{(x+3)(x-3)}$$
$$= \frac{(x+3) - (x-3) + 2(x^2-9)}{(x+3)(x-3)}$$
$$= \frac{x+3 - x+3 + 2x^2 - 18}{(x+3)(x-3)}$$
$$= \frac{2x^2 - 12}{x^2 - 9}$$

27.
$$\left(-4x^3 y^2\right)^3 = (-4)^3 \left(x^3\right)^3 \left(y^2\right)^3$$
$$= -64x^9 y^6$$

29.
$$\text{Thickness} = \frac{1}{8} + \frac{1}{8} + 1\frac{3}{4}$$
$$= \frac{1}{8} + \frac{1}{8} + 1\frac{6}{8}$$
$$= 1\frac{8}{8}$$
$$= 2$$

    Total $= 3(2) = 6$ inches

Putting Your Skills to Work

1. $-5.4x + y = 372$

    $y = 372$ million in 1980

    $y = 5.4(20) + 372$

    $= 480$ million in 2000

    $y = 5.4(0) + 372$

    $y = 534$ million in 2010

2. $-5.25x + y = 242$

    $y = 242$ million in 1980

    $y = 5.25(20) + 242$

    $y = 347$ million in 2000

    $y = 5.25(30) + 242$

    $y = 399.5$ million in 2010

3. North America $480 - 372 = 108$ million

    South America $347 - 242 = 105$ million

    North America experienced greater growth.
    It grew by 3 million more peole in the
    period from 1980-2000.

4. North America $y = 5.4(40) + 372$

    $y = 588$ million

    South America $y = 5.25(40) + 242$

    $y = 452$ million

    Difference: $588 - 452 = 136$ million

    The difference will be 136 million people
    in 2020. Yes

5.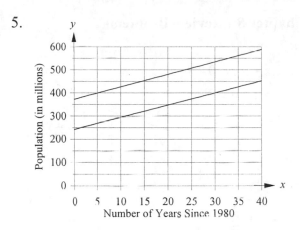

6. They do not intersect on the graph paper.
    For the time period shown the population
    of North America is never the same as the
    population of South America. If they
    intersect it would have to be for values of
    x less than 0.

7. $-5.4x + y = 372$ (1)

    $-5.25x + y = 242$ (2)

    Multiply (2) by -1

    $-5.4x + y = 372$

    $\underline{5.25x - y = -242}$

    $-0.15x \quad = 130$

    $x = -866.7$

    Substitute -866.67 for x in (1)

    $-5.4(-866.67) + y = 372$

    $y = -4308.0$

    $(-866.7, -4308.0)$

8. This would have no meaning since y is
    negative and you cannot have a negative
    population.

269

Chapter 8 - Review Problems

1. $2x + 3y = 0$
   $-x + 3y = 9$
   $(-3, 2)$

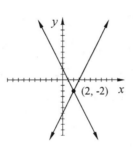

2. $-3x + y = -2$
   $-2x - y = -8$
   $(2, 4)$

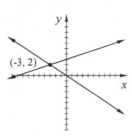

3. $2x - y = 6$
   $6x + 3y = 6$
   $(-3, 1)$

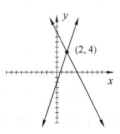

4. $2x - y = 1$
   $3x + y = -6$
   $(-1, -3)$

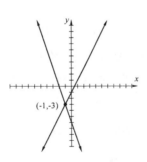

5. $x + y = 6$ (1)
   $-2x + y = -3$ (2)
   Solve (2) for y
   $y = 2x - 3$ (3)
   Substitute $2x - 3$ for y in (1)
   $x + (2x - 3) = 6$
   $x + 2x - 3 = 6$
   $3x = 9$
   $x = 3$

   Substitute 3 for x in (3)
   $y = 2(3) - 3 = 3$
   $(3, 3)$

   Check: $3 + 3 \overset{?}{=} 6$
   $6 = 6$

6. $x + 3y = 18$ (1)
   $2x + y = 11$ (2)
   Solve (2) for y
   $y = -2x + 11$ (3)
   Substitute $-2x + 11$ for y in (1)
   $x + 3(-2x + 11) = 18$
   $x - 6x + 33 = 18$
   $-5x = -15$
   $x = 3$
   Substitute 3 for x in (3)
   $y = -2(3) + 11 = 5$
   $(3, 5)$

   Check: $3 + 3(5) \overset{?}{=} 18$
   $18 = 18$

7. $3x - 2y = 3$ $\qquad$ (1)

$x - \dfrac{1}{3}y = 8$

$3x - y = 24$ $\qquad$ (2)

Solve (2) for y

$y = 3x - 24$ $\qquad$ (3)

Substitute $3x - 24$ for y in (1)

$3x - 2(3x - 24) = 3$

$\quad 3x - 6x + 48 = 3$

$\qquad\qquad -3x = -45$

$\qquad\qquad\quad x = 15$

Substitute 15 for x in (3)

$y = 3(15) - 24 = 21$

$(15, 21)$

Check: $15 - \dfrac{1}{3}(21) \overset{?}{=} 8$

$\qquad\qquad 15 - 7 \overset{?}{=} 6$

$\qquad\qquad\qquad 8 = 8$

8. $0.5x + y = 16$ $\qquad$ (1)

$\quad 4x - 2y = 8$ $\qquad$ (2)

Solve (1) for y

$y = -0.5x + 16$ $\qquad$ (3)

Substitute $-0.5x + 16$ for y in (2)

$4x - 2(-0.5x + 16) = 8$

$\qquad 4x + x - 32 = 8$

$\qquad\quad 5x - 32 = 8$

$\qquad\qquad\quad 5x = 40$

$\qquad\qquad\qquad x = 8$

Substitute 8 for x in (3)

$y = -0.5(8) + 16 \qquad y = 12$

Check: $4(8) - 2(12) \overset{?}{=} 8$

$\qquad\qquad\qquad 8 = 8$

$(8, 12)$

9. $6x - 2y = 10$ $\qquad$ (1)

$2x + 3y = 7$ $\qquad$ (2)

Multiply (1) by 3 and (2) by 2

$18x - 6y = 30$

$\underline{4x + 6y = 14}$

$22x \qquad = 44$

$\qquad x = 2$

Substitute 2 for x in (2)

$2(2) + 3y = 7$

$\qquad 3y = 3$

$\qquad\quad y = 1$

$(2, 1)$

Check: $6(2) - 2(1) \overset{?}{=} 10$

$\qquad\qquad\qquad 10 = 10$

10. $\quad 4x - 5y = -4$ $\qquad$ (1)

$-3x + 2y = 3$ $\qquad$ (2)

Multiply (1) by 2 and (2) by 5

$\quad 8x - 10y = -8$

$\underline{-15x + 10y = 15}$

$\quad -7x \qquad = 7$

$\qquad\quad x = -1$

Substitute -1 for x in (2)

$-3(-1) + 2y = 3$

$\qquad\quad 2y = 0$

$\qquad\qquad y = 0$

$(-1, 0)$

Check: $4(-1) - 5(0) \overset{?}{=} -4$

$\qquad\qquad\qquad -4 = -4$

11. $5x - 4y = 12$ (1)

$-2x + 3y = -9$ (2)

Multiply (1) by 3 and (2) by 4

$15x - 12y = 36$

$-8x + 12y = -36$

$7x \quad\quad = 0$

$x = 0$

Substitute 0 for x in (2)

$-2(0) + 3y = -9$

$3y = -9$

$y = -3$

$(0, -3)$

Check: $5(0) - 4(-3)\overset{?}{=}12$

$12 = 12$

12. $7x + 2y = 4$ (1)

$2x - 3y = 19$ (2)

Multiply (1) by 3 and (2) by 2

$21x + 6y = 12$

$4x - 6y = 38$

$25x \quad\quad = 50$

$x = 2$

Substitute 2 for x in (1)

$7(2) + 2y = 4$

$14 + 2y = 4$

$2y = -10$

$y = -5$

$(2, -5)$

Check: $2(2) - 3(-5)\overset{?}{=}19$

$19 = 19$

13. $5x - 3y = 32$ (1)

$5x + 7y = -8$ (2)

Multiply (2) by -1

$5x - 3y = 32$

$-5x - 7y = 8$

$-10y = 40$

$y = -4$

Substitute -4 for y in (1)

$5x - 3(-4) = 32$

$5x = 20$

$x = 4$

$(4, -4)$

14. $4x + 3y = 46$ (1)

$-2x + 3y = -14$ (2)

Multiply (2) by -1

$4x + 3y = 46$

$2x - 3y = 14$

$6x \quad\quad = 60$

$x = 10$

Substitute 10 for x in (1)

$4(10) + 3y = 46$

$3y = 6$

$y = 2$

$(10, 2)$

15. $7x + 3y = 2$ (1)
    $-8x - 7y = 2$ (2)

Multiply (1) by 7 and (2) by 3

$49x + 21y = 14$

$-24x - 21y = 6$

$25x \qquad = 20$

$$x = \frac{4}{5}$$

Substitute $\dfrac{4}{5}$ for x in (1)

$$7\left(\frac{4}{5}\right) + 3y = 2$$

$$3y = -\frac{18}{5}$$

$$y = -\frac{6}{5}$$

$$\left(\frac{4}{5}, -\frac{6}{5}\right)$$

16. $7x + 5y = 7$ (1)
    $-3x - 4y = 1$ (2)

Multiply (1) by 4 and (2) by 5

$28x + 20y = 28$

$-15x - 20y = 5$

$13x \qquad = 33$

$$x = \frac{33}{13}$$

Substitute $\dfrac{33}{13}$ for x in (1)

$$7\left(\frac{33}{13}\right) + 5y = 7$$

$$\frac{231}{13} + 5y = 7$$

$$5y = -\frac{140}{13}$$

$$y = -\frac{28}{13}$$

$$\left(\frac{33}{13}, -\frac{28}{13}\right)$$

17. $4x + 5y = 4$ (1)
    $-5x - 8y = 2$ (2)

Multiply (1) by 5 and (2) by 4

$20x + 25y = 20$

$-20x - 32y = 8$

$-7y = 28$

$$y = -4$$

Substitute -4 for y in (1)

$$4x + 5(-4) = 4$$

$$4x - 20 = 4$$

$$4x = 24$$

$$x = 6$$

$$(6, -4)$$

18. $7x - 2y = 1$ (1)
    $-5x + 3y = -7$ (2)

Multiply (1) by 3 and (2) by 2

$21x - 6y = 3$

$-10x + 6y = -14$

$11x \qquad = -11$

$$x = -1$$

Substitute -1 for x in (1)

$$7(-1) - 2y = 1$$

$$-7 - 2y = 1$$

$$-2y = 8$$

$$y = -4$$

$$(-1, -4)$$

19. $2x - 4y = 6$ (1)

     $-3x + 6y = 7$ (2)

     Multiply (1) by 3 and (2) by 2

     $6x - 12y = 18$

     $\underline{-6x + 12y = 14}$

          $0 = 32$

     No solution, inconsistent system.

20. $4x - 7y = 8$ (1)

     $5x + 9y = 81$ (2)

     Multiply (1) by 9 and (2) by 7

     $36x - 63y = 72$

     $\underline{35x + 63y = 567}$

     $71x \qquad = 639$

         $x = 9$

     Substitute 9 for x in (2)

     $5(9) + 9y = 81$

         $9y = 36$

         $y = 4$

     $(9, 4)$

21. $2x - 9y = 0$ (1)

     $3x + \;\; 5 = 6y$ (2)

     Rearrange (2)

     $3x - 6y = -5$ (3)

     Multiply (1) by 3 and (3) by -2

     $6x - 27y = 0$

     $\underline{-6x + 12y = 10}$

       $-15y = 10$

          $y = -\dfrac{2}{3}$

Substitute $-\dfrac{2}{3}$ for y in (1)

$2x - 9\left(-\dfrac{2}{3}\right) = 0$

       $2x = -6$

        $x = -3$

$\left(-3, \ -\dfrac{2}{3}\right)$

22. $2x + 10y = 1$ (1)

     $-4x - 20y = -2$ (2)

     Multiply (1) by 2

     $4x + 20y = 2$

     $\underline{-4x - 20y = -2}$

         $0 = 0$

     Infinite number of solutions,

     dependent equations

23. $5x - 8y = 3x + 12$ (1)

     $7x + \;\; y = 6y - 4$ (2)

     Rearrange and simplify

     $2x - 8y = 12$ (3)

     $7x - 5y = -4$ (4)

     Multiply (3) by 7 and (4) by -2

     $14x - 56y = 84$

     $\underline{-14x + 10y = 8}$

         $-46y = 92$

            $y = -2$

     Substitute -2 for y in (3)

     $2x - 8(-2) = 12$

          $2x = -4$

           $x = -2$

     $(-2, -2)$

24. $1 + x - y = y + 4$

    $4(x - y) = 3 - x$

    Rearrange and simplify

    $x - 2y = 3$ (1)

    $5x - 4y = 3$ (2)

    Multiply (1) by -5

    $-5x + 10y = -15$

    $\underline{5x - 4y = 3}$

          $6y = -12$

           $y = -2$

    Substitute -2 for y in (1)

    $x - 2(-2) = 3$

          $x = -1$

    $(-1, -2)$

25. $3x + y = 9$ (1)

    $x - 2y = 10$ (2)

    Multiply (1) by 2

    $6x + 2y = 18$

    $\underline{x - 2y = 10}$

    $7x = 28$

          $x = 4$

    Substitute 4 for x in (1)

    $3(4) + y = 9$

          $y = -3$

    $(4, -3)$

26. $x + 12y = 0$ (1)

    $3x - 5y = -2$ (2)

    Multiply (1) by -3

    $-3x - 36y = 0$

    $\underline{3x - 5y = -2}$

        $-41y = -2$

          $y = \dfrac{2}{41}$

    Substitute $\dfrac{2}{41}$ for y in (1)

    $x + 12\left(\dfrac{2}{41}\right) = 0$

          $x = -\dfrac{24}{41}$

    $\left(-\dfrac{24}{41}, \dfrac{2}{41}\right)$

27. $2(x + 3) = y + 4$

    $4x - 2y = -4$

    Expand, rearrange and simplify

    $2x - y = -2$ (1)

    $4x - 2y = -4$ (2)

    Multiply (1) by -2

    $-4x + 2y = 4$

    $\underline{4x - 2y = -4}$

         $0 = 0$

    Infinite number of solutions,

    dependent equations.

28. $x + y = 3000$ (1)

$x - 2y = -120$ (2)

Multiply (2) by -1

$x + y = 3000$

$\underline{-x + 2y = 120}$

$3y = 3120$

$y = 1040$

Substitute 1040 for y in (1)

$x + 1040 = 3000$

$x = 1960$

$(1960, 1040)$

29. $5x + 4y + 3 = 23$

$8x - 3y - 4 = 75$

Rearrange and simplify

$5x + 4y = 20$ (1)

$8x - 3y = 79$ (2)

Multiply (1) by 3 and (2) by 4

$15x + 12y = 60$

$\underline{32x - 12y = 316}$

$47x \qquad = 376$

$x = 8$

Substitute 8 for x in (1)

$5(8) + 4y = 20$

$4y = -20$

$y = -5$

$(8, -5)$

30. $4x - 3y + 1 = 6$ (1)

$5x + 8y + 2 = -74$ (2)

Rearrange and simplify

$4x - 3y = 5$ (3)

$5x + 8y = -76$ (4)

Multiply (3) by 8 and (4) by 3

$32x - 24y = 40$

$\underline{15x + 24y = -228}$

$47x = -188$

$x = -4$

Substitute -4 for x in (2)

$5(-4) + 8y + 2 = -74$

$8y = -56$

$y = -7$

$(-4, -7)$

31. $\dfrac{2x}{3} - \dfrac{3y}{4} = \dfrac{7}{12}$ (1)

$8x + 5y = 9$ (2)

Multiply (1) by -12

$-8x + 9y = -7$

$\underline{8x + 5y = 9}$

$14y = 2$

$y = \dfrac{1}{7}$

Substitute $\dfrac{1}{7}$ for y in (2)

$$8x + 5\left(\frac{1}{7}\right) = 9$$

$$8x = \frac{58}{7}$$

$$x = \frac{29}{28}$$

$$\left(\frac{29}{28}, \frac{1}{7}\right)$$

32. $\dfrac{x}{2} + \dfrac{y}{5} = 4$ (1)

$$\frac{x}{3} + \frac{y}{5} = \frac{10}{3} \qquad (2)$$

Multiply (1) by 10 and (2) by -15

$$5x + 2y = 40$$
$$\underline{-5x - 3y = -50}$$
$$-y = -10$$
$$y = 10$$

Substitute 10 for y in (1)

$$\frac{x}{2} + \frac{10}{5} = 4$$

$$\frac{x}{2} = 2$$

$$x = 4$$

$$(4, 10)$$

33. $\dfrac{1}{5}a + \dfrac{1}{2}b = 6$ (1)

$$\frac{3}{5}a - \frac{1}{2}b = 2 \qquad (2)$$

$$\underline{}$$

$$\frac{4}{5}a = 8$$

$$a = 10$$

Substitute 10 for a in (1)

$$\frac{1}{5}(10) + \frac{1}{2}b = 6$$

$$\frac{1}{2}b = 4$$

$$b = 8$$

$$(10,\ 8)$$

34. $\dfrac{2}{3}a + \dfrac{3}{5}b = -17$ (1)

$$\frac{1}{2}a - \frac{1}{3}b = -1 \qquad (2)$$

Multiply (1) by 30 and (2) by 54

$$20a + 18b = -510$$
$$\underline{27a - 18b = -54}$$
$$47a = -564$$
$$a = -12$$

Substitute -12 for a in (2)

$$\frac{1}{2}(-12) - \frac{1}{3}b = -1$$

$$-\frac{1}{3}b = 5$$

$$b = -15$$

$$(-12,\ -15)$$

35. $4.8 + 0.6m = 0.9n$

     $0.6m + 0.9n = -4.8$

       $6m - 9n = -48$ (1)

     $0.2m - 0.3n = 1.6$

       $2m - 3n = 16$ (2)

Multiply (2) by -3

       $6m - 9n = -48$

     $\underline{-6m + 9n = -48}$

        $0 + 0 = -9$

No solution. Inconsistent system.

Substitute $\dfrac{1}{2}$ for s in (4)

$$4\left(\dfrac{1}{2}\right) + 6t = -2$$

$$6t = -4$$

$$t = -\dfrac{2}{3}$$

$$\left(\dfrac{1}{2}, -\dfrac{2}{3}\right)$$

36. $8.4 - 0.8m = 0.4n$

$$-0.8m - 0.4n = -8.4$$

$$-8m - 4n = -84 \qquad (1)$$

$$0.2m + 0.1n = 2.1$$

$$2m + n = 21 \qquad (2)$$

Multiply (2) by 4

$$-8m - 4n = -84$$

$$\underline{8m + 4n = 84}$$

$$0 = 0$$

Infinite number of solutions.

Dependent equations.

37. $3s - 8t = 5 \qquad (1)$

     $4s + 3t = 2 \qquad (2)$

Multiply (1) by 4 and (2) by -3

$$12s - 32t = 20$$

$$\underline{-12s - 9t = -6}$$

$$-41t = 14$$

$$t = -\dfrac{14}{41}$$

Substitute $-\dfrac{14}{41}$ for t in (2)

$$4s + 3\left(-\dfrac{14}{41}\right) = 2$$

$$4s - \dfrac{42}{41} = 2$$

$$4s = \dfrac{42}{41} + \dfrac{82}{41}$$

$$4s = \dfrac{124}{41}$$

$$s = \dfrac{31}{41}$$

$$\left(\dfrac{31}{41}, -\dfrac{14}{41}\right)$$

38. $5s + 6t = 2 \qquad (1)$

     $3s - 5t = 4 \qquad (2)$

Multiply (1) by 5 and (2) by 6

$$25s + 30t = 10$$

$$\underline{18s - 30t = 24}$$

$$43s = 34$$

$$s = \dfrac{34}{43}$$

Substitute $\dfrac{34}{43}$ for s in (2)

$$3\left(\dfrac{34}{43}\right) - 5t = 4$$

$$102 - 215t = 172$$

$$-215t = 70$$

$$t = -\dfrac{70}{215}$$

$$t = -\dfrac{14}{43}$$

$$\left(\dfrac{34}{43}, -\dfrac{14}{43}\right)$$

39. $3(x+2) = -2-(x+3y)$

$3(x+y) = 3-2(y-1)$

Expand, rearrange and simplify

$4x+3y = -8$ (1)

$3x+5y = 5$ (2)

Multiply (1) by 3 and (2) by -4

$\quad 12x+9y = -24$

$\underline{-12x-20y = -20}$

$\qquad -11y = -44$

$\qquad\quad y = 4$

Substitute 4 for y in (1)

$4x+3(4) = -8$

$\quad 4x = -20$

$\qquad x = -5$

$(-5,\ 4)$

40. $13-x = 3(x+y)+1$

$14+2x = 5(x+y)+3x$

Expand, rearrange and simplify

$4x+3y = 12$ (1)

$6x+5y = 14$ (2)

Multiply (1) by -3 and (2) by 2

$-12x-\ 9y = -36$

$\underline{\ \ 12x+10y = 28\ }$

$\qquad\quad y = -8$

Substitute -8 for y in (1)

$4x+3(-8) = 12$

$\quad 4x = 36$

$\qquad x = 9$

$(9,\ -8)$

41. $\qquad 0.2b = 1.4-0.3a$

$0.1b+0.6 = 0.5a$

Rearrange

$0.3a+0.2b = 1.4$ (1)

$0.5a-0.1b = 0.6$ (2)

Multiply (1) by 10 and (2) by 20

$\quad 3a+2b = 14$

$\underline{10a-2b = 12\ }$

$13a \qquad = 26$

$\qquad a = 2$

Substitute 2 for a in (1)

$0.3(2)+0.2b = 1.4$

$\qquad 0.2b = 0.8$

$\qquad\quad b = 4$

$(2,\ 4)$

42. $0.3a = 1.1-0.2b$

$0.3b = 0.4a-0.9$

Rearrange and simplify

$0.3a+0.2b = 1.1$ (1)

$0.4a-0.3b = 0.9$ (2)

Multiply (1) by 30 and (2) by 20

$9a+6b = 33$

$\underline{8a-6b = 18\ }$

$17a \quad = 51$

$\qquad a = 3$

279

Substitute 3 for a in (1)

$$0.3(3) + 0.2b = 1.1$$
$$0.2b = -0.2$$
$$b = 1$$

$$(3, 1)$$

43. $$\frac{b}{5} = \frac{2}{5} - \frac{a-3}{2}$$
$$4(a-b) = 3b - 2(a-2)$$

Multiply the first equation by 10, then
Expand, rearrange, and simplify.

$$5a + 2b = 19 \qquad (1)$$
$$6a - 7b = 4 \qquad (2)$$

Multiply (1) by 7 and (2) by 2

$$35a + 14b = 133$$
$$\underline{12a - 14b = 8}$$
$$47a = 141$$
$$a = 3$$

Substitute 3 for a in (1)

$$5(3) + 2b = 19$$
$$2b = 4$$
$$b = 2$$

$$(3, 2)$$

44. $9(b+4) = 2(2a+5b)$

Expand and simplify

$$4a + b = 36 \qquad (1)$$

$$\frac{b}{5} + \frac{a}{2} = \frac{18}{5}$$

Rearrange and multiply by 10

$$5a + 2b = 36 \qquad (2)$$

Multiply (1) by -2

$$-8a - 2b = -72$$
$$\underline{5a + 2b = 36}$$
$$-3a \quad\;\; = -36$$
$$a = 12$$

Substitute 12 for a in (1)

$$4(12) + b = 36$$
$$b = -12$$

$$(12, -12)$$

45. $x =$ number of reserved seat tickets
$y =$ number of general admission tickets

$$x + \;\; y = 760 \qquad (1)$$
$$6x + 4y = 3280 \qquad (2)$$

Multiply (1) by -4

$$-4x - 4y = -3040$$
$$\underline{6x + 4y = 3280}$$
$$2x \qquad\;\; = 240$$

$$x = 120$$

Substitute 120 for x in (1)

$$120 + y = 760$$
$$y = 640$$

120 reserved seats

640 general admission seats

280

46. x = number of 2-pound bags

    y = number of 5-pound bags

$$2x + 5y = 252 \qquad (1)$$
$$y = 2x \qquad (2)$$

Substitute $2x$ for y in (1)

$$2x + 5(2x) = 252$$
$$2x + 10x = 252$$
$$12x = 252$$
$$x = 21$$

Substitute 21 for x in (2)

$$y = 2(21) = 42$$

He prepared 21 2-lb bags

and 42 5-lb bags

47. r = airspeed

    w = wind speed

$$\text{speed} = \frac{\text{distance}}{\text{time}}$$

$$r + w = \frac{1500}{5} \qquad (1)$$

$$r - w = \frac{1500}{6} \qquad (2)$$

$$2r \quad = 550$$

$$r = 275$$

Substitute 275 for r in (1)

$$275 + w = 300$$
$$w = 25$$

Speed in still air $= 275$ mph

Wind speed $= 25$ mph

48. x = amount of 30% acid solution

    y = amount of 20% acid solution

$$y = x + 40 \qquad (1)$$
$$0.30x + 0.12(40) = 0.20y$$

Multiply by 10 and rearrange

$$3x - 2y = -48 \qquad (2)$$

Substitute $x + 40$ for y in (2)

$$3x - 2(x + 40) = -48$$
$$3x - 2x - 80 = -48$$
$$x = 32$$

32 liters of 30% acid solution

should be added.

49. x = number of regular-sized cars

    y = number of compact cars

$$x + \quad y = 86 \qquad (1)$$
$$4x + 3.50y = 323 \qquad (2)$$

Multiply (1) by -4

$$-4x - \quad 4y = -344$$
$$\underline{4x + 3.50y = 323}$$
$$-0.50y = -21$$
$$y = 42$$

Substitute 42 for y in (1)

$$x + 42 = 86$$
$$x = 44$$

44 regular-sized cars

42 compact cars

50. x = tons of 15% salt mixture

    y = tons of 30% salt mixture

    $x + y = 24$ (1)

    $0.15x + 0.30y = 0.25(24)$

    Multiply by 100 and simplify

    $15x + 30y = 600$ (2)

    Solve (1) for x

    $x = 24 - y$ (3)

    Substitute $24 - y$ for x in (2)

    $15(24 - y) + 30y = 600$

    $360 - 15y + 30y = 600$

              $15y = 240$

                $y = 16$

    Substitute 16 for y in (3)

    $x = 24 - 16 = 8$

    8 tons of 15% salt mixture

    16 tons of 30% salt mixture

51. r = speed of boat in still water

    c = speed of current

    $r + c = 23$ (1)

    $\underline{r - c = 15}$ (2)

    $2r \quad = 38$

      $r = 19$

    Substitute 19 for r in (1)

    $19 + c = 23$

        $c = 4$

    Speed of boat = 19 kph

    Speed of current = 4 kph

52. x = cost of copper per gram

    y = hourly labor rate

    $5x + 3y = 27$ (1)

    $4x + 5y = 32$ (2)

    Multiply (1) by 5 and (2) by -3

    $25x + 15y = 135$

    $\underline{-12x - 15y = -96}$

      $13x \qquad = 39$

          $x = 3$

    Substitute 3 for x in (1)

    $5(3) + 3y = 27$

          $3y = 12$

          $y = 4$

    It costs \$3 per gram of copper.

    The hourly labor rate is \$4.

53. x = number of lower seats

    y = number of upper seats

    $x + \quad y = 23$ (1)

    $22x + 6.5y = 320$ (2)

    Solve (1) for x

    $x = 23 - y$ (3)

    Substitute $23 - y$ for x in (2)

    $22(23 - y) + 6.5y = 320$

    $506 - 22y + 6.5y = 320$

        $506 - 15.5y = 320$

            $-15.5y = -186$

                $y = 12$

    Substitute 12 for y in (3)

    $x = 23 - 12$

    $x = 11$

    11 lower seats

    9 upper seats

282

54. x = number of infield seats

y = number of bases seats

$$x + \quad y = 27 \qquad (1)$$
$$42x + 34y = 1070 \qquad (2)$$

Solve (1) for x

$$x = 27 - y \qquad (3)$$

Substitute $27 - y$ for x in (2)

$$42(27 - y) + 34y = 1070$$
$$1134 - 42y + 34y = 1070$$
$$1134 - 8y = 1070$$
$$-8y = -64$$
$$y = 8$$

19 upper infield seats

8 lower bases seats

How Am I Doing? Chapter 8 Test

1. $\quad 3x - \quad y = -5 \qquad (1)$

$\quad -2x + 5y = -14 \qquad (2)$

Solve (1) for y

$$y = 3x + 5 \qquad (3)$$

Substitute $3x + 5$ for y in (2)

$$-2x + 5(3x + 5) = -14$$
$$-2x + 15x + 25 = -14$$
$$13x = -39$$
$$x = -3$$

Substitute -3 for x in (1)

$$3(-3) - y = -5$$
$$-y = 4$$
$$y = -4$$

$$(-3, -4)$$

2. $3x + 4y = 7 \qquad (1)$

$\quad 2x + 3y = 6 \qquad (2)$

Multiply (1) by 2 and (2) by -3

$$6x + 8y = 14$$
$$\underline{-6x - 9y = -18}$$
$$-y = -4$$
$$y = 4$$

Substitute 4 for y in (2)

$$2x + 3(4) = 6$$
$$2x = -6$$
$$x = -3$$

$$(-3, 4)$$

3. $2x - y = 4$

$\quad 4x + y = 2$

$$(1, -2)$$

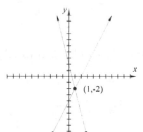

4. $\quad x + 3y = 12 \qquad (1)$

$\quad 2x - 4y = 4 \qquad (2)$

Multiply (1) by -2

$$-2x - 6y = -24$$
$$\underline{2x - 4y = 4}$$
$$-10y = -20$$
$$y = 2$$

Substitute 2 for y in (1)

$$x + 3(2) = 12$$
$$x = 6$$

$$(6, 2)$$

5. $2x - y = 5$ (1)

   $-x + 3y = 5$ (2)

Multiply (1) by 3

$6x - 3y = 15$

$\underline{-x + 3y = 5}$

$5x \quad\quad = 20$

       $x = 4$

Substitute 4 for x in (1)

$2(4) - y = 5$

     $-y = -3$

       $y = 3$

$(4, 3)$

6. $2x + 3y = 13$ (1)

   $3x - 5y = 10$ (2)

Multiply (1) by 5 and (2) by 3

$10x + 15y = 65$

$\underline{9x - 15y = 30}$

$19x \quad\quad = 95$

       $x = 5$

Substitute 5 for x in (1)

$2(5) + 3y = 13$

       $3y = 3$

         $y = 1$

$(5, 1)$

7. $\dfrac{2}{3}x - \dfrac{1}{5}y = 2$ (1)

   $\dfrac{4}{3}x + 4y = 4$ (2)

Multiply (1) by 15 and (2) by 3

$10x - 3y = 30$ (3)

$4x + 12y = 12$ (4)

Multiply (3) by 4

$40x - 12y = 120$

$\underline{4x + 12y = 12}$

$44x \quad\quad\quad = 132$

         $x = 3$

Substitute 3 for x in (2)

$\dfrac{4}{3}(3) + 4y = 4$

       $4y = 0$

        $y = 0$

$(3, 0)$

8. $3x - 6y = 5$ (1)

   $-\dfrac{1}{2}x + y = \dfrac{7}{2}$ (2)

Multiply (2) by 6

    $3x - 6y = 5$ (3)

$\underline{-3x + 6y = 21}$ (4)

          $0 = 26$

No solution, inconsistent system

9. $5x - 2 = y$ (1)

    $10x = 4 + 2y$ (2)

Substitute $5x - 2$ for y in (2)

$10x = 4 + 2(5x - 2)$

$10x = 4 + 10x - 4$

    $0 = 0$

Infinite number of solutions,

dependent equations.

10. $0.3x + 0.2y = 0$ (1)

   $1.0x + 0.5y = 0.5$ (2)

Multiply (1) by -50 and (2) by 20

$-15x - 10y = 0$ (3)

$\underline{20x + 10y = -10}$ (4)

    $5x = -10$

      $x = -2$

Substitute -2 for x in (4)

$20(-2) + 10y = -10$

        $10y = 30$

         $y = 3$

$(-2, 3)$

11. $2(x + y) = 2(1 - y)$ (1)

  $5(-x + y) = 2(23 - y)$ (2)

Expand, rearrange, and simplify

   $2x + 4y = 2$ (3)

$-5x + 7y = 46$ (4)

Multiply (3) by 5 and (4) by 2

  $10x + 20y = 10$

$\underline{-10x + 14y = 92}$

     $34y = 102$

      $y = 3$

Substitute 3 for y in (3)

$2x + 4(3) = 2$

  $2x = -10$

   $x = -5$

$(-5, 3)$

12. $3(x - y) = 12 + 2y$ (1)

  $8(y + 1) = 6x - 7$ (2)

Expand, rearrange, and simplify

  $3x - 5y = 12$ (3)

$-6x + 8y = -15$ (4)

Multiply (3) by 2

  $6x - 10y = 24$

$\underline{-6x + 8y = -15}$

    $-2y = 9$

      $y = -4.5$

Substitute -4.5 for y in (3)

$3x - 5(-4.5) = 12$

  $3x + 22.5 = 12$

    $3x = -10.5$

     $x = -3.5$

$(-3.5, -4.5)$

13. x = first number
     y = second number
     $2x + 3y = 1$ (1)
     $3x + 2y = 9$ (2)
     Multiply (1) by 3 and (2) by -2
     $6x + 9y = 3$
     $\underline{-6x - 4y = -18}$
     $\quad\quad 5y = -15$
     $\quad\quad\ y = -3$
     Substitute -3 for y in (1)
     $2x + 3(-3) = 1$
     $\quad\quad 2x = 10$
     $\quad\quad\ x = 5$
     The first number is 5 and
     the second number is -3

14. x = the number of $8 tickets
     y = the number of $12 tickets
     $x + \quad y = 30,500$ (1)
     $8x + 12y = 308,000$ (2)
     Solve (1) for y
     $y = 30,500 - x$ (3)
     Substitute $30,500 - x$ for y in (2)
     $8x + 12(30,500 - x) = 308,000$
     $8x + 366,000 - 12x = 308,000$

     $\quad\quad\quad -4x = -58,000$
     $\quad\quad\quad\ x = 14,500$
     Substitute 14,500 for x in (3)
     $y = 30,500 - 14,500 = 16,000$
     14,500 of the $8 tickets
     16,000 of the $12 tickets

15. x = cost of a shirt
     y = cost of a pair of slacks
     $5x + 3y = 172$ (1)
     $3x + 4y = 156$ (2)
     Multiply (1) by 4 and (2) by -3
     $20x + 12y = 688$
     $\underline{-9x - 12y = -468}$
     $11x \quad\quad = 220$
     $\quad\quad x = 20$
     Substitute 20 for x in (1)
     $5(20) + 3y = 172$
     $\quad\quad\quad 3y = 72$
     $\quad\quad\quad\ y = 24$
     A shirt costs $20
     A pair of slacks costs $24

16. x = number of booklets
     y = cost
     $y = 0.25x + 200$ (1)
     $y = 0.2x + 250$ (2)
     Substitute $0.25x + 200$ for y in (2)
     $0.25x + 200 = 0.2x + 250$
     $0.05x + 200 = 250$
     $\quad\quad 0.05x = 50$
     $\quad\quad\quad x = 1000$
     Substitute 1000 for x in (1)
     $y = 0.25(1000) + 200$
     $y = 450$
     Order 1000 booklets at a cost of $450.

17. r = airspeed

w = wind speed

$$r + w = \frac{2000}{4} \qquad (1)$$

$$r - w = \frac{2000}{5} \qquad (2)$$

$$2r \quad = 900$$

$$r = 450$$

Substitute 450 for r in (1)

$$450 + w = 500$$

$$w = 50$$

Speed of plane in still air = 450 kmph

Wind speed = 50 kmph

Cumulative Test for Chapters 0-8

1. 11% of $37.20 = 0.11(37.20) = \$4.09$

2. $\dfrac{-2^4\left(2^2\right)}{2^3} = \dfrac{-16(4)}{8} = -8$

3. $\left(3x^2 - 2x + 1\right)(5x - 3)$

$= \left(3x^2 - 2x + 1\right)(5x) - \left(3x^2 - 2x + 1\right)(3)$

$= 15x^3 - 10x^2 + 5x - 9x^2 + 6x - 3$

$= 15x^3 - 19x^2 + 11x - 3$

4. $\dfrac{x^2 - 7x + 12}{x^2 - 9} \div \dfrac{x^2 - 8x + 16}{1}$

$= \dfrac{x^2 - 7x + 12}{x^2 - 9} \cdot \dfrac{1}{x^2 - 8x + 16}$

$= \dfrac{(x-4)(x-3)}{(x+3)(x-3)} \cdot \dfrac{1}{(x-4)(x-4)}$

$= \dfrac{1}{(x+3)(x-4)}$

5. $2(x+3) < 3(x-5)$

$2x + 6 < 3x - 15$

$-x + 6 < -15$

$-x < -21$

$x > 21$

6. $6x^2 + x - 2 = 0$

$(2x - 1)(3x + 2) = 0$

$2x - 1 = 0 \qquad 3x + 2 = 0$

$2x = 1 \qquad\quad 3x = -2$

$x = \dfrac{1}{2} \qquad\quad x = -\dfrac{2}{3}$

7. 12% of x is 360

$0.12x = 360$

$x = 3000$

8. $\dfrac{1}{10}x + \dfrac{1}{3} = \dfrac{2}{5}x - \dfrac{1}{6}$

$30\left(\dfrac{1}{10}x\right) + 30\left(\dfrac{1}{3}\right) = 30\left(\dfrac{2}{5}\right)x - 30\left(\dfrac{1}{6}\right)$

$3x + 10 = 12x - 5$

$$10 = 9x - 5$$
$$15 = 9x$$
$$\frac{5}{3} = x$$

9. $10t^2 - 25t^3 + 15t^4$

$$= 5t^2\left(3t^2 - 5t + 2\right)$$

$$= 5t^2\left(3t - 2\right)\left(t - 1\right)$$

10. $4x = 2\left(12 - 2x\right)$

$$4x = 24 - 4x$$
$$8x = 24$$
$$x = 3$$

11. $2x + \ y = 8$ \qquad (1)

$3x + 4y = -8$ \qquad (2)

Multiply (1) by -4

$$-8x - 4y = -32$$
$$\underline{\ \ 3x + 4y = -8\ \ }$$
$$-5x \qquad = -40$$
$$x = 8$$

Substitute 8 for x in (1)

$$2(8) + y = 8$$
$$y = -8$$

$(8, -8)$

12. $\dfrac{1}{3}x - \dfrac{1}{2}y = 4$

$\dfrac{3}{8}x - \dfrac{1}{4}y = 7$

Clear the fractions

$2x - 3y = 24$ \qquad (1)

$3x - 2y = 56$ \qquad (2)

Multiply (1) by -3 and (2) by 2

$$-6x + 9y = -72$$
$$\underline{\ \ 6x - 4y = 112\ \ }$$
$$5y = 40$$
$$y = 8$$

Substitute 8 for y in (1)

$$2x - 3(8) = 24$$
$$2x = 48$$
$$x = 24$$

$(24, 8)$

13. $1.3x - 0.7y = 0.4$ \qquad (1)

$-3.9x + 2.1y = -1.2$ \qquad (2)

Multiply (1) by 30 and (2) by 10

$$39x - 21y = 12$$
$$\underline{-39x + 21y = -12}$$
$$0 = 0$$

Infinite number of solutions, dependent system.

14. $10x - 5y = 45$ \qquad (1)

$3x - 8y = 7$ \qquad (2)

Multiply (1) by -8 and (2) by 5

$$-80x + 40y = -360$$
$$\underline{\ \ 15x - 40y = 35\ \ }$$
$$-65x = -325$$
$$x = 5$$

Substitute 5 for x in (2)

$$3(5) - 8y = 7$$
$$-8y = -8$$
$$y = 1$$

$(5, 1)$

15. Parallel lines represent an inconsistent system for which there is no solution.

16. x = amount of 8% solution

    y = amount of 20% solution

    $x + y = 12,000$ (1)

    $0.08x + 0.20y = 0.16(12,000)$

    Multiply by 100 and simplify

    $8x + 20y = 192,000$ (2)

    Solve (1) for x

    $x = 12,000 - y$ (3)

    Substitute $24 - y$ for x in (2)

    $8(12,000 - y) + 20y = 192,000$

    $96,000 \quad 8y + 20y = 192,000$

    $12y = 96,000$

    $y = 8000$

    Substitute 8000 for y in (3)

    $x = 12,000 - 8000 = 4000$

    4000 liters of 8% solution

    8000 liters of 20% solution

17. r = speed of boat in still water

    s = speed of the stream

    $r - s = \dfrac{6}{3}$ (1)

    $r + s = \dfrac{6}{1.5}$ (2)

    Multiply (1) by -1

    $-r + s = -2$

    $\underline{r + s = 4}$

    $2s = 2$

    $s = 1$

    Speed of the stream is 1 mph.

18. x = first printer's rate

    y = second printer's rate

    $5x + 5y = 15,000$ (1)

    $7x + 2y = 15,000$ (2)

    Multiply (1) by 2 and (2) by -5

    $10x + 10y = 30,000$

    $\underline{-35x - 10y = -75,000}$

    $-25x \qquad\quad = -45,000$

    $x = 1800$

    Substitute 1800 for x in (1)

    $5(1800) + 5y = 15,000$

    $9000 + 5y = 15,000$

    $5y = 6000$

    $y = 1200$

    The printer that broke prints 1200 labels/hr. The other printer prints 1800 labels/hr.

Chapter 9

9.1 Exercises

1. Answers will vary.

3. No, because $(0.3)(0.3) = 0.09$.

5. $\pm\sqrt{9} = \pm 3$

7. $\pm\sqrt{49} = \pm 7$

9. $\sqrt{16} = 4$

11. $\sqrt{81} = 9$

13. $-\sqrt{36} = -6$

15. $\sqrt{0.81} = 0.9$

17. $\sqrt{\dfrac{36}{121}} = \dfrac{6}{11}$

19. $\sqrt{\dfrac{49}{64}} = \dfrac{7}{8}$

21. $\sqrt{400} = 20$

23. $-\sqrt{10,000} = -100$

25. $\sqrt{169} = 13$

27. $-\sqrt{\dfrac{1}{64}} = -\dfrac{1}{8}$

29. $\sqrt{\dfrac{9}{16}} = \dfrac{3}{4}$

31. $\sqrt{0.0036} = 0.06$

33. $\sqrt{16,900} = 130$

35. $-\sqrt{289} = -17$

37. $\sqrt{27} = 5.176$

39. $\sqrt{74} \approx 8.602$

41. $-\sqrt{133} = -11.533$

43. $-\sqrt{195} = -13.964$

45. $\sqrt{169} = 13$ feet

47. If $a = 900$,
$$t = \frac{1}{4}\sqrt{a} = \frac{1}{4}\sqrt{900} = 7.5 \text{ seconds}$$

49. If $a = 1444$,
$$t = \frac{1}{4}\sqrt{a} = \frac{1}{4}\sqrt{1444} = 9.5 \text{ seconds}$$

51. $\sqrt[3]{27} = 3$

53. $\sqrt[3]{-216} = -6$

55. $\sqrt[4]{81} = 3$

57. $\sqrt[5]{243} = 3$

59. No; a fourth power of a real number must be nonnegative.

Cumulative Review

61. $3x + 2y = 8$ (1)

$7x - 3y = 11$ (2)

Multiply (1) by 3 and (2) by 2

$9x + 6y = 24$

$\underline{14x - 6y = 22}$

$23x \qquad = 46$

$x = 2$

Substitute 2 for x in (1)

$3(2) + 2y = 8$

$2y = 2$

$y = 1$

$(2, 1)$

63. s = cost per snowboard

g = cost per pair of goggles

$3s + 2g = 850$ (1)

$4s + 3g = 1150$ (2)

Multiply (1) by -3 and (2) by 2.

$-9s - 6g = -2550$

$\underline{8s + 6g = \;\; 2300}$

$-s = -250$

$s = 250$

Substitute 250 for s in (1).

$3(250) + 2g = 850$

$750 + 2g = 850$

$2g = 100$

$g = 50$

$250 per snowboard

$50 per pair of goggles

65. $2000 - 2010$:

Decrease $= 10.6 - 9.4 = 1.2$

Percent decrease $= \dfrac{1.2}{10.6} = 0.113 = 11.3\%$

$2010 - 2020$:

$100\% - 11.3\% = 88.7\%$

Length of stay $= 88.7\%$ of 9.4

$= 0.887(9.4)$

$= 8.3$ days

9.2 Exercises

1. Yes. $\sqrt{6^2} = \sqrt{6 \cdot 6} = \sqrt{6} \cdot \sqrt{6} = \left(\sqrt{6}\right)^2$

3. No. $\sqrt{(-9)^2} = \sqrt{81} = \sqrt{9^2}$

5. $\sqrt{8^2} = 8$

7. $\sqrt{18^4} = \sqrt{\left(18^2\right)^2} = 18^2$

9. $\sqrt{9^6} = \sqrt{\left(9^3\right)^2} = 9^3$

11. $\sqrt{33^8} = \sqrt{\left(33^4\right)^2} = 33^4$

13. $\sqrt{5^{140}} = \sqrt{\left(5^{70}\right)^2} = 5^{70}$

15. $\sqrt{x^{12}} = \sqrt{\left(x^6\right)^2} = x^6$

17. $\sqrt{t^{18}} = \sqrt{\left(t^9\right)^2} = t^9$

19. $\sqrt{y^{26}} = \sqrt{\left(y^{13}\right)^2} = y^{13}$

21. $\sqrt{36x^8} = \sqrt{6^2\left(x^4\right)^2} = 6x^4$

23. $\sqrt{144x^2} = \sqrt{144}\sqrt{x^2} = 12x$

25. $\sqrt{x^6y^4} = \sqrt{\left(x^3\right)^2\left(y^2\right)^2} = x^3y^2$

27. $\sqrt{16x^2y^{20}} = \sqrt{4^2x^2\left(y^{10}\right)^2} = 4xy^{10}$

29. $\sqrt{100x^{12}y^8} = \sqrt{10^2\left(x^6\right)^2\left(y^4\right)^2} = 10x^6y^4$

31. $\sqrt{24} = \sqrt{4\cdot6} = 2\sqrt{6}$

33. $\sqrt{45} = \sqrt{9\cdot5} = 3\sqrt{5}$

35. $\sqrt{18} = \sqrt{9\cdot2} = 3\sqrt{2}$

37. $\sqrt{72} = \sqrt{36\cdot2} = 6\sqrt{2}$

39. $\sqrt{90} = \sqrt{9\cdot10} = 3\sqrt{10}$

41. $\sqrt{128} = \sqrt{64\cdot2} = 8\sqrt{2}$

43. $\sqrt{8x^3} = \sqrt{4\cdot2x^2x} = 2x\sqrt{2x}$

45. $\sqrt{27w^5} = \sqrt{9\cdot3w^4w}$
$$= \sqrt{3^2\cdot3\left(w^2\right)^2w}$$
$$= 3w^2\sqrt{3w}$$

47. $\sqrt{32z^9} = \sqrt{16\cdot2z^8z} = 4z^4\sqrt{2z}$

49. $\sqrt{28x^5y^7} = \sqrt{4\cdot7x^4xy^6y} = 2x^2y^3\sqrt{7xy}$

51. $\sqrt{48y^3w} = \sqrt{16\cdot3y^2yw} = 4y\sqrt{3yw}$

53. $\sqrt{75x^2y^3} = \sqrt{25\cdot3x^2y^2y} = 5xy\sqrt{3y}$

55. $\sqrt{81x^8} = 9x^4$

57. $\sqrt{y^7} = \sqrt{y^6 y} = y^3\sqrt{y}$

59. $\sqrt{x^5 y^{11}} = \sqrt{x^4 xy^{10} y} = x^2 y^5 \sqrt{xy}$

61. $\sqrt{135x^5 y^7} = \sqrt{9 \cdot 15x^4 xy^6 y} = 3x^2 y^3 \sqrt{15xy}$

63. $\sqrt{80a^3 b^3 c^6} = \sqrt{16 \cdot 5a^2 ab^2 bc^6} = 4abc^3 \sqrt{5ab}$

65. $\sqrt{169a^3 b^8 c^5} = \sqrt{169a^2 ab^8 c^4 c}$
$= 13ab^4 c^2 \sqrt{ac}$

67. $\sqrt{(x+5)^2} = x+5$

69. $\sqrt{16x^2 + 8x + 1} = \sqrt{(4x+1)^2} = 4x+1$

71. $\sqrt{x^2 y^2 + 14xy^2 + 49y^2} = \sqrt{y^2 (x^2 + 14x + 49)}$
$= \sqrt{y^2 (x+7)^2}$
$= y(x+7)$

73. $\sqrt{75} = \sqrt{25 \cdot 3} = 5\sqrt{3}$ mm^2

75. (a) $\sqrt{1200} = \sqrt{400 \cdot 3} = 20\sqrt{3}$ mm^2

    (b) $\dfrac{20\sqrt{3}}{5\sqrt{3}} = 4$ times larger

Cumulative Review

77. $3x - 2y = 14$ (1)
    $y = x - 5$ (2)
    $3x - 2(x - 5) = 14$ Substitute $x - 5$ into (1)
    $3x - 2x + 10 = 14$
              $x = 4$
    $y = 4 - 5 = -1$ Substitute 4 into (2)
    $(4, -1)$

79. $1984 - 1994$
    Rate of increase $= \dfrac{560 - 310}{10} = 25$
    Use in $2007 = 560 + 13(25)$
               $= 885$ million tons

81. Rate of increase $= \dfrac{990 - 560}{560} \approx 0.768 = 76.8\%$

9.3 Exercises

1. (1) Simplify each radical term.
    (2) Combine like radicals.

3. $3\sqrt{5} - \sqrt{5} + 4\sqrt{5} = 6\sqrt{5}$

5. $\sqrt{2} + 8\sqrt{3} - 5\sqrt{3} + 4\sqrt{2}$
    $= 5\sqrt{2} + 3\sqrt{3}$

7. $\sqrt{5} + \sqrt{45} = \sqrt{5} + \sqrt{9 \cdot 5}$
              $= \sqrt{5} + 3\sqrt{5}$
              $= 4\sqrt{5}$

9. $\sqrt{80} + 4\sqrt{20} = \sqrt{16 \cdot 5} + 4\sqrt{4 \cdot 5}$

$\qquad = 4\sqrt{5} + 8\sqrt{5}$

$\qquad = 12\sqrt{5}$

11. $2\sqrt{8} - 3\sqrt{2} = 2\sqrt{4 \cdot 2} - 3\sqrt{2}$

$\qquad = 4\sqrt{2} - 3\sqrt{2}$

$\qquad = \sqrt{2}$

13. $-\sqrt{2} + \sqrt{18} + \sqrt{98}$

$\qquad = -\sqrt{2} + \sqrt{9 \cdot 2} + \sqrt{49 \cdot 2}$

$\qquad = -\sqrt{2} + 3\sqrt{2} + 7\sqrt{2}$

$\qquad = 9\sqrt{2}$

15. $\sqrt{25} + \sqrt{72} + 3\sqrt{12} = \sqrt{25} + \sqrt{36 \cdot 2} + 3\sqrt{4 \cdot 3}$

$\qquad\qquad\qquad = 5 + 6\sqrt{2} + 6\sqrt{3}$

17. $2\sqrt{48} - 3\sqrt{8} + \sqrt{50}$

$\qquad = 2\sqrt{16 \cdot 3} - 3\sqrt{4 \cdot 2} + \sqrt{25 \cdot 2}$

$\qquad = 8\sqrt{3} - \sqrt{2}$

19. $8\sqrt{2x} + \sqrt{50x} = 8\sqrt{2x} + \sqrt{25 \cdot 2x}$

$\qquad\qquad = 8\sqrt{2x} + 5\sqrt{2x}$

$\qquad\qquad = 13\sqrt{2x}$

21. $1.2\sqrt{3x} - 0.5\sqrt{12x} = 1.2\sqrt{3x} - 0.5\sqrt{4 \cdot 3x}$

$\qquad\qquad\qquad = 1.2\sqrt{3x} - \sqrt{3x}$

$\qquad\qquad\qquad = 0.2\sqrt{3x}$

23. $\sqrt{20y} + 2\sqrt{45y} - \sqrt{5y}$

$\qquad = \sqrt{4 \cdot 5y} + 2\sqrt{9 \cdot 5y} - \sqrt{5y}$

$\qquad = 2\sqrt{5y} + 6\sqrt{5y} - \sqrt{5y}$

$\qquad = 7\sqrt{5y}$

25. $\sqrt{50} - 3\sqrt{8} = \sqrt{25 \cdot 2} - 3\sqrt{4 \cdot 2}$

$\qquad\qquad = 5\sqrt{2} - 6\sqrt{2}$

$\qquad\qquad = -\sqrt{2}$

27. $3\sqrt{28x} - 5x\sqrt{63x}$

$\qquad = 3\sqrt{4 \cdot 7x} - 5x\sqrt{9 \cdot 7x}$

$\qquad = 6\sqrt{7x} - 15x\sqrt{7x}$

29. $5\sqrt{8x^3} - 3x\sqrt{50x}$

$\qquad = 5\sqrt{4 \cdot 2xx^2} - 3x\sqrt{25 \cdot 2x}$

$\qquad = 10x\sqrt{2x} - 15x\sqrt{2x}$

$\qquad = -5x\sqrt{2x}$

31. $5x\sqrt{48} - 2x\sqrt{75}$

$\qquad = 5x\sqrt{16 \cdot 3} - 2x\sqrt{25 \cdot 3}$

$\qquad = 5x(4)\sqrt{3} - 2x(5)\sqrt{3}$

$\qquad = 20x\sqrt{3} - 10x\sqrt{3}$

$\qquad = 10x\sqrt{3}$

33. $2\sqrt{6y^3} - 2y\sqrt{54} = 2\sqrt{6yy^2} - 2y\sqrt{9 \cdot 6}$

$\qquad\qquad\qquad = 2y\sqrt{6y} - 6y\sqrt{6}$

35. $5x\sqrt{8x} - 24\sqrt{50x^3}$

$= 5x\sqrt{4 \cdot 2x} - 24\sqrt{25 \cdot 2xx^2}$

$= 10x\sqrt{2x} - 120x\sqrt{2x}$

$= -110x\sqrt{2x}$

37. $P = 2\left(\sqrt{5} + 2\sqrt{3}\right) + 2\left(3\sqrt{5} + \sqrt{3}\right)$

$= 2\sqrt{5} + 4\sqrt{3} + 6\sqrt{5} + 2\sqrt{3}$

$= 8\sqrt{5} + 6\sqrt{3}$ miles

39. $\left(50\sqrt{3} + 70\sqrt{2}\right) - \left(42\sqrt{3} + 16\sqrt{2}\right)$

$= 50\sqrt{3} + 70\sqrt{2} - 42\sqrt{3} - 16\sqrt{2}$

$= 8\sqrt{3} + 54\sqrt{2}$ meters above

41. $7 - 3x \le 11$

$-3x \le 4$

$x \ge -\dfrac{4}{3}$

- 4/3   0

43. x = number of levels above the lobby

$\dfrac{1}{6}(5280) = 45 + 31 + 17x$

$880 = 76 + 17x$

$804 = 17x$

$x \approx 47$ levels above the lobby

Total number of levels is 48.

9.4 Exercises

1. $\sqrt{3}\sqrt{10} = \sqrt{30}$

3. $\sqrt{2}\sqrt{22} = 2\sqrt{11}$

5. $\sqrt{18}\sqrt{3} = \sqrt{18 \cdot 3} = \sqrt{54} = \sqrt{9 \cdot 6} = 3\sqrt{6}$

7. $\left(3\sqrt{5}\right)\left(2\sqrt{6}\right) = 6\sqrt{30}$

9. $\sqrt{5}\sqrt{10a} = \sqrt{50a} = \sqrt{25 \cdot 2a} = 5\sqrt{2a}$

11. $\left(2\sqrt{14x}\right)\left(3x\sqrt{7x}\right) = 6x\sqrt{98x^2}$

$= 6x\sqrt{49 \cdot 2x^2}$

$= 42x^2\sqrt{2}$

13. $\left(-4\sqrt{8a}\right)\left(-2\sqrt{3a}\right) = 8\sqrt{24a^2}$

$= 8\sqrt{4 \cdot 6a^2}$

$= 16a\sqrt{6}$

15. $\left(-3\sqrt{ab}\right)\left(2\sqrt{b}\right) = -6\sqrt{ab^2}$

$= -6b\sqrt{a}$

17. $\left(3\sqrt{5}\right)\left(2\sqrt{8}\right) = 6\sqrt{40}$

$= 6\sqrt{4 \cdot 10}$

$= 12\sqrt{10}$

19. $\sqrt{3}\left(2\sqrt{6}+5\sqrt{15}\right)=2\sqrt{18}+5\sqrt{45}$
$$=2\sqrt{9\cdot2}+5\sqrt{9\cdot5}$$
$$=6\sqrt{2}+15\sqrt{5}$$

21. $2\sqrt{x}\left(\sqrt{x}-8\sqrt{5}\right)=2\sqrt{x^2}-16\sqrt{5x}$
$$=2x-16\sqrt{5x}$$

23. $\sqrt{6}\left(\sqrt{2}-3\sqrt{6}+2\sqrt{10}\right)$
$$=\sqrt{12}-3\sqrt{36}+2\sqrt{60}$$
$$=\sqrt{4\cdot3}-18+2\sqrt{4\cdot15}$$
$$=2\sqrt{3}-18+4\sqrt{15}$$

25. $\left(2\sqrt{3}+\sqrt{6}\right)\left(\sqrt{3}-2\sqrt{6}\right)$
$$=2\sqrt{9}-4\sqrt{18}+\sqrt{18}-2\sqrt{36}$$
$$=6-3\sqrt{9\cdot2}-12$$
$$=-6-9\sqrt{2}$$

27. $\left(5+3\sqrt{2}\right)\left(3+\sqrt{2}\right)$
$$=15+5\sqrt{2}+9\sqrt{2}+3\sqrt{4}$$
$$=15+14\sqrt{2}+6$$
$$=21+14\sqrt{2}$$

29. $\left(2\sqrt{7}-3\sqrt{3}\right)\left(\sqrt{7}+\sqrt{3}\right)$
$$=2\sqrt{49}+2\sqrt{21}-3\sqrt{21}-3\sqrt{9}$$
$$=14-\sqrt{21}-9$$
$$=5-\sqrt{21}$$

31. $\left(\sqrt{3}+2\sqrt{6}\right)\left(2\sqrt{3}-\sqrt{6}\right)$
$$=2\sqrt{9}-\sqrt{18}+4\sqrt{18}-2\sqrt{36}$$
$$=6+3\sqrt{18}-12$$
$$=-6+3\sqrt{9\cdot2}$$
$$=-6+9\sqrt{2}$$

33. $\left(3\sqrt{7}-\sqrt{8}\right)\left(\sqrt{8}+2\sqrt{7}\right)$
$$=3\sqrt{56}+6\sqrt{49}-\sqrt{64}-2\sqrt{56}$$
$$=\sqrt{56}+42-8$$
$$=\sqrt{4\cdot14}+34$$
$$=2\sqrt{14}+34$$

35. $\left(2\sqrt{5}-3\right)^2=4\sqrt{25}+2\left(-6\sqrt{5}\right)+9$
$$=20-12\sqrt{5}+9$$
$$=29-12\sqrt{5}$$

37. $\left(\sqrt{3}+5\sqrt{2}\right)^2=\sqrt{9}+2\left(5\sqrt{6}\right)+25\sqrt{4}$
$$=3+10\sqrt{6}+50$$
$$=53+10\sqrt{6}$$

39. $\left(3\sqrt{5}-\sqrt{3}\right)^2$
$$=9\sqrt{25}-6\sqrt{15}+\sqrt{9}$$
$$=45-6\sqrt{15}+3$$
$$=48-6\sqrt{15}$$

41. $\left(3\sqrt{5}\right)\left(2\sqrt{8}\right)=6\sqrt{40}$
$$=6\sqrt{4\cdot10}$$
$$=12\sqrt{10}$$

43. $\sqrt{7}\left(\sqrt{2} + 3\sqrt{14} - \sqrt{6}\right)$

$\quad = \sqrt{14} + 3\sqrt{98} - \sqrt{42}$

$\quad = \sqrt{14} + 3\sqrt{49 \cdot 2} - \sqrt{42}$

$\quad = \sqrt{14} + 2\sqrt{2} - \sqrt{42}$

45. $\left(5\sqrt{2} - 3\sqrt{7}\right)\left(3\sqrt{2} + \sqrt{7}\right)$

$\quad = 15\sqrt{4} + 5\sqrt{14} - 9\sqrt{14} - 3\sqrt{49}$

$\quad = 30 - 4\sqrt{14} - 21$

$\quad = 9 - 4\sqrt{14}$

47. $2\sqrt{a}\left(3\sqrt{b} + \sqrt{ab} - 2\sqrt{a}\right)$

$\quad = 6\sqrt{ab} + 2\sqrt{a^2 b} - 4\sqrt{a^2}$

$\quad = 6\sqrt{ab} + 2a\sqrt{b} - 4a$

49. $\left(3x\sqrt{y} + \sqrt{5}\right)\left(3x\sqrt{y} - \sqrt{5}\right)$

$\quad = \left(3x\sqrt{y}\right)^2 - \left(\sqrt{5}\right)^2$

$\quad = 9x^2 y - 5$

51. (a) $\sqrt{a} \cdot \sqrt{a} = a$ is not true when a
       is negative.

    (b) The restriction " for any nonnegative
       real number" is necessary in order
       to deal with real numbers and it is
       not true when 'a' is negative.

53. $A = \dfrac{1}{2}bh,\ b = \sqrt{288},\ h = \sqrt{2}$

$\quad A = \dfrac{1}{2}\sqrt{288} \cdot \sqrt{2} = \dfrac{1}{2}\left(12\sqrt{2}\right)\left(\sqrt{2}\right) = 12$

The area is 12 square feet

55. $A = \sqrt{12}\sqrt{27}$

$\quad = \sqrt{324}$

$\quad = 18$ square feet

Cumulative Review

57. $36x^2 - 49y^2 = \left(6x\right)^2 - \left(7y\right)^2$

$\qquad\qquad\qquad = \left(6x + 7y\right)\left(6x - 7y\right)$

59. $m = ak$

$\quad m = \left(\dfrac{6076}{5280}\right)k$

$\quad m = \left(\dfrac{1519}{1320}\right)k$

Destroyer is going

$\quad m = \left(\dfrac{1519}{1320}\right)(35) \approx 40.3$ mph

How Am I Doing? Sections 9.1-9.4

1. $\sqrt{49} = 7$

2. $\sqrt{\dfrac{25}{64}} = \dfrac{5}{8}$

3. $\sqrt{81} = 9$

4. $-\sqrt{100} = -10$

5. $\sqrt{5} = 2.236$

6. $-\sqrt{121} = -11$

7. $\sqrt{0.04} = 0.2$

8. $\sqrt{0.36} = 0.6$

9. $\sqrt{x^4} = x^2$

10. $\sqrt{25x^4y^6} = 5x^2y^3$

11. $\sqrt{50} = \sqrt{25 \cdot 2} = 5\sqrt{2}$

12. $\sqrt{x^5} = \sqrt{x^4 x} = x^2\sqrt{x}$

13. $\sqrt{36x^3} = \sqrt{36x^2 x} = 6x\sqrt{x}$

14. $\sqrt{8a^4b^3} = \sqrt{4 \cdot 2a^4b^2b}$
    $$= 2a^2b\sqrt{2b}$$

15. $\sqrt{98} + \sqrt{128} = \sqrt{49 \cdot 2} + \sqrt{64 \cdot 2}$
    $$= 7\sqrt{2} + 8\sqrt{2}$$
    $$= 15\sqrt{2}$$

16. $3\sqrt{2} - \sqrt{8} + \sqrt{18} = 3\sqrt{2} - \sqrt{4 \cdot 2} + \sqrt{9 \cdot 2}$
    $$= 3\sqrt{2} - 2\sqrt{2} + 3\sqrt{2}$$
    $$= 4\sqrt{2}$$

17. $2\sqrt{28} + 3\sqrt{63} - \sqrt{49}$
    $$= 2\sqrt{4 \cdot 7} + 3\sqrt{9 \cdot 7} - \sqrt{49}$$
    $$= 4\sqrt{7} + 9\sqrt{7} - 7$$
    $$= 13\sqrt{7} - 7$$

18. $3\sqrt{8} + \sqrt{12} + \sqrt{50} - 4\sqrt{85}$
    $$= 3\sqrt{4 \cdot 2} + \sqrt{4 \cdot 3} + \sqrt{25 \cdot 2} - 4\sqrt{25 \cdot 3}$$
    $$= 6\sqrt{2} + 2\sqrt{3} + 5\sqrt{2} - 20\sqrt{3}$$

19. $5\sqrt{2x} - 7\sqrt{8x} = 5\sqrt{2x} - 7\sqrt{4 \cdot 2x}$
    $$= 5\sqrt{2x} - 14\sqrt{2x}$$
    $$= -9\sqrt{2x}$$

20. $-4x\sqrt{75} - 2x\sqrt{27}$
    $$= -4x\sqrt{25 \cdot 3} - 2x\sqrt{9 \cdot 3}$$
    $$= -20x\sqrt{3} - 6x\sqrt{3}$$
    $$= -26x\sqrt{3}$$

21. $\left(3\sqrt{5}\right)\left(2\sqrt{10}\right) = 6\sqrt{50}$
    $$= 6\sqrt{25 \cdot 2}$$
    $$= 30\sqrt{2}$$

22. $\left(5x\sqrt{7}\right)\left(3x\sqrt{14}\right) = 15x^2\sqrt{98}$
    $$= 15x^2\sqrt{49 \cdot 2}$$
    $$= 105x^2\sqrt{2}$$

23. $\sqrt{2}\left(\sqrt{6} + 3\sqrt{2}\right) = \sqrt{12} + 3\sqrt{4}$
    $$= \sqrt{4 \cdot 3} + 3\sqrt{4}$$
    $$= 2\sqrt{3} + 6$$

24. $\left(\sqrt{7}+4\right)^2 = \sqrt{49}+2\sqrt{7}\left(4\right)+16$
$$= 7+8\sqrt{7}+16$$
$$= 23+8\sqrt{7}$$

25. $\left(\sqrt{11}-\sqrt{10}\right)\left(\sqrt{11}+\sqrt{10}\right)$
$$= \sqrt{121}-\sqrt{100}$$
$$= 11-10$$
$$= 1$$

26. $\left(2\sqrt{3}-\sqrt{5}\right)^2$
$$= 4\sqrt{9}-2\left(2\sqrt{3}\right)\left(\sqrt{5}\right)+\sqrt{25}$$
$$= 12-4\sqrt{15}+5$$
$$= 17-4\sqrt{15}$$

27. $\left(\sqrt{x}+3\right)\left(\sqrt{x}-4\right)$
$$= \sqrt{x^2}-4\sqrt{x}+3\sqrt{x}-12$$
$$= x-\sqrt{x}-12$$

28. $\left(3\sqrt{7}+4\sqrt{3}\right)\left(5\sqrt{7}-2\sqrt{3}\right)$
$$= 15\sqrt{49}-6\sqrt{21}+20\sqrt{21}-8\sqrt{9}$$
$$= 105+14\sqrt{21}-24$$

9.5 Exercises

1. $\dfrac{\sqrt{12}}{\sqrt{3}} = \sqrt{\dfrac{12}{3}} = \sqrt{4} = 2$

3. $\dfrac{\sqrt{7}}{\sqrt{63}} = \sqrt{\dfrac{7}{63}} = \sqrt{\dfrac{1}{9}} = \dfrac{1}{3}$

5. $\dfrac{\sqrt{98}}{\sqrt{2}} = \sqrt{\dfrac{98}{2}} = \sqrt{49} = 7$

7. $\dfrac{\sqrt{6}}{\sqrt{x^4}} = \dfrac{\sqrt{6}}{x^2}$

9. $\dfrac{\sqrt{18}}{\sqrt{a^4}} = \dfrac{\sqrt{9\cdot 2}}{\sqrt{\left(a^2\right)^2}} = \dfrac{3\sqrt{2}}{a^2}$

11. $\dfrac{3}{\sqrt{7}} = \dfrac{3}{\sqrt{7}}\cdot\dfrac{\sqrt{7}}{\sqrt{7}} = \dfrac{3\sqrt{7}}{\sqrt{49}} = \dfrac{3\sqrt{7}}{7}$

13. $\dfrac{5}{\sqrt{13}} = \dfrac{5}{\sqrt{13}}\cdot\dfrac{\sqrt{13}}{\sqrt{13}} = \dfrac{5\sqrt{13}}{13}$

15. $\dfrac{x\sqrt{x}}{\sqrt{2}} = \dfrac{x\sqrt{x}}{\sqrt{2}}\cdot\dfrac{\sqrt{2}}{\sqrt{2}}$
$$= \dfrac{x\sqrt{2x}}{\sqrt{4}}$$
$$= \dfrac{x\sqrt{2x}}{x}$$

17. $\dfrac{\sqrt{8}}{\sqrt{x}} = \dfrac{\sqrt{4\cdot 2}}{\sqrt{x}}\cdot\dfrac{\sqrt{x}}{\sqrt{x}} = \dfrac{2\sqrt{2x}}{\sqrt{x^2}} = \dfrac{2\sqrt{2x}}{x}$

19. $\dfrac{3}{\sqrt{12}} = \dfrac{3}{\sqrt{4\cdot 3}} = \dfrac{3}{2\sqrt{3}} = \dfrac{3}{2\sqrt{3}}\cdot\dfrac{\sqrt{3}}{\sqrt{3}}$
$$= \dfrac{3\sqrt{3}}{2\sqrt{9}} = \dfrac{\sqrt{3}}{2}$$

21. $\dfrac{6}{\sqrt{a}} = \dfrac{6}{\sqrt{a}} = \dfrac{\sqrt{a}}{\sqrt{a}} = \dfrac{6\sqrt{a}}{\sqrt{a^2}} = \dfrac{6\sqrt{a}}{a}$

23. $\dfrac{x}{\sqrt{2x^5}} = \dfrac{x}{\sqrt{2xx^4}} = \dfrac{x}{x^2\sqrt{2x}}$

$= \dfrac{1}{x\sqrt{2x}} \cdot \dfrac{\sqrt{2x}}{\sqrt{2x}}$

$= \dfrac{\sqrt{2x}}{x\sqrt{4x^2}} = \dfrac{\sqrt{2x}}{2x^2}$

25. $\sqrt{\dfrac{18}{2x^3}} = \sqrt{\dfrac{18}{2x^3}} = \sqrt{\dfrac{9}{x^3}} = \dfrac{3}{x\sqrt{x}} \cdot \dfrac{\sqrt{x}}{\sqrt{x}}$

$= \dfrac{3\sqrt{x}}{x^2}$

27. $\sqrt{\dfrac{3}{5}} = \dfrac{\sqrt{3}}{\sqrt{5}} \cdot \dfrac{\sqrt{5}}{\sqrt{5}} = \dfrac{\sqrt{15}}{\sqrt{25}} = \dfrac{\sqrt{5}}{5}$

29. $\sqrt{\dfrac{13}{14}} = \dfrac{\sqrt{13}}{\sqrt{14}} = \dfrac{\sqrt{13}}{\sqrt{14}} \cdot \dfrac{\sqrt{14}}{\sqrt{14}} = \dfrac{\sqrt{182}}{\sqrt{196}} = \dfrac{\sqrt{182}}{14}$

31. $\dfrac{9}{\sqrt{32x}} = \dfrac{9}{\sqrt{16 \cdot 2x}} = \dfrac{9}{4\sqrt{2x}} \cdot \dfrac{\sqrt{2x}}{\sqrt{2x}}$

$= \dfrac{9\sqrt{2x}}{4\sqrt{4x^2}}$

$= \dfrac{9\sqrt{2x}}{8x}$

33. $\dfrac{4}{\sqrt{3}-1} = \dfrac{4}{\sqrt{3}-1} \cdot \dfrac{\sqrt{3}+1}{\sqrt{3}+1}$

$= \dfrac{4\sqrt{3}+4}{\sqrt{9}-\sqrt{1}} = \dfrac{4\sqrt{3}+4}{3-1}$

$= \dfrac{4\left(\sqrt{3}+1\right)}{2} = 2\sqrt{3}+2$

35. $\dfrac{6}{\sqrt{5}+\sqrt{2}} = \dfrac{6}{\sqrt{5}+\sqrt{2}} \cdot \dfrac{\sqrt{5}-\sqrt{2}}{\sqrt{5}-\sqrt{2}}$

$= \dfrac{6\sqrt{5}-6\sqrt{2}}{\sqrt{25}-\sqrt{4}}$

$= \dfrac{6\sqrt{5}-6\sqrt{2}}{3}$

$= 2\sqrt{5}-2\sqrt{2}$

37. $\dfrac{\sqrt{6}}{\sqrt{6}-\sqrt{3}} = \dfrac{\sqrt{6}}{\sqrt{6}-\sqrt{3}} \cdot \dfrac{\sqrt{6}+\sqrt{3}}{\sqrt{6}+\sqrt{3}}$

$= \dfrac{\sqrt{36}+\sqrt{18}}{\left(\sqrt{6}\right)^2 - \left(\sqrt{3}\right)^2}$

$= \dfrac{6+\sqrt{9 \cdot 2}}{6-3}$

$= \dfrac{6+3\sqrt{2}}{3}$

$= 2+\sqrt{2}$

39. $\dfrac{\sqrt{7}}{\sqrt{8}+\sqrt{7}} = \dfrac{\sqrt{7}}{\sqrt{8}+\sqrt{7}} \cdot \dfrac{\sqrt{8}-\sqrt{7}}{\sqrt{8}-\sqrt{7}}$

$= \dfrac{\sqrt{56}-\sqrt{49}}{\left(\sqrt{8}\right)^2 - \left(\sqrt{7}\right)^2}$

$= \dfrac{\sqrt{4 \cdot 14}-7}{8-7}$

$= 2\sqrt{14}-7$

41.
$$\frac{3x}{2\sqrt{2}-\sqrt{5}} = \frac{3x}{2\sqrt{2}-\sqrt{5}} \cdot \frac{2\sqrt{2}+\sqrt{5}}{2\sqrt{2}+\sqrt{5}}$$
$$= \frac{6x\sqrt{2}+3x\sqrt{5}}{\left(2\sqrt{2}\right)^2 - \left(\sqrt{5}\right)^2}$$
$$= \frac{3x\left(2\sqrt{2}+\sqrt{5}\right)}{8-5}$$
$$= x\left(2\sqrt{2}+\sqrt{5}\right)$$

43.
$$\frac{\sqrt{x}}{\sqrt{6}+\sqrt{2}} = \frac{\sqrt{x}}{\sqrt{6}+\sqrt{2}} \cdot \frac{\sqrt{6}-\sqrt{2}}{\sqrt{6}-\sqrt{2}}$$
$$= \frac{\sqrt{6x}-\sqrt{2x}}{\sqrt{36}-\sqrt{4}}$$
$$= \frac{\sqrt{6x}-\sqrt{2x}}{4}$$

45.
$$\frac{\sqrt{5}-\sqrt{2}}{\sqrt{5}+\sqrt{2}} = \frac{\sqrt{5}-\sqrt{2}}{\sqrt{5}+\sqrt{2}} \cdot \frac{\sqrt{5}-\sqrt{2}}{\sqrt{5}-\sqrt{2}}$$
$$= \frac{\sqrt{25}+2\left(-\sqrt{10}\right)+\sqrt{4}}{\left(\sqrt{5}\right)^2 - \left(\sqrt{2}\right)^2}$$
$$= \frac{5-2\sqrt{10}+2}{5-2}$$
$$= \frac{7-2\sqrt{10}}{3}$$

47.
$$\frac{4\sqrt{7}+3}{\sqrt{5}-\sqrt{2}} = \frac{4\sqrt{7}+3}{\sqrt{5}-\sqrt{2}} \cdot \frac{\sqrt{5}+\sqrt{2}}{\sqrt{5}+\sqrt{2}}$$
$$= \frac{4\sqrt{35}+4\sqrt{14}+3\sqrt{5}+3\sqrt{2}}{\sqrt{25}-\sqrt{4}}$$
$$= \frac{4\sqrt{35}+4\sqrt{14}+3\sqrt{5}+3\sqrt{2}}{3}$$

49.
$$\frac{4\sqrt{3}+2}{\sqrt{8}-\sqrt{6}} = \frac{4\sqrt{3}+2}{\sqrt{8}-\sqrt{6}} \cdot \frac{\sqrt{8}+\sqrt{6}}{\sqrt{8}+\sqrt{6}}$$
$$= \frac{4\sqrt{24}+4\sqrt{18}+2\sqrt{8}+2\sqrt{6}}{\left(\sqrt{8}\right)^2 - \left(\sqrt{6}\right)^2}$$
$$= \frac{8\sqrt{6}+12\sqrt{2}+4\sqrt{2}+2\sqrt{6}}{8-6}$$
$$= \frac{10\sqrt{6}+16\sqrt{2}}{2} = 5\sqrt{6}+8\sqrt{2}$$

51.
$$\frac{x-25}{\sqrt{x}+5} = \frac{x-25}{\sqrt{x}+5} \cdot \frac{\sqrt{x}-5}{\sqrt{x}-5}$$
$$= \frac{(x-25)\left(\sqrt{x}-5\right)}{x-25}$$
$$= \sqrt{x}-5$$

53. (a) $\left(x+\sqrt{2}\right)\left(x-\sqrt{2}\right) = (x)^2 - \left(\sqrt{2}\right)^2$
$$= x^2 - 2$$

    (b) $x^2 - 2 = (x)^2 - \left(\sqrt{2}\right)^2$
$$= \left(x+\sqrt{2}\right)\left(x-\sqrt{2}\right)$$

    (c) $x^2 - 12 = (x)^2 - \left(2\sqrt{3}\right)^2$
$$= \left(x+2\sqrt{3}\right)\left(x-2\sqrt{3}\right)$$

55. $s = \sqrt{\dfrac{3V}{h}}$

    a. $s = \dfrac{\sqrt{3V}}{\sqrt{h}} \cdot \dfrac{\sqrt{h}}{\sqrt{h}}$

    $= \dfrac{\sqrt{3Vh}}{h}$

    b. $V = 24,\ h = 8$

    $s = \sqrt{\dfrac{3(24)}{8}} = 3$ feet

57. $x = $ width, $l = \sqrt{5} + 2$

    $A = lw$

    $3 = \left(\sqrt{5} + 2\right)x$

    $x = \dfrac{3}{\sqrt{5}+2} = \dfrac{3}{\sqrt{5}+2} \cdot \dfrac{\sqrt{5}-2}{\sqrt{5}-2}$

    $= \dfrac{3\sqrt{5}-6}{\sqrt{25}-4} = \dfrac{3\sqrt{5}-6}{5-4}$

    $= \left(3\sqrt{5}-6\right)$ meters

59. $l = \sqrt{5} + 2 = 2.236 + 2 = 4.236$ meters

    $w = 3\sqrt{5} - 6 = 3(2.236) - 6 = 0.708$ meters

Cumulative Review

61. $3(2x-6) = 5x - 7(x-2) + 27$

    $6x - 18 = 5x - 7x + 14 + 27$

    $6x - 18 = -2x + 41$

    $8x - 18 = 41$

    $8x = 59$

    $x = \dfrac{59}{8} \approx 7.38$

63. Let $x = $ mg per cup in instant coffee

    $x + 0.7x = 120$

    $1.7x = 120$

    $x \approx 70.6$

    Approximately 71 mg per cup in the instant coffee.

9.6 Exercises

1. $c^2 = 5^2 + 12^2$

    $c^2 = 25 + 144$

    $= 169$

    $c = \sqrt{169} = 13$

3. $9^2 = 5^2 + b^2$

    $81 = 25 + b^2$

    $56 = b^2$

    $\sqrt{56} = b$

    $\sqrt{4 \cdot 14} = b$

    $2\sqrt{14} = b$

5. $a = 7,\ b = 7$

    $7^2 + 7^2 = c^2$

    $49 + 49 = c^2$

    $98 = c^2$

    $c = \sqrt{98}$

    $c = \sqrt{49 \cdot 2}$

    $c = 7\sqrt{2}$

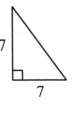

7. $a = \sqrt{14},\ b = 7$

$c^2 = \left(\sqrt{14}\right)^2 + 7^2$

$= 14 + 49$

$= 63$

$c = \sqrt{63} = \sqrt{9 \cdot 7} = 3\sqrt{7}$

9. $c = 20,\ \ b = 18$

$a^2 + 18^2 = 20^2$

$a^2 + 324 = 400$

$a^2 = 76$

$a = \sqrt{76} = 2\sqrt{19}$

11. $c = \sqrt{82},\ a = 5$

$5^2 + b^2 = \left(\sqrt{82}\right)^2$

$25 + b^2 = 82$

$b^2 = 57$

$b = \sqrt{57}$

13. $c = 12.96,\ \ b = 8.35$

$a^2 + \left(8.35\right)^2 = \left(12.96\right)^2$

$a^2 + 69.7225 = 167.9616$

$a^2 = 98.2391$

$a \approx 9.91$

15. $c^2 = 8^2 + 5^2$

$c^2 = 64 + 25$

$= 89$

$c = \sqrt{89}$

$c \approx 9.4$ feet

17.

$a^2 + b^2 = c^2$

$a^2 + 20^2 = 100^2$

$a^2 + 400 = 10{,}000$

$a^2 = 9600$

$a = 98.0$

98 feet

19.   Bottom cable

$c^2 = \left(54\right)^2 + \left(130\right)^2$

$= 2916 + 16{,}900$

$= 19{,}816$

$c = \sqrt{19{,}816} \approx 140.77$ feet

     Top cable

$c^2 = \left(54\right)^2 + \left(135\right)^2$

$= 2916 + 18{,}225$

$= 21{,}141$

$c = \sqrt{21{,}141} \approx 145.40$ feet

21. $\sqrt{x + 2} = 3$

$x + 2 = 9$

$x = 7$

Check:

$\sqrt{7 + 2} \overset{?}{=} 3$

$\sqrt{9} \overset{?}{=} 3$

$3 = 3$

23. $\sqrt{2x+7} = 5$

$2x+7 = 5^2$

$2x+7 = 25$

$2x = 18$

$x = 9$

25. $\sqrt{2x+2} = \sqrt{3x-5}$

$2x+2 = 3x-5$

$2 = x-5$

$7 = x$

Check: $\sqrt{2(7)+2} \overset{?}{=} \sqrt{3(7)-5}$

$\sqrt{16} \overset{?}{=} \sqrt{16}$

$4 = 4$

27. $\sqrt{2x}-5 = 4$

$\sqrt{2x} = 9$

$2x = 9^2$

$2x = 81$

$x = \dfrac{81}{2}$

Check: $\sqrt{2\left(\dfrac{81}{2}\right)-5} \overset{?}{=} 4$

$\sqrt{81}-5 \overset{?}{=} 4$

$9-5 \overset{?}{=} 4$

$4 = 4$

29. $\sqrt{2x+15} = x$

$2x+15 = x^2$

$x^2 - 2x - 15 = 0$

$(x-5)(x+3) = 0$

Check:

$\sqrt{2(5)+15} \overset{?}{=} 5$　　$\sqrt{2(-3)+15} \overset{?}{=} -3$

$\sqrt{25} \overset{?}{=} 5$　　　　　$\sqrt{9} \overset{?}{=} -3$

$5 = 5$　　　　　　　　$3 \neq -3$

$x = 5$ only

31. $\sqrt{5y+1} = y+1$

$5y+1 = (y+1)^2$

$5y+1 = y^2 + 2y + 1$

$y^2 - 3y = 0$

$y(y-3) = 0$

$y = 0, \quad y - 3 = 0$

$y = 3$

Check:

$\sqrt{5(0)+1} \overset{?}{=} 0+1$　　$\sqrt{5(3)+1} \overset{?}{=} 3+1$

$\sqrt{1} \overset{?}{=} 1$　　　　　　$\sqrt{16} \overset{?}{=} 4$

$1 = 1$　　　　　　　　$4 = 4$

$y = 0, 3$

33.　　　　　$\sqrt{x+3} = 3x-1$

$x+3 = (3x-1)^2$

$x+3 = 9x^2 - 6x + 1$

$9x^2 - 7x - 2 = 0$

$(9x+2)(x-1) = 0$

$9x+2 = 0$　　　　$x-1 = 0$

$9x = -2$　　　　　$x = 1$

$x = -\dfrac{2}{9}$

Check:

$$\sqrt{-\frac{2}{9}+3} \overset{?}{=} 3\left(-\frac{2}{9}\right)-1$$

$$\sqrt{\frac{25}{9}} \overset{?}{=} -\frac{5}{3}$$

$$\frac{5}{3} \neq -\frac{5}{3} \text{ Doens't check}$$

$$\sqrt{1+3} \overset{?}{=} 3(1)-1$$

$$\sqrt{4} \overset{?}{=} 2$$

$$2=2$$

The only solution is $x = 1$.

35. $\sqrt{3y+1} - y = 1$

$$\sqrt{3y+1} = y+1$$

$$3y+1 = (y+1)^2$$

$$3y+1 = y^2 + 2y + 1$$

$$y^2 - y = 0$$

$$y(y-1) = 0$$

$$y = 0 \qquad y-1=0$$

$$y = 1$$

Check:

$$\sqrt{3(0)+1} - 0 \overset{?}{=} 1 \qquad\qquad \sqrt{3(1)+1} - 1 \overset{?}{=} 1$$

$$\sqrt{1} - 0 \overset{?}{=} 1 \qquad\qquad \sqrt{4} - 1 \overset{?}{=} 1$$

$$1 = 1 \qquad\qquad\qquad 2-1 \overset{?}{=} 1$$

$$1 = 1$$

$$y = 0, 1$$

37. $\sqrt{6y+1} - 3y = y$

$$\sqrt{6y+1} = 4y$$

$$6y+1 = 16y^2$$

$$0 = 16y^2 - 6y - 1$$

$$0 = (8y+1)(2y-1)$$

$$8y+1 = 0 \qquad\qquad 2y-1 = 0$$

$$y = -\frac{1}{8} \qquad\qquad y = \frac{1}{2}$$

Check:

$$\sqrt{6\left(-\frac{1}{8}\right)+1} - 3\left(-\frac{1}{8}\right) \overset{?}{=} -\frac{1}{8}$$

$$\sqrt{\frac{1}{4}} + \frac{3}{8} \overset{?}{=} -\frac{1}{8}$$

$$\frac{1}{2} + \frac{3}{8} \overset{?}{=} -\frac{1}{8}$$

$$\frac{7}{8} \neq -\frac{1}{8}$$

Check:

$$\sqrt{6\left(\frac{1}{2}\right)+1} - 3\left(\frac{1}{2}\right) \overset{?}{=} \frac{1}{2}$$

$$\sqrt{4} - \frac{3}{2} \overset{?}{=} \frac{1}{2}$$

$$2 - \frac{3}{2} \overset{?}{=} \frac{1}{2}$$

$$\frac{1}{2} = \frac{1}{2}$$

$$y = \frac{1}{2} \text{ only}$$

39. $\sqrt{12x+1} = 2\sqrt{6x} - 1$

$$12x+1 = \left(2\sqrt{6x} - 1\right)^2$$
$$12x+1 = 4\sqrt{36x^2} - 2\left(2\sqrt{6x}\right) + 1$$
$$12x+1 = 24x - 4\sqrt{6x} + 1$$
$$-12x+1 = -4\sqrt{6x} + 1$$
$$-12x = -4\sqrt{6x}$$
$$3x = \sqrt{6x}$$
$$(3x)^2 = 6x$$
$$9x^2 - 6x = 0$$
$$3x(3x-2) = 0$$

$3x = 0 \qquad 3x - 2 = 0$
$x = 0 \qquad 3x = 2$
$\qquad\qquad x = \dfrac{2}{3}$

Check:

$$\sqrt{12(0)+1} \overset{?}{=} 2\sqrt{6(0)} - 1$$
$$\sqrt{1} \overset{?}{=} -1$$
$$1 \neq -1$$

$x = \dfrac{2}{3}$ only

$$\sqrt{12\left(\dfrac{2}{3}\right)+1} \overset{?}{=} 2\sqrt{6\left(\dfrac{2}{3}\right)} - 1$$
$$\sqrt{9} \overset{?}{=} 2(2) - 1$$
$$3 = 3$$

Cumulative Review

41.
$$\frac{5x}{x-4} = 5 + \frac{4x}{x-4}$$
$$(x-4)\left(\frac{5x}{x-4}\right) = 5(x-4) + (x-4)\left(\frac{4x}{x-4}\right)$$
$$5x = 5x - 20 + 4x$$
$$5x = 9x - 20$$
$$-4x = -20$$
$$x = 5$$

43. $f(x) = 2x^2 - 3x + 6$
$$f(-2) = 2(-2)^2 - 3(-2) + 6$$
$$= 2(4) + 6 + 6 = 20$$

45. $x =$ number of birds at the start
$$x + 50(25) = 1700$$
$$x + 1250 = 1700$$
$$x = 450 \text{ birds at the start}$$

9.7 Exercises

1. $y = kx, \;\; y = 9, \;\; x = 2$
$$9 = 2k \Rightarrow k = \frac{9}{2}$$
$$y = \frac{9}{2}x, \;\; x = 16$$
$$y = \frac{9}{2}(16) = 72$$

306

3. $y = kx^3$, $y = 12$, $x = 2$

$$12 = k(2)^3 \Rightarrow k = \frac{12}{8} = \frac{3}{2}$$

$$y = \frac{3}{2}x^3, \quad x = 7$$

$$y = \frac{3}{2}(7)^3 = \frac{3}{2}(343) = \frac{1029}{2}$$

5. $y = kx^2$, $y = 900$, $x - 25$

$$900 = k(25)^2 \Rightarrow k = \frac{900}{625} = \frac{36}{25}$$

$$y = \frac{36}{25}x^2, \quad x = 30$$

$$y = \frac{36}{25}(30)^2 = 1296$$

7. $c = kw$, $c = 200$, $w = 50$

$$200 - k(50)$$
$$4 = k$$
$$c = 4w, \quad w = 70$$
$$c = 4(70)$$
$$c = 280 \text{ calories}$$

9. $T = $ time, $s = $ length of side

$T = ks^3$, $T = 7$, $s = 2.0$

$$7 = k(2.0)^3 \Rightarrow k = \frac{7}{8}$$

$$T = \frac{7}{8}s^3, \quad s = 4.0$$

$$T = \frac{7}{8}(4.0)^3 = 56 \text{ min.}$$

11. $y = \frac{k}{x}$, $y = 18$, $x = 5$

$$18 = \frac{k}{5} \Rightarrow k = 90$$

$$y = \frac{90}{x}, \quad x = 8$$

$$y = \frac{90}{8} = \frac{45}{4}$$

13. $y = \frac{k}{x}$, $y = \frac{1}{4}$, $x = 8$

$$\frac{1}{4} = \frac{k}{8} \Rightarrow k = 2$$

$$y = \frac{2}{x}, \quad x = 1$$

$$y = \frac{2}{1} = 2$$

15. $y = \frac{k}{x^2}$, $y = 30$, $x = 2$

$$30 = \frac{k}{(2)^2} \Rightarrow k = 120$$

$$y = \frac{120}{x^2}, \quad x = 9$$

$$y = \frac{120}{(9)^2} = \frac{120}{81} = \frac{40}{27}$$

17. $T = $ time, $F = $ temperature

$$T = \frac{k}{F}$$

$$2.3 = \frac{k}{60}$$

$$138 = k$$

$$T = \frac{138}{F}$$

$T = \dfrac{138}{40}$

$T = 3.45$

3.45 minutes

19. W = weight, D = distance from center

$W = \dfrac{k}{D^2}, \quad W = 1000, \quad D = 4000$

$1000 = \dfrac{k}{(4000)^2} \Rightarrow k = 16,000,000,000$

$W = \dfrac{16,000,000,000}{D^2}, \quad D = 6000$

$W = \dfrac{16,000,000,000}{(6000)^2} = \dfrac{4000}{9}$

$= 444\dfrac{4}{9}$ pounds

21. $d = \dfrac{15}{11}\sqrt{h}$

  (a) $h = 121; \; d = \dfrac{15}{11}\sqrt{121} = 15$ km

  $h = 36; \; d = \dfrac{15}{11}\sqrt{36} \approx 8.2$ km

  $h = 4; \; d = \dfrac{15}{11}\sqrt{4} \approx 2.7$ km

  (b) $h = 81; \; d = \dfrac{15}{11}\sqrt{81} \approx 12.3$ km

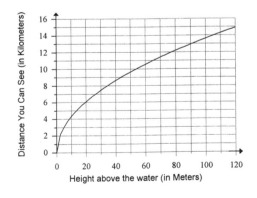

23. $t^2 = kd^3$

  a. $1^1 = k(1)^3$

  $1 = k$

  b. $t^2 = 1(1.5)^3$

  $t^2 = 3.375$

  $t = \sqrt{3.375}$

  ≈ 1.837 earth years

Cumulative Review

25. $\cdot \; \dfrac{80,000}{320} = \dfrac{120,000}{320 + a}$

  $\dfrac{2}{320} = \dfrac{3}{320 + a}$

  $2(320 + a) = 3(320)$

  $640 + 2a = 960$

  $2a = 320$

  $a = 160$

27. $12x^2 - 20x - 48,$

  $= 4(3x^2 - 5x - 12)$

  Grouping number $= 36$

  $= 4(3x^2 - 9x + 4x - 12)$

  $= 4[3x(x - 3) + 4(x - 3)]$

  $= 4(x - 3)(3x + 4)$

29. $x = $ second side

$x + 5 = $ first side

$2x = $ third side

$x + x + 5 + 2x = 69$

$4x + 5 = 69$

$4x = 64$

$x = 16$

First side: $x + 5 = 16 + 5 = 21$ feet

Second side: $x = 16$ feet

Third side: $2x = 2(16) = 32$ feet

Putting Your Skills to Work

1. $A = 112(39) = 4368$ square feet

2. $\dfrac{3750}{4} = 937.5$ watts

3. $\dfrac{937.5 \text{ watts}}{4368 \text{ sq. ft}} = 0.21$ watts/sq. ft.

4. $A = 150(39) = 5850$ sq. ft.

$4(5850)(0.21) = 4914$ watts

Increase $= 4914 - 3750 = 1164$ watts

5. $p = k\sqrt{l},\ l = 130,\ p = 400$

$400 = k\sqrt{130}$

$\dfrac{400}{\sqrt{130}} = k$

$p = \dfrac{400}{\sqrt{130}}\sqrt{l},\ l = 190$

$p = \dfrac{400}{\sqrt{130}} \cdot \sqrt{190}$

$= 400\sqrt{\dfrac{190}{130}}$

$= 484$ watts

6. $p = k\sqrt{w},\ w = 30,\ p = 4400$

$4400 = k\sqrt{30}$

$\dfrac{4400}{\sqrt{30}} = k$

$p = \dfrac{4400}{\sqrt{30}}\sqrt{w},\ w = 50$

$p = 4400 \cdot \sqrt{\dfrac{50}{30}}$

$= 5680$ watts

Chapter 9 Review Problems

1. $\sqrt{36} = 6$

2. $\sqrt{25} = 5$

3. $\sqrt{169} = 13$

4. $\sqrt{196} = 14$

5. $-\sqrt{81} = -9$

6. $\sqrt{64} = 8$

7. $\sqrt{49} = 7$

8. $-\sqrt{121} = -11$

9. $-\sqrt{144} = -12$

10. $\sqrt{289} = 17$

11. $\sqrt{0.04} = 0.2$

12. $\sqrt{0.49} = 0.7$

13. $\sqrt{\dfrac{1}{25}} = \dfrac{1}{5}$

14. $\sqrt{\dfrac{36}{49}} = \dfrac{6}{7}$

15. $\sqrt{105} \approx 10.247$

16. $\sqrt{198} \approx 14.071$

17. $\sqrt{77} = 8.775$

18. $\sqrt{88} \approx 9.381$

19. $\sqrt{27} = \sqrt{9 \cdot 3} = 3\sqrt{3}$

20. $\sqrt{52} = \sqrt{4 \cdot 13} = 2\sqrt{13}$

21. $\sqrt{28} = \sqrt{4 \cdot 7} = 2\sqrt{7}$

22. $\sqrt{125} = \sqrt{25 \cdot 5} = 5\sqrt{5}$

23. $\sqrt{40} = \sqrt{4 \cdot 10} = 2\sqrt{10}$

24. $\sqrt{80} = \sqrt{16 \cdot 5} = 4\sqrt{5}$

25. $\sqrt{x^8} = \sqrt{\left(x^4\right)^2} = x^4$

26. $\sqrt{y^{10}} = \sqrt{\left(y^5\right)^2} = y^5$

27. $\sqrt{x^5 y^6} = \sqrt{x^4 xy^6} = x^2 y^3 \sqrt{x}$

28. $\sqrt{a^3 b^4} = \sqrt{a^2 \cdot a \cdot \left(b^2\right)^2} = ab^2 \sqrt{a}$

29. $\sqrt{16x^3 y^5} = \sqrt{16x^2 xy^4 y} = 4xy^2 \sqrt{xy}$

30. $\sqrt{98x^4 y^6} = \sqrt{49 \cdot 2 \cdot \left(x^2\right)^2 \left(y^3\right)^2}$
$= 7x^2 y^3 \sqrt{2}$

31. $\sqrt{12x^5} = \sqrt{4 \cdot 3x^4 x} = 2x^2 \sqrt{3x}$

32. $\sqrt{27x^7} = \sqrt{9 \cdot 3(x^3)^2 x} = 3x^3\sqrt{3x}$

33. $\sqrt{75x^{10}} = \sqrt{25 \cdot 3x^{10}} = 5x^5\sqrt{3}$

34. $\sqrt{125x^{12}} = \sqrt{25 \cdot 5(x^6)^2} = 5x^6\sqrt{5}$

35. $\sqrt{120a^3b^4c^5} = \sqrt{4 \cdot 30a^2 ab^4 c^4 c}$
$\qquad = 2ab^2c^2\sqrt{30ac}$

36. $\sqrt{121a^6b^4c} = \sqrt{11^2 (a^3)^2 (b^2)^2 c}$
$\qquad = 11a^3 b^2 \sqrt{c}$

37. $\sqrt{56x^7 y^9} = \sqrt{4 \cdot 14x^6 xy^8 y}$
$\qquad = 2x^3 y^4 \sqrt{14xy}$

38. $\sqrt{99x^{13} y^7} = \sqrt{9 \cdot 11(x^6)^2 x(y^3)^2 y}$
$\qquad = 3x^6 y^3 \sqrt{11xy}$

39. $\sqrt{63} - \sqrt{7} + \sqrt{28} = \sqrt{9 \cdot 7} - \sqrt{7} + \sqrt{4 \cdot 7}$
$\qquad = 3\sqrt{7} - \sqrt{7} + 2\sqrt{7}$
$\qquad = 4\sqrt{7}$

40. $5\sqrt{6} - \sqrt{24} + 2\sqrt{54}$
$\quad = 5\sqrt{6} - \sqrt{4 \cdot 6} + 2\sqrt{9 \cdot 6}$
$\quad = 5\sqrt{6} - 2\sqrt{6} + 6\sqrt{6}$
$\quad = 9\sqrt{6}$

41. $x\sqrt{3} + 3x\sqrt{3} + \sqrt{27x^2} = 4x\sqrt{3} + \sqrt{9 \cdot 3x^2}$
$\qquad = 4x\sqrt{3} + 3x\sqrt{3}$
$\qquad = 7x\sqrt{3}$

42. $a\sqrt{2} + \sqrt{12a^2} + a\sqrt{98}$
$\quad = a\sqrt{2} + 2a\sqrt{3} + 7a\sqrt{2}$
$\quad = 8a\sqrt{2} + 2a\sqrt{3}$

43. $5\sqrt{5} - 6\sqrt{20} + 2\sqrt{10}$
$\quad = 5\sqrt{5} - 6\sqrt{4 \cdot 5} + 2\sqrt{10}$
$\quad = 5\sqrt{5} - 12\sqrt{5} + 2\sqrt{10}$
$\quad = -7\sqrt{5} + 2\sqrt{10}$

44. $3\sqrt{6} - 5\sqrt{18} + 3\sqrt{24}$
$\quad = 3\sqrt{6} - 15\sqrt{2} + 6\sqrt{6}$
$\quad = 9\sqrt{6} - 15\sqrt{2}$

45. $\left(2\sqrt{x}\right)\left(3\sqrt{x^3}\right) = 6\sqrt{x^4} = 6x^2$

46. $\left(-5\sqrt{a}\right)\left(2\sqrt{ab}\right) = -10\sqrt{a^2 b} = -10a\sqrt{b}$

47. $\left(\sqrt{2a^3}\right)\left(\sqrt{8b^2}\right) = \sqrt{16a^2 ab^2}$
$\qquad = 4ab\sqrt{a}$

48. $\left(5x\sqrt{x}\right)\left(-3x^2\sqrt{x}\right) = -15x^3(x) = -15x^4$

49. $\sqrt{7}\left(\sqrt{28} - 3\sqrt{7}\right) = \sqrt{196} - 3\sqrt{49}$
$$= 14 - 21$$
$$= -7$$

50. $\sqrt{8}\left(5\sqrt{2} - 3\sqrt{8}\right) = 5\sqrt{16} - 3\sqrt{64}$
$$= 20 - 24$$
$$= -4$$

51. $\sqrt{2}\left(\sqrt{5} - \sqrt{3} - 2\sqrt{2}\right) = \sqrt{10} - \sqrt{6} - 2\sqrt{4}$
$$= \sqrt{10} - \sqrt{6} - 4$$

52. $\sqrt{5}\left(\sqrt{6} - 2\sqrt{5} + \sqrt{10}\right)$
$$= \sqrt{30} - 2(5) + \sqrt{50}$$
$$= \sqrt{30} - 10 + 5\sqrt{2}$$

53. $\left(\sqrt{11} + 2\right)\left(2\sqrt{11} - 1\right)$
$$= 2\sqrt{121} - \sqrt{11} + 4\sqrt{11} - 2$$
$$= 22 + 3\sqrt{11} - 2$$
$$= 20 + 3\sqrt{11}$$

54. $\left(\sqrt{10} + 3\right)\left(3\sqrt{10} - 1\right)$
$$= 3(10) - \sqrt{10} + 9\sqrt{10} - 3$$
$$= 30 + 8\sqrt{10} - 3 = 27 + 8\sqrt{10}$$

55. $\left(2 + 3\sqrt{6}\right)\left(4 - 2\sqrt{3}\right)$
$$= 8 - 4\sqrt{3} + 12\sqrt{6} - 6\sqrt{18}$$
$$= 8 - 4\sqrt{3} + 12\sqrt{6} - 18\sqrt{2}$$

56. $\left(5 - \sqrt{2}\right)\left(3 - \sqrt{12}\right)$
$$= \left(5 - \sqrt{2}\right)\left(3 - 2\sqrt{3}\right)$$
$$= 15 - 10\sqrt{3} - 3\sqrt{2} + 2\sqrt{6}$$

57. $\left(2\sqrt{3} + 3\sqrt{6}\right)^2 = 4\sqrt{9} + 2(6)\sqrt{18} + 9\sqrt{36}$
$$= 12 + 36\sqrt{2} + 54$$
$$= 66 + 36\sqrt{2}$$

58. $\left(5\sqrt{2} - 2\sqrt{6}\right)^2$
$$= \left(5\sqrt{2}\right)^2 - 2\left(5\sqrt{2}\right)\left(2\sqrt{6}\right) + \left(2\sqrt{6}\right)^2$$
$$= 25(2) - 20\sqrt{12} + 4(6)$$
$$= 50 - 40\sqrt{3} + 24$$
$$= 74 - 40\sqrt{3}$$

59. $\dfrac{1}{\sqrt{3x}} = \dfrac{1}{\sqrt{3x}} \cdot \dfrac{\sqrt{3x}}{\sqrt{3x}} = \dfrac{\sqrt{3x}}{3x}$

60. $\dfrac{2y}{\sqrt{5}} = \dfrac{2y}{\sqrt{5}} \cdot \dfrac{\sqrt{5}}{\sqrt{5}} = \dfrac{2y\sqrt{5}}{5}$

61. $\dfrac{x^2 y}{\sqrt{8}} = \dfrac{x^2 y}{2\sqrt{2}} = \dfrac{x^2 y}{2\sqrt{2}} \cdot \dfrac{\sqrt{2}}{\sqrt{2}} = \dfrac{x^2 y\sqrt{2}}{4}$

62. $\dfrac{3ab}{\sqrt{2b}} = \dfrac{3ab}{\sqrt{2b}} \cdot \dfrac{\sqrt{2b}}{\sqrt{2b}} = \dfrac{3ab\sqrt{2b}}{2b} = \dfrac{3a\sqrt{2b}}{2}$

63. $\sqrt{\dfrac{5}{6}} = \dfrac{\sqrt{5}}{\sqrt{6}} \cdot \dfrac{\sqrt{6}}{\sqrt{6}} = \dfrac{\sqrt{30}}{\sqrt{36}} = \dfrac{\sqrt{30}}{6}$

64. $\sqrt{\dfrac{6}{11}} = \dfrac{\sqrt{6}}{\sqrt{11}} \cdot \dfrac{\sqrt{11}}{\sqrt{11}} = \dfrac{\sqrt{66}}{\sqrt{121}} = \dfrac{\sqrt{66}}{11}$

65. $\dfrac{\sqrt{a^5}}{\sqrt{2a}} = \dfrac{\sqrt{a^5}}{\sqrt{2a}} \cdot \dfrac{\sqrt{2a}}{\sqrt{2a}} = \dfrac{\sqrt{2a^6}}{2a} = \dfrac{a^3\sqrt{2}}{2a}$

$= \dfrac{a^2\sqrt{2}}{2}$

66. $\dfrac{\sqrt{x^3}}{\sqrt{3x}} = \sqrt{\dfrac{x^3}{3x}} = \sqrt{\dfrac{x^2}{3}} = \dfrac{\sqrt{x^2}}{\sqrt{3}} = \dfrac{x}{\sqrt{3}}$

$= \dfrac{x}{\sqrt{3}} \cdot \dfrac{\sqrt{3}}{\sqrt{3}} = \dfrac{x\sqrt{3}}{3}$

67. $\dfrac{3}{\sqrt{5}+\sqrt{2}} - \dfrac{3}{\sqrt{5}+\sqrt{2}} \cdot \dfrac{\sqrt{5}-\sqrt{2}}{\sqrt{5}-\sqrt{2}}$

$= \dfrac{3\sqrt{5}-3\sqrt{2}}{\left(\sqrt{5}\right)^2 - \left(\sqrt{2}\right)^2}$

$= \dfrac{3\sqrt{5}-3\sqrt{2}}{3}$

$= \sqrt{5} - \sqrt{2}$

68. $\dfrac{2}{\sqrt{6}-\sqrt{3}} = \dfrac{2}{\sqrt{6}-\sqrt{3}} \cdot \dfrac{\sqrt{6}+\sqrt{3}}{\sqrt{6}+\sqrt{3}}$

$= \dfrac{2\left(\sqrt{6}+\sqrt{3}\right)}{6-3} = \dfrac{2\left(\sqrt{6}+\sqrt{3}\right)}{3}$

69. $\dfrac{1-\sqrt{5}}{2+\sqrt{5}} = \dfrac{1-\sqrt{5}}{2+\sqrt{5}} \cdot \dfrac{2-\sqrt{5}}{2-\sqrt{5}}$

$= \dfrac{2-3\sqrt{5}+5}{2^2 - \left(\sqrt{5}\right)^2}$

$= \dfrac{7-3\sqrt{5}}{-1}$

$= -7+3\sqrt{5}$

70. $\dfrac{1-\sqrt{3}}{3+\sqrt{3}} = \dfrac{1-\sqrt{3}}{3+\sqrt{3}} \cdot \dfrac{3-\sqrt{3}}{3-\sqrt{3}} = \dfrac{3-4\sqrt{3}+3}{9-3}$

$= \dfrac{6-4\sqrt{3}}{6} = \dfrac{2\left(3-2\sqrt{3}\right)}{6} = \dfrac{3-2\sqrt{3}}{3}$

71. $c^2 = a^2 + b^2, \quad a = 5, \quad b = 8$

$c^2 = 5^2 + 8^2$

$c = \sqrt{25+64}$

$c = \sqrt{89}$

72. $a^2 + b^2 = c^2$

$a^2 + 3^2 = \left(\sqrt{11}\right)^2$

$a^2 + 9 = 11$

$a^2 = 2$

$a = \sqrt{2}$

73. $c^2 = a^2 + b^2, \quad c = 5, \quad a = 3.5$

$5^2 = (3.5)^2 + b^2$

$25 = 12.25 + b^2$

$12.75 = b^2$

$\sqrt{12\frac{3}{4}} = b$

$\sqrt{\frac{51}{4}} = b$

$\frac{\sqrt{51}}{2} = b$

74. $a^2 + b^2 = c^2$

$(2.400)^2 + (2.000)^2 = c^2$

$5.760 + 4.000 = c^2$

$9.760 = c^2$

$3.124 = c$

75. $x^2 = 18^2 + 24^2$

$x^2 = 324 + 576$

$x^2 = 900$

$x = 30$

It is 30 meters from his feet to the top of the pole.

76. $a^2 + b^2 = c^2$

$(20.0)^2 + b^2 = (50.0)^2$

$400.0 + b^2 = 2500.0$

$b^2 = 2100.0$

$b \approx 45.8$

It is 45.8 miles

77. $x =$ length of a side

$x^2 + x^2 = \left(\sqrt{455}\right)^2$

$2x^2 = 455$

$x^2 = 227.5$

$x = 15.1$ feet

78. $\sqrt{x-4} = 5$

$x - 4 = 25$

$x = 29$

Check:

$\sqrt{29-4} \overset{?}{=} 5$

$\sqrt{25} = 5$

$5 = 5$

79. $\sqrt{3x+1} = 8$

$3x + 1 = 64$

$3x = 63$

$x = 21$

Check:

$\sqrt{3(21)+1} \overset{?}{=} 8$

$\sqrt{64} \overset{?}{=} 8$

$8 = 8$

314

80. $\sqrt{1-3x} = \sqrt{5+x}$

$$\left(\sqrt{1-3x}\right)^2 = \left(\sqrt{5+x}\right)^2$$

$$1-3x = 5+x$$

$$1 = 5+4x$$

$$-4 = 4x$$

$$-1 = x$$

Check:

$$\sqrt{1-3(-1)} \overset{?}{=} \sqrt{5+(-1)}$$

$$\sqrt{1+3} = \sqrt{4}$$

$$x = -1$$

81. $\sqrt{-5+2x} = \sqrt{1+x}$

$$-5+2x = 1+x$$

$$x = 6$$

Check:

$$\sqrt{-5+2(6)} \overset{?}{=} \sqrt{1+6}$$

$$\sqrt{-5+12} \overset{?}{=} \sqrt{7}$$

$$\sqrt{7} = \sqrt{7}$$

$$x = 6$$

82. $\sqrt{10x+9} = -1+2x$

$$\left(\sqrt{10x+9}\right)^2 = (-1+2x)^2$$

$$10x+9 = 1-4x+4x^2$$

$$0 = 4x^2 - 14x - 8$$

$$0 = 2\left(2x^2 - 7x - 4\right)$$

$$0 = 2(2x+1)(x-4)$$

$$2x+1 = 0 \qquad\qquad x-4 = 0$$

$$x = -\frac{1}{2} \qquad\qquad x = 4$$

Check: $x = -\dfrac{1}{2}$

$$\sqrt{10\left(-\frac{1}{2}\right)+9} \overset{?}{=} -1+2\left(-\frac{1}{2}\right)$$

$$\sqrt{4} \overset{?}{=} -2$$

$$2 \neq -2$$

Check: $x = 4$

$$\sqrt{10(4)+9} \overset{?}{=} -1+2(4)$$

$$\sqrt{49} \overset{?}{=} 7$$

$$7 = 7$$

$$x = 4$$

83. $\sqrt{2x-5} - 10 \quad x$

$$2x-5 = (10-x)^2$$

$$2x-5 = 100 - 20x + x^2$$

$$0 = x^2 - 22x + 105$$

$$0 = (x-7)(x-15)$$

$$x-7 = 0 \qquad\qquad x-15 = 0$$

$$x = 7 \qquad\qquad x = 15$$

Check: $x = 7$

$$\sqrt{2(7)-5} \overset{?}{=} 10-7$$

$$\sqrt{9} \overset{?}{=} 3$$

$$3 = 3$$

Check: $x = 15$

$$\sqrt{2(15)-5} \overset{?}{=} 10-5$$

$$\sqrt{25} \overset{?}{=} -5$$

$$5 \neq -5$$

$$x = 7 \text{ only}$$

84. $6 - \sqrt{5x-1} = x+1$

$-\sqrt{5x-1} = x-5$

$\left(-\sqrt{5x-1}\right)^2 = (x-5)^2$

$5x - 1 = x^2 - 10x + 25$

$0 = x^2 - 15x + 26$

$0 = (x-13)(x-2)$

$x - 13 = 0 \qquad x - 2 = 0$

$\qquad x = 13 \qquad\qquad x = 2$

Check: $x = 13$

$6 - \sqrt{5(13)-1} \overset{?}{=} 13+1$

$6 - \sqrt{64} \overset{?}{=} 14$

$6 - 8 \neq 14$

Check: $x = 2$

$6 - \sqrt{5(2)-1} \overset{?}{=} 2+1$

$6 - \sqrt{9} \overset{?}{=} 3$

$6 - 3 = 3$

$x = 2$

85. $4x + \sqrt{x+2} = 5x - 4$

$\sqrt{x+2} = x - 4$

$x + 2 = (x-4)^2$

$x + 2 = x^2 - 8x + 16$

$0 = x^2 - 9x + 14$

$0 = (x-2)(x-7)$

$x - 2 = 0 \qquad x - 7 = 0$

$\qquad x = 2 \qquad\qquad x = 7$

Check: $x = 7$

$4(7) + \sqrt{7+2} \overset{?}{=} 5(7) - 4$

$28 + \sqrt{9} \overset{?}{=} 31$

$31 = 31$

$x = 7$ only

86. $y = k\sqrt{x}$

$35 = k\sqrt{25}$

$35 = 5k$

$7 = k$

$y = 7\sqrt{x} = 7\sqrt{121} = 7(11) = 77$

87. $y = \dfrac{k}{x^2}, \quad y = \dfrac{6}{5}, \quad x = 5$

$\dfrac{6}{5} = \dfrac{k}{5^2} \Rightarrow k = 30$

$y = \dfrac{30}{x^2}, \quad x = 15$

$y = \dfrac{30}{(15)^2} = \dfrac{2}{15}$

88. $y = \dfrac{k}{x^3}$

$4 = \dfrac{k}{2^3}$

$4 = \dfrac{k}{8}$

$32 = k$

$y = \dfrac{32}{x^3} = \dfrac{32}{4^3} = \dfrac{32}{64} = \dfrac{1}{2}$

89. $I = \dfrac{k}{d^2}, \quad I = I_1, \quad d = 1$

     $I_1 = \dfrac{k}{1} \Rightarrow k = I_1$

       $I = \dfrac{I_1}{d^2}, \quad d = 4$

       $I_4 = \dfrac{I_1}{4^2} = \dfrac{I_1}{16}$

   $\dfrac{I_4}{I_1} = \dfrac{\frac{I_1}{16}}{I_1} = \dfrac{1}{16}$

   The intensity is $\dfrac{1}{16}$ as great.

90. l = length of skid mark, s = speed of car

    $l = ks^2$

    $40 = k(30)^2$

    $40 = 900k$

    $\dfrac{2}{45} = k$

    $l = \dfrac{2}{45}s^2 = \dfrac{2}{45}(55)^2 = 134$

    134 feet

91. H = horsepower, s = speed

    $H = ks^3, \quad s = s_m, \quad H = H_m$

    $H_1 = k(s_m)^3 \Rightarrow k = \dfrac{H_1}{(s_m)^3}$

    $H_1 = \dfrac{H_m}{s_m^3}s^3, \quad s = 2s_m$

    $H = \dfrac{H_m}{s_m^3}(2s_m)^3 = 8H_m$

   The horsepower is 8 times as much.

92. $\sqrt{\dfrac{36}{121}} = \dfrac{6}{11}$

93. $\sqrt{0.0004} = 0.02$

94. $\sqrt{98x^6y^3} = \sqrt{49 \cdot 2x^6y^2 y}$

             $= 7x^3y\sqrt{2y}$

95. $3\sqrt{27} - 2\sqrt{75} + \sqrt{48}$

    $= 3\sqrt{9 \cdot 3} - 2\sqrt{25 \cdot 3} + \sqrt{16 \cdot 3}$

    $= 9\sqrt{3} - 10\sqrt{3} + 4\sqrt{3}$

    $= 3\sqrt{3}$

96. $\left(2\sqrt{3} + \sqrt{5}\right)\left(3\sqrt{3} - \sqrt{10}\right)$

    $= 6\sqrt{9} - 2\sqrt{30} + 3\sqrt{15} - \sqrt{50}$

    $= 18 - 2\sqrt{30} + 3\sqrt{15} - \sqrt{25 \cdot 2}$

    $= 18 - 2\sqrt{30} + 3\sqrt{15} - 5\sqrt{2}$

97. $\left(3\sqrt{5} + 2\right)^2 = 9\sqrt{25} + 2\left(3\sqrt{5}\right)(2) + 4$

               $= 45 + 12\sqrt{5} + 4$

               $= 49 + 12\sqrt{5}$

98. $\dfrac{5}{\sqrt{12}} = \dfrac{5}{\sqrt{4 \cdot 3}} = \dfrac{5}{2\sqrt{3}} = \dfrac{5}{2\sqrt{3}} \cdot \dfrac{\sqrt{3}}{\sqrt{3}} = \dfrac{5\sqrt{3}}{6}$

99. $\dfrac{\sqrt{3}+\sqrt{6}}{2\sqrt{3}+\sqrt{2}} = \dfrac{\sqrt{3}+\sqrt{6}}{2\sqrt{3}+\sqrt{2}} \cdot \dfrac{2\sqrt{3}-\sqrt{2}}{2\sqrt{3}-\sqrt{2}}$

$= \dfrac{2\sqrt{9}-\sqrt{6}+2\sqrt{18}-\sqrt{12}}{4\sqrt{9}-\sqrt{4}}$

$= \dfrac{6-\sqrt{6}+2\sqrt{9\cdot2}-\sqrt{4\cdot3}}{12-2}$

$= \dfrac{6-\sqrt{6}+6\sqrt{2}-2\sqrt{3}}{10}$

100. $\sqrt{2x-3} = 9$

$2x-3 = 81$

$2x = 84$

$x = 42$

101. $\sqrt{10x+5} = 2x+1$

$10x+5 = 4x^2+4x+1$

$0 = 4x^2-6x-4$

$0 = 2(2x^2-3x-2)$

$0 = 2(2x+1)(x-2)$

$2x+1 = 0 \qquad x-2 = 0$

$2x = -1 \qquad x = 2$

$x = -\dfrac{1}{2}$

How Am I Doing? Chapter 9 Test

1. $\sqrt{121} = 11$

2. $\sqrt{\dfrac{9}{100}} = \dfrac{3}{10}$

3. $\sqrt{48x^2 y^7} = \sqrt{3 \cdot 16x^2 y^6 y}$

$= 4xy^3 \sqrt{3y}$

4. $\sqrt{100x^3 yz^4} = \sqrt{100 \cdot x^2 \cdot xy\left(z^2\right)^2}$

$= 10xz^2 \sqrt{xy}$

5. $8\sqrt{3}+5\sqrt{27}-5\sqrt{48} = 8\sqrt{3}+5\sqrt{9\cdot3}-5\sqrt{16\cdot3}$

$= 8\sqrt{3}+15\sqrt{3}-20\sqrt{3}$

$= 3\sqrt{3}$

6. $\sqrt{4a}+\sqrt{8a}+\sqrt{36a}+\sqrt{18a}$

$= 2\sqrt{a}+2\sqrt{2a}+6\sqrt{a}+3\sqrt{2a}$

$= 8\sqrt{a}+5\sqrt{2a}$

7. $\left(2\sqrt{a}\right)\left(3\sqrt{b}\right)\left(2\sqrt{ab}\right) = 12\sqrt{a^2 b^2}$

$= 12ab$

8. $\sqrt{5}\left(\sqrt{10}+2\sqrt{3}-3\sqrt{5}\right)$

$= \sqrt{50}+2\sqrt{15}-3\sqrt{25}$

$= \sqrt{25\cdot2}+2\sqrt{15}-15$

$= 5\sqrt{2}+2\sqrt{15}-15$

9. $\left(2\sqrt{3}\right)^2 = 4\sqrt{9}+2\left(2\sqrt{3}\right)(5)+25$

$= 12+20\sqrt{3}+25$

$= 37+20\sqrt{3}$

10. $\left(4\sqrt{2}-\sqrt{5}\right)\left(3\sqrt{2}+\sqrt{5}\right)$

$= 12(2)+4\sqrt{10}-3\sqrt{10}-5$

$= 24+\sqrt{10}-5 = 19+\sqrt{10}$

11. $\sqrt{\dfrac{x}{5}} = \dfrac{\sqrt{x}}{\sqrt{5}} = \dfrac{\sqrt{x}}{\sqrt{5}}\cdot\dfrac{\sqrt{5}}{\sqrt{5}} = \dfrac{\sqrt{5x}}{5}$

12. $\dfrac{3}{\sqrt{12}} = \dfrac{3}{2\sqrt{3}} = \dfrac{3}{2\sqrt{3}}\cdot\dfrac{\sqrt{3}}{\sqrt{3}} = \dfrac{3\sqrt{3}}{2(3)} = \dfrac{\sqrt{3}}{2}$

13. $\dfrac{\sqrt{3}+4}{5+\sqrt{3}} = \dfrac{\sqrt{3}+4}{5+\sqrt{3}}\cdot\dfrac{5-\sqrt{3}}{5-\sqrt{3}}$

$= \dfrac{5\sqrt{3}-\sqrt{9}+20-4\sqrt{3}}{25-\sqrt{9}}$

$= \dfrac{\sqrt{3}-3+20}{25-3}$

$= \dfrac{17+\sqrt{3}}{22}$

14. $\dfrac{3a}{\sqrt{5}+\sqrt{2}} = \dfrac{3a}{\sqrt{5}+\sqrt{2}}\cdot\dfrac{\sqrt{5}-\sqrt{2}}{\sqrt{5}-\sqrt{2}}$

$= \dfrac{3a\left(\sqrt{5}-\sqrt{2}\right)}{5-2} = \dfrac{3a\left(\sqrt{5}-\sqrt{2}\right)}{3}$

$= a\left(\sqrt{5}-\sqrt{2}\right)$

15. $\sqrt{156} = 12.49$

16. $c^2 = a^2 + b^2$

$13^2 = 6^2 + x^2$

$169 = 36 + x^2$

$133 = x^2$

$\sqrt{133} = x$

17. $x^2 = \left(3\sqrt{2}\right)^2 + 3^2 = 9\sqrt{4}+9 = 27$

$x = \sqrt{27} = \sqrt{9\cdot3} = 3\sqrt{3}$

18. $6-\sqrt{2x+1} = 0$

$6 = \sqrt{2x+1}$

$6^2 = \left(\sqrt{2x+1}\right)^2$

$36 = 2x+1$

$35 = 2x$

$\dfrac{35}{2} = x$

Check:

$6-\sqrt{2\left(\dfrac{35}{2}\right)+1} \overset{?}{=} 0$

$6-\sqrt{36} \overset{?}{=} 0$

$6-6 = 0$

$x = \dfrac{35}{2}$

19. $x = 5+\sqrt{x+7}$

$x-5 = \sqrt{x+7}$

$x^2-10x+25 = x+7$

$x^2-11x+18 = 0$

$(x-2)(x-9) = 0$

$$x - 2 = 0 \qquad x - 9 = 0$$
$$x = 2 \qquad\quad x = 9$$

2 is an extraneous solution. $x = 9$

20. i = illumination, d = distance

$$i = \frac{k}{d^2}$$

$$i = \frac{k}{8^2}$$

$$64i = k$$

$$i = \frac{64i}{d^2}$$

$$\frac{1}{4}i = \frac{64i}{d^2}$$

$$d^2 = 256$$

$$d = 16$$

16 inches

21. $c = ks,\ c = 23.40,\ s = 780$

$$23.40 = k(780)$$

$$0.03 = k$$

$$c = 0.03s,\ s = 2859$$

$$c = 0.03(2859)$$

$$c = \$85.77$$

22. A = area, p = perimeter

$$A = kp^2$$

$$6.93 = k(12)^2$$

$$6.93 = 144k$$

$$0.048125 = k$$

$$A = 0.048125p^2$$

$$= 0.048125(21)^2 = 21.2 \text{ cm}^2$$

Cumulative Test Chapters 0 - 9

1. $\dfrac{28}{42} = \dfrac{2 \cdot 2 \cdot 7}{2 \cdot 3 \cdot 7} = \dfrac{2}{3}$

2. $3\dfrac{1}{4} + 5\dfrac{2}{3} = 3\dfrac{3}{12} + 5\dfrac{8}{12} = 8\dfrac{11}{12}$

3. $6\dfrac{1}{4} \div 6\dfrac{2}{3} = \dfrac{25}{4} \div \dfrac{20}{3}$

$$= \frac{25}{4} \cdot \frac{3}{20}$$

$$= \frac{5(5)}{4} \cdot \frac{3}{4(5)}$$

$$= \frac{15}{16}$$

4. $0.07\% = 0.0007$

5. $-11 - 16 + 8 + 4 - 13 + 31$

$$= -27 + 8 + 4 - 13 + 31$$

$$= -19 + 4 - 13 + 31$$

$$= -15 - 13 + 31$$

$$= -28 + 31$$

$$= 3$$

6. $(-3)^2 \cdot 4 - 8 \div 2 - (3 - 2)^3$

$$= 9 \cdot 4 - 8 \div 2 - 1^3$$

$$= 9 \cdot 4 - 8 \div 2 - 1$$

$$= 36 - 4 - 1 = 31$$

7. $4a^2bc^3 - 2abc^2 - 7a^2bc^3 = -3a^2bc^3 - 2abc^2$

8. $(x+3)(x-2)(x+2) = (x+3)(x^2-4)$
$$= x^3 - 4x + 3x^2 - 12$$
$$= x^3 + 3x^2 - 4x - 12$$

9. $(4x-5)^2 = 16x^2 - 2(4x)(5) + 25$
$$= 16x^2 - 40x + 25$$

10. $(3x-11)(3x+11) = (3x)^2 - 11^2$
$$= 9x^2 - 121$$

11. $\dfrac{4x}{x+2} + \dfrac{4}{x+2} = \dfrac{4x+4}{x+2}$

12. $\dfrac{x^2-5x+6}{x^2-5x-6} \div \dfrac{x^2-4}{x^2+2x+1}$
$$= \dfrac{x^2-5x+6}{x^2-5x-6} \cdot \dfrac{x^2+2x+1}{x^2-4}$$
$$= \dfrac{(x-2)(x-3)}{(x-6)(x+1)} \cdot \dfrac{(x+1)^2}{(x-2)(x+2)}$$
$$= \dfrac{(x-3)(x+1)}{(x-6)(x+2)}$$

13. $\sqrt{98x^5y^6} = \sqrt{49 \cdot 2x^4xy^6}$
$$= 7x^2y^3\sqrt{2x}$$

14. $\sqrt{50} - \sqrt{98} + \sqrt{162}$
$$= \sqrt{25 \cdot 2} - \sqrt{49 \cdot 2} + \sqrt{81 \cdot 2}$$
$$= 5\sqrt{2} - 7\sqrt{2} + 9\sqrt{2}$$
$$= 7\sqrt{2}$$

15. $\left(\sqrt{6} - \sqrt{3}\right)^2 = \sqrt{36} + 2(-\sqrt{3})(\sqrt{6}) + \sqrt{9}$
$$= 6 - 2\sqrt{18} + 3$$
$$= 9 - 2\sqrt{9 \cdot 2}$$
$$= 9 - 6\sqrt{2}$$

16. $\dfrac{\sqrt{3}+\sqrt{2}}{\sqrt{3}-\sqrt{2}} = \dfrac{\sqrt{3}+\sqrt{2}}{\sqrt{3}-\sqrt{2}} \cdot \dfrac{\sqrt{3}+\sqrt{2}}{\sqrt{3}+\sqrt{2}}$
$$= \dfrac{3+2\sqrt{6}}{3-2} = 5 + 2\sqrt{6}$$

17. $\left(3\sqrt{6} - \sqrt{2}\right)\left(\sqrt{6} + 4\sqrt{2}\right)$
$$= 3\sqrt{36} + 12\sqrt{12} - \sqrt{12} - 4\sqrt{4}$$
$$= 18 + 11\sqrt{12} - 8$$
$$= 10 + 11\sqrt{4 \cdot 3}$$
$$= 10 + 22\sqrt{3}$$

18. $\dfrac{1}{3-\sqrt{2}} = \dfrac{1}{3-\sqrt{2}} \cdot \dfrac{3+\sqrt{2}}{3+\sqrt{2}}$
$$= \dfrac{3+\sqrt{2}}{9-2} = \dfrac{3+\sqrt{2}}{7}$$

19. $-\sqrt{16} = -4$

20. Not a real number

21. $c^2 = a^2 + b^2, \quad a = 4, b = \sqrt{7}$
$$c^2 = 4^2 + \left(\sqrt{7}\right)^2 = 16 + 7 = 23$$
$$c = \sqrt{23}$$

22. $a^2 + b^2 = c^2$
$$19^2 + b^2 = 21^2$$
$$361 + b^2 = 441$$
$$b^2 = 80$$
$$b = 4\sqrt{5}$$

23. $\sqrt{4x + 5} = x$
$$4x + 5 = x^2$$
$$0 = x^2 - 4x - 5$$
$$0 = (x - 5)(x + 1)$$

$x - 5 = 0 \qquad x + 1 = 0$

$\quad x = 5 \qquad\qquad x = -1$

-1 is an extraneous solution. $x = 5$

24. $\sqrt{3y - 2} + 2 = y$
$$\sqrt{3y - 2} = y - 2$$
$$\left(\sqrt{3y - 2}\right)^2 = (y - 2)^2$$
$$3y - 2 = y^2 - 4y + 4$$
$$0 = y^2 - 7y + 6$$
$$0 = (y - 6)(y - 1)$$

$y - 6 = 0 \qquad\qquad y - 1 = 0$

$\quad y = 6 \qquad\qquad\quad y = 1$

Check: $y = 6$

$\sqrt{3(6) - 2} + 2 \overset{?}{=} 6$

$\sqrt{16} + 2 \overset{?}{=} 6$

$4 + 2 = 6$

Check: $y = 1$

$\sqrt{3(1) - 2} + 2 \overset{?}{=} 1$

$\sqrt{1} + 2 \overset{?}{=} 1$

$1 + 2 \neq 1$

$\quad y = 6$

25. $y = \dfrac{k}{x}, \quad y = 4, \quad x = 5$

$$4 = \frac{k}{5} \Rightarrow k = 20$$

$$y = \frac{20}{x}, \quad x = 2$$

$$y = \frac{20}{2} = 10$$

26. A = surface area, r = radius

$$A = kr^2$$
$$1256 = k(2)^2$$
$$1256 = 4k$$
$$314 = k$$
$$A = 314r^2 = 314(0.5)^2$$
$$= 314(0.25) = 78.5$$

78.5 m^2

Chapter 10

10.1 Exercises

1. $x^2 + 8x + 7 = 0$
$a = 1, \quad b = 8, \quad c = 7$

3. $8x^2 - 11x = 0$
$a = 8, \quad b = -11, \quad c = 0$

5. $x^2 + 15x - 7 = 12x + 8$
$x^2 + 3x - 15 = 0$
$a = 1, \quad b = 3, \quad c = -15$

7. $27x^2 \quad 9x - 0$
$9x(3x - 1) = 0$
$9x = 0 \qquad 3x - 1 = 0$
$x = 0 \qquad x = \dfrac{1}{3}$

9. $5x^2 - 7x = 3x$
$5x^2 - 10x = 0$
$5x(x - 2) = 0$
$5x = 0 \qquad x - 2 = 0$
$x = 0 \qquad x = 2$

11. $11x^2 - 13x = 8x - 3x^2$
$14x^2 - 21x = 0$
$7x(2x - 3) = 0$
$7x = 0 \qquad 2x - 3 = 0$
$x = 0 \qquad x = \dfrac{3}{2}$

13. $x^2 - 3x - 28 = 0$
$(x + 4)(x - 7) = 0$
$x + 4 = 0 \qquad x - 7 = 0$
$x = -4 \qquad x = 7$

15. $2x^2 + 11x - 6 = 0$
$(2x - 1)(x + 6) = 0$
$2x - 1 = 0 \qquad x + 6 = 0$
$2x = 1 \qquad x = -6$
$x = \dfrac{1}{2}$

17. $3x^2 - 16x + 5 - 0$
$(3x - 1)(x - 5) = 0$
$3x - 1 = 0 \qquad x - 5 = 0$
$3x = 1 \qquad x = 5$
$x = \dfrac{1}{3}$

19. $x^2 = 3x + 18$
$x^2 - 3x - 18 = 0$
$(x + 3)(x - 6) = 0$
$x + 3 = 0 \qquad x - 6 = 0$
$x = -3 \qquad x = 6$

21. $12x^2 + 17x + 6 = 0$

$(4x+3)(3x+2) = 0$

$4x+3 = 0 \qquad 3x+2 = 0$

$4x = -3 \qquad\quad 3x = -2$

$x = -\dfrac{3}{4} \qquad x = -\dfrac{2}{3}$

23. $m^2 + 13m + 24 = 2m - 6$

$m^2 + 11m + 30 = 0$

$(m+6)(m+5) = 0$

$m+6 = 0 \qquad m+5 = 0$

$m = -6 \qquad\quad m = -5$

25. $\qquad\qquad 8y^2 = 14y - 3$

$8y^2 - 14y + 3 = 0$

$(4y-1)(2y-3) = 0$

$4y-1 = 0 \qquad 2y-3 = 0$

$4y = 1 \qquad\quad 2y = 3$

$y = \dfrac{1}{4} \qquad\quad y = \dfrac{3}{2}$

27. $25x^2 - 60x + 36 = 0$

$(5x-6)(5x-6) = 0$

$5x-6 = 0$

$5x = 6$

$x = \dfrac{6}{5}$

29. $(x-5)(x+2) = -10$

$x^2 - 3x - 10 = -10$

$x^2 - 3x = 0$

$x(x-3) = 0$

$x = 0 \qquad x-3 = 0$

$x = 3$

31. $3x^2 + 8x - 10 = -6x - 10$

$3x^2 + 14x = 0$

$x(3x+14) = 0$

$x = 0 \qquad 3x+14 = 0$

$3x = -14$

$x = -\dfrac{14}{3}$

33. $\qquad y(y-7) = 2(5-2y)$

$y^2 - 7y- = 10 - 4y$

$y^2 - 3y = 10$

$y^2 - 3y - 10 = 0$

$(y+2)(y-5) = 0$

$y+2 = 0 \qquad y-5 = 0$

$y = -2 \qquad\quad y = 5$

35. $(x-6)(x-4) = 3$

$x^2 - 10x + 24 = 3$

$x^2 - 10x + 21 = 0$

$(x-3)(x-7) = 0$

$x-3 = 0 \qquad x-7 = 0$

$x = 3 \qquad\quad x = 7$

37. $2x(x+3) = (3x+1)(x+1)$

$$2x^2 + 6x = 3x^2 + 4x + 1$$
$$0 = x^2 - 2x + 1$$
$$0 = (x-1)(x-1)$$
$$0 = x - 1$$
$$1 = x$$

39.
$$x + \frac{8}{x} = 6$$
$$x^2 + 8 = 6x$$
$$x^2 - 6x + 8 = 0$$
$$(x-2)(x-4) = 0$$

$$x - 2 = 0 \qquad x - 4 = 0$$
$$x = 2 \qquad\quad x = 4$$

Check: $2 + \dfrac{8}{2} \overset{?}{=} 6 \qquad 4 + \dfrac{8}{4} \overset{?}{=} 6$

$$6 = 6 \qquad\qquad 6 = 6$$

41.
$$\frac{x}{4} - \frac{7}{x} = -\frac{3}{4}$$
$$x^2 - 28 = -3x$$
$$x^2 + 3x - 28 = 0$$
$$(x+7)(x-4) = 0$$

$$x + 7 = 0 \qquad x - 4 = 0$$
$$x = -7 \qquad\quad x = 4$$

Check: $\dfrac{-7}{4} - \dfrac{7}{-7} \overset{?}{=} -\dfrac{3}{4} \qquad \dfrac{4}{4} - \dfrac{7}{4} \overset{?}{=} -\dfrac{3}{4}$

$$-\frac{3}{4} = -\frac{3}{4} \qquad\qquad -\frac{3}{4} = -\frac{3}{4}$$

43.
$$\frac{3y-8}{2} = \frac{2}{y+1}$$
$$(y+1)(3y-8) = 4$$
$$3y^2 - 5y - 8 = 4$$
$$3y^2 - 5y - 12 = 0$$
$$(3y+4)(y-3) = 0$$

$$3y + 4 = 0 \qquad y - 3 = 0$$
$$3y = -4 \qquad\quad y = 3$$
$$y = -\frac{4}{3}$$

Check: $\dfrac{3\left(-\dfrac{4}{3}\right) - 8}{2} \overset{?}{=} \dfrac{2}{-\dfrac{4}{3}+1}$

$$-6 = -6$$

$$\frac{3(3)-8}{2} \overset{?}{=} \frac{2}{3+1}$$
$$\frac{1}{2} = \frac{1}{2}$$

45.
$$\frac{4}{x} + \frac{3}{x+5} = 2$$
$$(x+5)(4) + 3x = 2x(x+5)$$
$$4x + 20 + 3x = 2x^2 + 10x$$
$$2x^2 + 3x - 20 = 0$$
$$(2x-5)(x+4) = 0$$

$$2x - 5 = 0 \qquad x + 4 = 0$$
$$x = \frac{5}{2} \qquad\qquad x = -4$$

47. $\dfrac{24}{x^2-4}=1+\dfrac{2x-6}{x-2}$

$24=(x^2-4)(1)+(x+2)(2x-6)$

$24=x^2-4+2x^2-2x-12$

$0=3x^2-2x-40$

$0=(3x+10)(x-4)$

$3x+10=0 \qquad x-4=0$

$x=-\dfrac{10}{3} \qquad x=4$

Check:

$\dfrac{24}{(-10/3)^2-4}\overset{?}{=}1+\dfrac{2(-10/3)-6}{-10/3-2}$

$\dfrac{27}{8}=\dfrac{27}{8}$

$\dfrac{24}{4^2-4}\overset{?}{=}1+\dfrac{2(4)-6}{4-2}$

$2=2$

49. You can always factor out x.

51. $ax^2-7x+c=0$

$x=-\dfrac{3}{2}\Rightarrow\dfrac{9}{4}a+\dfrac{21}{2}+c=0 \qquad (1)$

$x=6\Rightarrow 36a-42+c=0 \qquad (2)$

Multiply (1) by -1 and add it to (2)

$\dfrac{135}{4}a-\dfrac{105}{2}=0$

$a=\dfrac{14}{9}$

Substitute $\dfrac{14}{9}$ for a in (2)

$36\left(\dfrac{14}{9}\right)-42+c=0$

$c=-14$

$a=\dfrac{14}{9}, \quad c=-14$

53. $t=\dfrac{n^2-n}{2}, \quad n=20$

$t=\dfrac{(20)^2-20}{2}=190$

190 truck routes.

55. $t=\dfrac{n^2-n}{2}, \quad t=15$

$15=\dfrac{n^2-n}{2}$

$0=n^2-n-30$

$0=(n-6)(n+5)$

$n-6=0 \qquad n+5=0$

$n=6 \qquad n=-5, \text{ has no meaning}$

6 cities can be serviced.

57. $t=\dfrac{n^2-n}{2}, \quad t=45$

$45=\dfrac{n^2-n}{2}$

$0=n^2-n-90$

$0=(n-10)(n+9)$

$$n - 10 = 0 \qquad n + 9 = 0$$
$$n = 10 \qquad n = -9$$
$$\text{has no meaning}$$

10 cities can be serviced.

For Exercises 59-63 use

$$R = -2.5n^2 + 80n - 280$$

59. $320 = -2.5n^2 + 80n - 280$

       $0 = -2.5n^2 + 80n - 600$

       $0 = -2.5\left(n^2 - 32n + 240\right)$

       $0 = -2.5(n-12)(n-20)$

     $n - 12 = 0 \quad n - 20 = 0$

       $n = 12 \qquad n = 20$

They may produce 1200 or 2000 labels.

61. $\dfrac{12 + 20}{2} = 16$, average $= 1600$ labels

     $R = -2.5(16)^2 + 80(16) - 280 = 360$

     The revenue for producing 1600 labels is \$360, which is more than producing either 1200 or 2000 labels.

63. $R = -2.5(15)^2 + 80(15) - 280 = \$357.5$

     $R = -2.5(17)^2 + 80(17) - 280 = \$357.5$

     It appears that the maximum revenue is at 1600 labels.

Cumulative Review

65. $\dfrac{\dfrac{1}{x} + \dfrac{3}{x-2}}{\dfrac{4}{x^2 - 4}} = \dfrac{\dfrac{1}{x} + \dfrac{3}{x-2}}{\dfrac{4}{(x+2)(x-2)}} \cdot \dfrac{x(x+2)(x-2)}{x(x+2)(x-2)}$

     $= \dfrac{(x+2)(x-2) + 3x(x+2)}{\cdot \, 4x}$

     $= \dfrac{x^2 - 4 + 3x^2 + 6x}{4x}$

     $= \dfrac{4x^2 + 6x - 4}{4x}$

     $= \dfrac{2x^2 - 3x - 2}{2x}$

     $= \dfrac{(2x-1)(x+2)}{2x}$

67.   Dust $= 0.12(36) = 4.32$ mg

10.2 Exercises

1. $x^2 = 64$

     $x = \pm\sqrt{64}$

     $x = \pm 8$

3. $x^2 = 98$

     $x = \pm\sqrt{98}$

     $x = \pm 7\sqrt{2}$

5. $x^2 - 28 = 0$

$$x^2 = 28$$
$$x = \pm\sqrt{28}$$
$$x = \pm 2\sqrt{7}$$

7. $5x^2 = 45$

$$x^2 = 9$$
$$x = \pm\sqrt{9}$$
$$x = \pm 3$$

9. $6x^2 = 120$

$$x^2 = 20$$
$$x = \pm\sqrt{20}$$
$$x = \pm 2\sqrt{5}$$

11. $3x^2 - 375 = 0$

$$3x^2 = 375$$
$$x^2 = 125$$
$$x = \pm\sqrt{125}$$
$$x = \pm 5\sqrt{5}$$

13. $5x^2 + 13 = 73$

$$5x^2 = 60$$
$$x^2 = 12$$
$$x = \pm\sqrt{12}$$
$$x = \pm 2\sqrt{3}$$

15. $13x^2 + 17 = 82$

$$13x^2 = 65$$
$$x^2 = 5$$
$$x = \pm\sqrt{5}$$

17. $(x-7)^2 = 16$

$$x - 7 = \pm 4$$
$$x = 7 \pm 4$$
$$x = 7 + 4 = 11$$
$$x = 7 - 4 = 3$$

19. $(x+4)^2 = 6$

$$x + 4 = \pm\sqrt{6}$$
$$x = -4 \pm \sqrt{6}$$

21. $(2x+5)^2 = 2$

$$2x + 5 = \pm\sqrt{2}$$
$$2x = -5 \pm \sqrt{2}$$
$$x = \frac{-5 \pm \sqrt{2}}{2}$$

23. $(3x-1)^2 = 7$

$$3x - 1 = \pm\sqrt{7}$$
$$3x = 1 \pm \sqrt{7}$$
$$x = \frac{1 \pm \sqrt{7}}{3}$$

25. $(7x+2)^2 = 12$

$$7x + 2 = \pm\sqrt{12}$$
$$7x = -2 \pm 2\sqrt{3}$$
$$x = \frac{-2 \pm 2\sqrt{3}}{7}$$

27. $(4x-5)^2 = 54$

$$4x-5 = \pm\sqrt{54}$$
$$4x = 5 \pm 3\sqrt{6}$$
$$x = \frac{5 \pm 3\sqrt{6}}{4}$$

29. $x^2 - 6x = 11, \quad \left[\frac{1}{2}(6)\right]^2 = 3^2 = 9$

$$x^2 - 6x + 9 = 11 + 9$$
$$(x-3)^2 = 20$$
$$x - 3 = \pm\sqrt{20}$$
$$x = 3 \pm 2\sqrt{5}$$

31. $x^2 + 6x - 7 = 0$

$$x^2 + 6x = 7$$
$$x^2 + 6x + 9 = 7 + 9$$
$$(x+3)^2 = 16$$
$$x + 3 = \pm 4$$
$$x = -3 \pm 4$$
$$x = -3 + 4 = 1$$
$$x = -3 - 4 = -7$$

33. $x^2 - 12x - 5 = 0$

$$x^2 - 12x = 5, \quad \left[\frac{1}{2}(-12)\right]^2 = 6^2 = 36$$
$$x^2 - 12x + 36 = 5 + 36$$
$$(x-6)^2 = 41$$
$$x - 6 = \pm\sqrt{41}$$
$$x = 6 \pm \sqrt{41}$$

35. $x^2 - 7x = 0$

$$x^2 - 7x + \frac{49}{4} = \frac{49}{4}$$
$$\left(x - \frac{7}{2}\right)^2 = \frac{49}{4}$$
$$x - \frac{7}{2} = \pm\sqrt{\frac{49}{4}}$$
$$x - \frac{7}{2} = \pm\frac{7}{2}$$
$$x = \frac{7}{2} \pm \frac{7}{2}$$
$$x = \frac{7}{2} + \frac{7}{2} = 7$$
$$x = \frac{7}{2} - \frac{7}{2} = 0$$

37. $5x^2 - 25x = 0$

$$x^2 - 5x = 0$$
$$x^2 - 5x + \frac{25}{4} = \frac{25}{4}$$
$$\left(x - \frac{5}{2}\right)^2 = \frac{25}{4}$$
$$x - \frac{5}{2} = \pm\sqrt{\frac{25}{4}}$$
$$x - \frac{5}{2} = \pm\frac{5}{2}$$
$$x = \frac{5}{2} \pm \frac{5}{2}$$
$$x = \frac{5}{2} + \frac{5}{2} = 5$$
$$x = \frac{5}{2} - \frac{5}{2} = 0$$

39. $2x^2 - 7x = 9$

$$x^2 - \frac{7}{2}x = \frac{9}{2}, \quad \left[\frac{1}{2}\left(-\frac{7}{2}\right)\right]^2 = \frac{49}{16}$$

$$x^2 - \frac{7}{2}x + \frac{49}{16} = \frac{9}{2} + \frac{49}{16}$$

$$\left(x - \frac{7}{4}\right)^2 = \frac{121}{16}$$

$$x - \frac{7}{4} = \pm\sqrt{\frac{121}{16}}$$

$$x = \frac{7}{4} \pm \frac{11}{4}$$

$$x = \frac{7}{4} - \frac{11}{4} \qquad x = \frac{7}{4} + \frac{11}{4}$$

$$x = -\frac{4}{4} = -1 \qquad x = \frac{18}{4} = \frac{9}{2}$$

41. $x^2 + bx - 7 = 0$

$$x^2 + bx = 7, \quad \left(\frac{b}{2}\right)^2 = \frac{b^2}{4}$$

$$x^2 + bx + \frac{b^2}{4} = 7 + \frac{b^2}{4}$$

$$\left(x + \frac{b}{2}\right)^2 = \frac{28 + b^2}{4}$$

$$x + \frac{b}{2} = \pm\sqrt{\frac{28 + b^2}{4}}$$

$$x = -\frac{b}{2} \pm \frac{\sqrt{28 + b^2}}{2}$$

$$x = \frac{-b \pm \sqrt{28 + b^2}}{2}$$

Cumulative Review

43. $3a - 5b = 8 \qquad$ (1)
$5a - 7b = 8 \qquad$ (2)

Multiply (1) by 5 and (2) by -3

$$15a - 25b = 40$$
$$\underline{-15a + 21b = -24}$$
$$-4b = 16$$
$$b = -4$$

Substitute -4 for b in (1)

$$3a - 5(-4) = 8$$
$$3a = -12$$
$$a = -4$$

$a = -4, \quad b = -4$

45. $P = \dfrac{F}{A}, \quad A = LW$

$F = 16, \; L = 8, \; W = 0.01$

$$P = \frac{16}{8(0.01)}$$

$$= \frac{16}{0.08}$$

$$= 200$$

The pressure is 200 pounds per square inch.

47. $21 - 7 = 14$ single men

$$\frac{14}{24} \approx 0.583 = 58.3\% \text{ were single}$$

330

10.3 Exercises

Use $x = \dfrac{-b \pm \sqrt{b^2 - 4ac}}{2a}$ in Exercises 1 - 31.
*

1. $3x^2 + 4x - 7 = 0$

    $a = 3, \quad b = 4, \quad c = -7$

    $\sqrt{b^2 - 4ac} = \sqrt{16 + 84}$

    $\qquad\qquad = \sqrt{100}$

    $\qquad\qquad = 10$

    There are two rational roots.

3. $4x^2 = -5x + 6$, no

    $4x^2 + 5x - 6 = 0$

    $a = 4, \quad b = 5, \quad c = -6$

5. $x^2 + 3x - 10 = 0$

    $a = 1, \quad b = 3, \quad c = -10$

    $x = \dfrac{-3 \pm \sqrt{(3)^2 - 4(1)(-10)}}{2(1)}$

    $\quad = \dfrac{-3 \pm \sqrt{49}}{2} = \dfrac{-3 \pm 7}{2}$

    $x = \dfrac{-3 \pm 7}{2}$

    $x = \dfrac{-3 + 7}{2} = 2$

    $x = \dfrac{-3 - 7}{2} = -5$

7. $x^2 - 3x - 8 = 0$

    $a = 1, \quad b = -3, \quad c = -8$

    $x = \dfrac{-(-3) \pm \sqrt{(-3)^2 - 4(1)(-8)}}{2(1)}$

    $\quad = \dfrac{3 \pm \sqrt{41}}{2}$

9. $4x^2 - 5x - 6 = 0$

    $a = 4, \quad b = -5, \quad c = -6$

    $x = \dfrac{-(-5) \pm \sqrt{(-5)^2 - 4(4)(-6)}}{2(4)}$

    $\quad = \dfrac{5 \pm \sqrt{121}}{8} = \dfrac{5 \pm 11}{8}$

11. $2x^2 = 3x + 20$

    $a = 2, \quad b = -3, \quad c = -20$

    $x = \dfrac{-(-3) \pm \sqrt{(-3)^2 - 4(2)(-20)}}{2(2)}$

    $x = \dfrac{3 \pm \sqrt{169}}{4}$

    $x = \dfrac{3 \pm 13}{4}$

    $x = \dfrac{3 \pm 13}{4}$

    $x = \dfrac{3 + 13}{4} = 4$

    $x = \dfrac{3 - 13}{4} = -\dfrac{5}{2}$

13. $6x^2 - 3x = 1$

$6x^2 - 3x - 1 = 0$

$a = 6, \ b = -3, \ c = -1$

$x = \dfrac{-(-3) \pm \sqrt{(-3)^2 - 4(6)(-1)}}{2(6)}$

$= \dfrac{3 \pm \sqrt{33}}{12}$

15. $x + \dfrac{3}{2} = 3x^2$

$3x^2 - x - \dfrac{3}{2} = 0$

$6x^2 - 2x - 3 = 0$

$a = 6, \ b = -2, \ c = -3$

$x = \dfrac{-(-2) \pm \sqrt{(-2)^2 - 4(6)(-3)}}{2(6)}$

$= \dfrac{2 \pm \sqrt{76}}{12} = \dfrac{2 \pm 2\sqrt{19}}{12} = \dfrac{1 \pm \sqrt{19}}{6}$

17. $\dfrac{x}{2} + \dfrac{5}{x} = \dfrac{7}{2}$

$x^2 + 10 = 7x$

$x^2 - 7x + 10 = 0$

$a = 1, \ b = -7, \ c = 10$

$x = \dfrac{-(-7) \pm \sqrt{(-7)^2 - 4(1)(10)}}{2(1)}$

$= \dfrac{7 \pm \sqrt{9}}{2} = \dfrac{7 \pm 3}{2}$

$x = \dfrac{7 + 3}{2} = 5$

$x = \dfrac{7 - 3}{2} = 2$

$(x - 7)^2 = 16$

$x - 7 = \pm 4$

$x = 7 \pm 4$

$x = 7 + 4 = 11$

$x = 7 - 4 = 3$

19. $5x^2 + 6x + 2 = 0$

$a = 5, \ b = 6, \ c = 2$

$x = \dfrac{-(6) \pm \sqrt{(6)^2 - 4(5)(2)}}{2(5)} = \dfrac{-6 \pm \sqrt{-4}}{10}$

No real solution.

21. $3y^2 = 8y - 3$

$3y^2 - 8y + 3 = 0$

$a = 3, \ b = -8, \ c = 3$

$y = \dfrac{-(-8) \pm \sqrt{(-8)^2 - 4(3)(3)}}{2(3)}$

$y = \dfrac{8 \pm \sqrt{28}}{6}$

$y = \dfrac{8 \pm 2\sqrt{7}}{6}$

$y = \dfrac{4 \pm \sqrt{7}}{3}$

23. $\dfrac{d^2}{2} + \dfrac{5d}{6} - 2 = 0$

$3d^2 + 5d - 12 = 0$

$a = 3, \ b = 5, \ c = -12$

$$d = \frac{-(5) \pm \sqrt{(5)^2 - 4(3)(-12)}}{2(3)}$$

$$= \frac{-5 \pm \sqrt{169}}{6} = \frac{-5 \pm 13}{6}$$

$$d = \frac{-5 - 13}{6} \qquad d = \frac{-5 + 13}{6}$$

$$d = -3 \qquad d = \frac{4}{3}$$

25. $4x^2 + 8x + 11 = 0$

$a = 4, \quad b = 8, \quad c = 11$

$$x = \frac{-8 \pm \sqrt{(8)^2 - 4(4)(11)}}{2(4)}$$

$$x = \frac{-8 \pm \sqrt{-24}}{8}$$

$\sqrt{-24}$ is not real

There is no real solution.

27. $x^2 - 10x + 25 = 0$

$a = 1, \quad b = -10, \quad c = 25$

$$x = \frac{-(-10) \pm \sqrt{(-10)^2 - 4(1)(25)}}{2(1)}$$

$$x = \frac{10 \pm \sqrt{0}}{2}$$

$x = 5$

29. $x^2 + 5x - 2 = 0$

$a = 1, \quad b = 5, \quad c = -2$

$$x = \frac{-(5) \pm \sqrt{(5)^2 - 4(1)(-2)}}{2(1)} = \frac{-5 \pm \sqrt{33}}{2}$$

$x = 0.372, \; -5.372$

31. $2x^2 - 7x - 5 = 0$

$a = 2, \quad b = -7, \quad c = -5$

$$x = \frac{-(-7) \pm \sqrt{(-7)^2 - 4(2)(-5)}}{2(2)}$$

$$x = \frac{7 \pm \sqrt{89}}{4}$$

$$x = \frac{7 + \sqrt{89}}{4} \approx 4.108$$

$$x = \frac{7 - \sqrt{89}}{4} \approx -0.608$$

33. $5x^2 + 10x + 1 = 0$

$a = 5, \quad b = 10, \quad c = 1$

$$x = \frac{-(10) \pm \sqrt{(10)^2 - 4(5)(1)}}{2(5)}$$

$$= \frac{-10 \pm \sqrt{80}}{10} = \frac{-10 \pm 4\sqrt{5}}{10} = \frac{-5 \pm 2\sqrt{5}}{5}$$

$x = -0.106, \; -1.894$

35. $6x^2 - 13x + 6 = 0$

$(3x - 2)(2x - 3) = 0$

$3x - 2 = 0 \qquad 2x - 3 = 0$

$3x = 2 \qquad \quad 2x = 3$

$$x = \frac{2}{3} \qquad \qquad x = \frac{3}{2}$$

37. $3(x^2+1)=10x$

$$3x^2+3=10x$$

$$3x^2-10x+3=0$$

$$(3x-1)(x-3)=0$$

$3x-1=0 \qquad x-3=0$

$3x=1 \qquad\quad x=3$

$$x=\frac{1}{3}$$

39. $(t+5)(t-3)=7$

$$t^2+2t-15=7$$

$$t^2+2t=22$$

$$t^2+2t+1=22+1$$

$$(t+1)^2=23$$

$$t+1=\pm\sqrt{23}$$

$$t=-1\pm\sqrt{23}$$

41. $y^2-\dfrac{2}{5}y=2$

$$5y^2-2y=10$$

$$5y^2-2y-10=0$$

$$a=5,\quad b=-2,\quad c=-10$$

$$y=\frac{-(-2)\pm\sqrt{(-2)^2-4(5)(-10)}}{2(5)}$$

$$=\frac{2\pm\sqrt{204}}{10}=\frac{2\pm2\sqrt{51}}{10}=\frac{1\pm\sqrt{51}}{5}$$

43. $3x^2-13=0$

$$3x^2=13$$

$$x^2=\frac{13}{3}$$

$$x=\pm\sqrt{\frac{13}{3}}=\pm\frac{\sqrt{13}}{\sqrt{3}}=\pm\frac{\sqrt{39}}{3}$$

45. $x(x-2)=7$

$$x^2-2x=7$$

$$x^2-2x-7=0$$

$$a=1,\quad b=-2,\quad c=-7$$

$$x=\frac{-(-2)\pm\sqrt{(-2)^2-4(1)(-7)}}{2(1)}$$

$$=\frac{2\pm\sqrt{32}}{2}=\frac{2\pm4\sqrt{2}}{2}=1\pm2\sqrt{2}$$

47. Total area – Pool area = Tile area

$$(2x+30)(2x+20)-20(30)=216$$

$$4x^2+100x+600-600=216$$

$$4x^2+100x-216=0$$

$$x^2+25x-54=0$$

$$(x+27)(x-2)=0$$

$x+27=0 \qquad x-2=0$

$x=-27 \qquad x=2$

Width can't be negative.

Width is 2 feet.

Cumulative Review

How Am I Doing? Sections 10.1–10.3

49. $\dfrac{3x}{x-2} + \dfrac{4}{x+2} - \dfrac{x+22}{x^2-4}$

$= \dfrac{3x}{x-2} \cdot \dfrac{x+2}{x+2} + \dfrac{4}{x+2} \cdot \dfrac{x-2}{x-2} - \dfrac{x+22}{x^2-4}$

$= \dfrac{3x^2 + 6x + 4x - 8 - x - 22}{(x-2)(x+2)}$

$= \dfrac{3x^2 + 9x - 30}{(x-2)(x+2)}$

$= \dfrac{3(x+5)(x-2)}{(x-2)(x+2)}$

$= \dfrac{3(x+5)}{x+2}$

1. $x^2 - 13x - 48 = 0$

$(x-16)(x+3) = 0$

$x - 16 = 0 \qquad x + 3 = 0$

$\qquad x = 16 \qquad\qquad x = -3$

2. $5x^2 + 7x = 14x$

$5x^2 - 7x = 0$

$x(5x-7) = 0$

$5x - 7 = 0 \qquad x = 0$

$5x = 7$

$x = \dfrac{7}{5}$

51.

$$
\begin{array}{r}
x^2 + 5x + 2 \\
x+3\overline{)x^3 + 8x^2 + 17x + 6} \\
\underline{x^3 + 3x^2} \\
5x^2 + 17x \\
\underline{5x^2 + 15x} \\
2x + 6 \\
\underline{2x + 6}
\end{array}
$$

$\left(x^3 + 8x^2 + 17x + 6\right) \div (x+3) = x^2 + 5x + 2$

3. $\qquad 5x^2 = 22x - 8$

$5x^2 - 22x + 8 = 0$

$(5x-2)(x-4) = 0$

$5x - 2 = 0 \qquad x - 4 = 0$

$5x = 2 \qquad\qquad x = 4$

$x = \dfrac{2}{5}$

53. $V = \pi r^2 h$

$\approx 3.14(2.40)^2(5.35)$

$\approx 96.76 \ \text{cubic feet}$

4. $\qquad -2x + 1 = 8x^2$

$8x^2 + 2x - 1 = 0$

$(4x-1)(2x+1) = 0$

$4x - 1 = 0 \qquad 2x + 1 = 0$

$4x = 1 \qquad\qquad 2x = -1$

$x = \dfrac{1}{4} \qquad\qquad x = -\dfrac{1}{2}$

5. $x(x+9) = 4(x+6)$

$x^2 + 9x = 4x + 24$

$x^2 + 5x - 24 = 0$

$(x+8)(x-3) = 0$

$x+8 = 0 \qquad x-3 = 0$

$x = -8 \qquad x = 3$

6. $\dfrac{5}{x+2} = \dfrac{2x-1}{5}$

$25 = (x+2)(2x-1)$

$25 = 2x^2 + 3x - 2$

$0 = 2x^2 + 3x - 27$

$0 = (2x+9)(x-3)$

$2x+9 = 0 \qquad x-3 = 0$

$2x = -9 \qquad x = 3$

$x = -\dfrac{9}{2}$

7. $x^2 - 18 = 0$

$x^2 = 18$

$x = \pm\sqrt{18}$

$x = \pm 3\sqrt{2}$

8. $3x^2 + 1 = 0$

$3x^2 = 75$

$x^2 = 25$

$x = \pm\sqrt{25}$

$x = \pm 5$

9. $x^2 + 8x + 5 = 0$

$x^2 + 8x = -5$

$x^2 + 8x + 16 = -5 + 16$

$(x+4)^2 = 11$

$x + 4 = \pm\sqrt{11}$

$x = -4 \pm \sqrt{11}$

10. $2x^2 + 3x - 7 = 0$

$2x^2 + 3x = 7$

$x^2 + \dfrac{3}{2}x = \dfrac{7}{2}$

$x^2 + \dfrac{3}{2}x + \dfrac{9}{16} = \dfrac{7}{2} + \dfrac{9}{16}$

$\left(x + \dfrac{3}{4}\right)^2 = \dfrac{65}{16}$

$x + \dfrac{3}{4} = \pm\sqrt{\dfrac{65}{16}}$

$x = -\dfrac{3}{4} \pm \sqrt{\dfrac{65}{4}}$

$x = \dfrac{-3 \pm \sqrt{65}}{4}$

11. $2x^2 + 4x - 5 = 0$

$a = 2, \quad b = 4, \quad c = -5$

$x = \dfrac{-4 \pm \sqrt{(4)^2 - 4(2)(-5)}}{2(2)}$

$x = \dfrac{-4 \pm \sqrt{56}}{4}$

$x = \dfrac{-4 \pm 2\sqrt{14}}{4}$

$x = \dfrac{-2 \pm \sqrt{14}}{2}$

12. $2x^2 = 7x - 4$

$2x^2 - 7x + 4 = 0$

$a = 2, \quad b = -7, \quad c = 4$

$x = \dfrac{-(-7) \pm \sqrt{(-7)^2 - 4(2)(4)}}{2(2)}$

$x = \dfrac{7 \pm \sqrt{17}}{4}$

13. $3x^2 + 8x + 1 = 0$

$a = 3, \quad b = 8, \quad c = 1$

$x = \dfrac{-8 \pm \sqrt{(8)^2 - 4(3)(1)}}{2(3)}$

$x = \dfrac{-8 \pm \sqrt{52}}{6}$

$x = \dfrac{-8 \pm 2\sqrt{13}}{6}$

$x = \dfrac{-4 \pm \sqrt{13}}{3}$

14. $5x^2 + 3 = 4x$

$5x^2 - 4x + 3 = 0$

$a = 5, \quad b = -4, \quad c = 3$

$x = \dfrac{-(-4) \pm \sqrt{(-4)^2 - 4(5)(3)}}{2(5)}$

$x = \dfrac{4 \pm \sqrt{-44}}{10}$

$\sqrt{-44}$ is not a real number
There is no real solution.

10.4 Exercises

1. It may have 2, 1, or none.

3. If $b = 0$, then the parabola always has a vertex at $(0, c)$ that is on the y-axis.

5. $y = x^2 + 2$

x	y
-2	6
-1	3
0	2
1	3
2	6

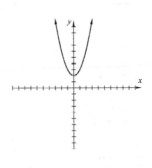

7. $y = -\dfrac{1}{3}x^2$

x	y
-6	-12
-3	-3
0	0
3	-3
6	-12

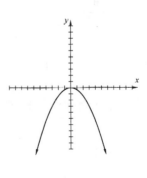

9. $y = 2x^2 - 3$

x	y
-2	5
-1	-1
0	-3
1	-1
2	5

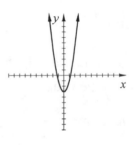

11. $y = (x-2)^2$

x	y
0	4
1	1
2	0
3	1
4	4

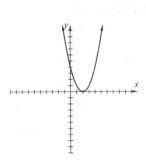

x	y
-4	0
-3	-3
-2	-4
-1	-3
0	0

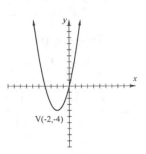

13. $y = -\dfrac{1}{2}x^2 + 4$

x	y
-4	-4
-2	2
0	4
2	2
4	-4

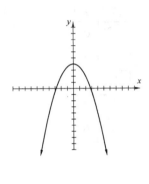

19. $y = -x^2 - 4x, \quad a = -1, \quad b = -4$

$a < 0$: opens down

Vertex: $x = -\dfrac{(-4)}{2(-1)} = -2$

$y = -(-2)^2 - 4(-2) = 4$

$V(-2, 4)$

x	y
-4	0
-3	3
-2	4
-1	3
0	0

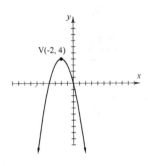

15. $y = \dfrac{1}{2}(x-3)^2$

x	y
-1	8
1	2
3	0
5	2
7	8

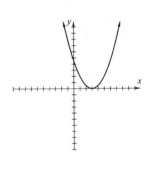

21. $y = -2x^2 + 8x, \quad a = -2, \quad b = 8$

$a < 0$: opens down

Vertex: $x = -\dfrac{8}{2(-2)} = 2$

$y = -2(2)^2 + 8(2) = 8$

$V(2, 8)$

17. $y = x^2 + 4x, \quad a = 1, \quad b = 4$

$a > 0$: opens up

Vertex: $x = -\dfrac{b}{2a} = -\dfrac{4}{2(1)} = -2$

$y = (-2)^2 + 4(-2) = -4$

$V(-2, -4)$

338

x	y
-1	-10
0	0
1	8
4	0
5	-10

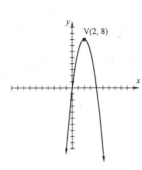

x – intercepts: $0 = -x^2 - 6x - 5$

$$0 = -(x+5)(x+1)$$

$$x = -5, \; -1$$

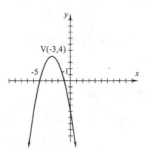

23. $y = x^2 + 2x - 3, \quad a = 1, \quad b = 2$

Vertex: $x = -\dfrac{2}{2(1)} = -1$

$$y = (-1)^2 + 2(-1) - 3 = -4$$

$V(-1, -4)$

y – intercept: $y = 0^2 + 2(0) - 3 = -3$

x – intercepts: $0 = x^2 + 2x - 3$

$$0 = (x+3)(x-1)$$

$$x = 1, \; -3$$

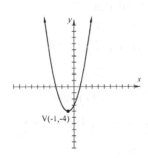

27. $y = x^2 + 6x + 9, \quad a = 1, \quad b = 6$

Vertex: $x = -\dfrac{6}{2(1)} = -3$

$$y = (-3)^2 + 6(-3) + 9 = 0$$

$V(-3, 0)$

y – intercept: $y = 0^2 + 6(0) + 9 = 9$

x – intercepts: $0 = x^2 + 6x + 9$

$$0 = (x+3)^2$$

$$x = -3$$

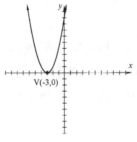

25. $y = -x^2 - 6x - 5, \quad a = -1, \quad b = -6$

Vertex: $x = -\dfrac{(-6)}{2(-1)} = -3$

$$y = -(-3)^2 - 6(-3) - 5 = 4$$

$V(-3, 4)$

y – intercept: $y = -0^2 - 6(0) - 5 = -5$

$h = -4.9t^2 + 39.2t + 4,$

$a = -4.9, \ b = 39.2$

Vertex: $t = -\dfrac{39.2}{2(-4.9)} = 4$

29. $h = -4.9(4)^2 + 39.2(4) + 4 = 82.4$

$V(4, 82.4)$

h – intercept: $h = 4$

t – intercept: $0 = -4.9t^2 + 39.2t + 10$

$t \approx -0.1, \ 8.1$

(a)

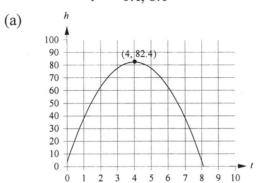

(b) $t = 2$

$h = -4.9(2)^2 + 39.2(2) + 4 = 62.8$

It is 62.8 m high.

(c) $V(4, 82.4)$

The maximum height is 82.4 m.

(d) The x – intercept is 8.1

After $8.1s$ it will strike the earth.

31. $N = 9x - x^2, \ a = -1, \ b = 9$

(a) Vertex: $x = -\dfrac{9}{2(-1)} = 4.5$

$N = 9(4.5) - (4.5)^2 = 20.25$

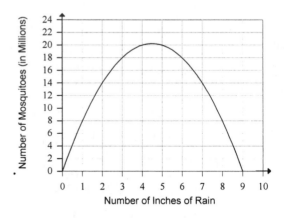

(a) Maximum is at the vertex: 4.5 inches

(b) Maximum is at the vertex:
20.25 million

33. $y = x^2 + 10.6x - 212.16$

Vertex: $x = -\dfrac{10.6}{2(1)} = -5.3$

$y = (-5.3)^2 + 10.6(-5.3) - 212.16$

$= -240.25$

$V(-5.3, -240.25)$

y-intercept: $(0, -212.16)$

x-intercepts:

$x = \dfrac{-10.6 \pm \sqrt{(10.6)^2 - 4(1)(-212.16)}}{2(1)}$

$= -20.8, \ 10.2$

$(-20.8, 0)$ and $(10.2, 0)$

35. $y = -301x^2 - 167x + 1528$

Vertex: $x = -\dfrac{-167}{2(-301)} \approx -0.277$

$y = -301(-0.277)^2 - 167(-0.277) + 1528$

≈ 1551.164

$V(-0.277, 1551.164)$

y-intercept: $(0, 1528)$

x-intercepts:

$x = \dfrac{167 \pm \sqrt{(-167)^2 - 4(-301)(1528)}}{2(-301)}$

$= -2.548,\ 1.993$

$(-2.548, 0)$ and $(1.993, 0)$

Cumulative Review

37. $y = kx^2,\ \ y = 12,\ \ x = 2$

$12 = k(2)^2 \Rightarrow k = 3$

$y = 3x^2,\ \ x = 5$

$y = 3(5)^2 = 75$

39. $a = \dfrac{V_2 - V_1}{T_2 - T_1} = \dfrac{360 - 355}{49 - 40} = \dfrac{5}{9}$

$V = aT + b$

$355 = \dfrac{5}{9}(40) + b$

$3195 = 200 + 9b$

$2995 = 9b$

$V = \dfrac{5}{9}T + \dfrac{2995}{9}$

10.5 Exercises

1. $A = \dfrac{1}{2}ba,\ x = $ altitude, $x - 5 = $ base

$88 = \dfrac{1}{2}(x - 5)(x)$

$176 = x^2 - 5x$

$0 = x^2 - 5x - 176$

$0 = (x - 16)(x + 11)$

$x - 16 = 0 \qquad x + 11 = 0$

$\qquad x = 16 \qquad\qquad x = -11$

Length can't be negative.

$x - 5 = 16 - 5 = 11$

The altitude is 16 centimeters.

The base is 11 centimeters

3. $x = $ length of the sides of the old garden

New garden area $= (x + 7)(x + 11)$

$x^2 + 18x + 77 = 396$

$x^2 + 18x - 319 = 0$

$(x - 11)(x + 29) = 0$

$x - 11 = 0 \qquad x + 29 = 0$

$\quad x = 11, \qquad\qquad x = -29,$

Length can't be negative.

The old garden was 11 feet by 11 feet.

5. s = original number of people

c = cost per person

$$s \cdot c = 420 \qquad (1)$$

$$(s+7)(c-5) = 420 \qquad (2)$$

Substitute $\dfrac{420}{5}$ for c in (2)

$$(s+7)\left(\frac{420}{s} - 5\right) = 420$$

$$(s+7)(420 - 5s) = 420s$$

$$(s+7)(84 - s) = 84s$$

$$s^2 + 7s - 588 = 0$$

$$(s+28)(s-21) = 0$$

$$s = -28, \quad s = 21$$

Number of people can't be negative.

Original number of people was 21.

7. s = number of members

c = cost

$$s \cdot c = 400 \qquad (1)$$

$$(s+20)(c-1) = 400 \qquad (2)$$

Substitute $\dfrac{400}{s}$ for c in (2)

$$(s+20)\left(\frac{400}{s} - 1\right) = 400$$

$$(s+20)(400 - s) = 400s$$

$$s^2 - 380s - 8000 = -400s$$

$$s^2 + 20s - 8000 = 0$$

$$(s+100)(s-80) = 0$$

$$s + 100 = 0 \qquad s - 80 = 0$$

$$s = -100 \qquad s = 80$$

Number of members can't be negative.

$$s + 20 = 100$$

80 were expected, 100 attended.

9. x = width, y = length

Length: $2x + y = 100 \qquad (1)$

Area: $xy = 1250 \qquad (2)$

Substitute $\dfrac{1250}{y}$ for x in (1)

$$2\left(\frac{1250}{y}\right) + y = 100$$

$$2500 + y^2 = 100y$$

$$y^2 - 100y + 2500 = 0$$

$$(y-50)(y-50) = 0$$

$$y - 50 = 0$$

$$y = 50$$

$$x = \frac{1250}{y} = \frac{1250}{50} = 25$$

The length is 50 feet, width is 25 feet.

11. x = actual speed

$x + 200$ = proposed speed

Actual test: time $= \dfrac{2400}{x}$

Proposed test: time $= \dfrac{2400}{x + 200}$

$$\frac{2400}{x+200} = \frac{2400}{x} - 1$$

$$2400x = 2400(x+200) - x(x+200)$$

$$2400x = 2400x + 480,000 - x^2 - 200x$$

$$0 = -x^2 - 200x + 480,000$$

342

$$0 = -(x+800)(x-600)$$

$$x = -800 \qquad x = 600$$

Speed can't be negative.

The actual speed was 600 mph.

Use $y = -2.5x^2 + 22.5x + 50$
in Exercises 13 – 17.

13. $x = 1991 - 1990 = 1$

$$y = -2.5(1)^2 + 22.5(1) + 50 = 70$$

15. $x = 1992 - 1990 = 2$

$$y = -2.5(2)^2 + 22.5(2) + 50 = 85$$

$$x = 1993 - 1990 = 3$$

$$y = -2.5(3)^2 + 22.5(3) + 50 = 95$$

$$95 - 85 = 10 \text{ more centers}$$

17. $-2.5x^2 + 22.5x + 50 = 100$

$$2.5x^2 - 22.5x + 50 = 0$$

$$x^2 - 9x + 20 = 0$$

$$(x-5)(x-4) = 0$$

$$x - 5 = 0 \qquad x - 4 = 0$$

$$x = 5 \qquad\qquad x = 4$$

$$\text{1995 and 1994}$$

19. $y = -0.018x^2 + 1.336x, \; y = 0$

$$0 = -0.018x^2 + 1.336x$$

$$0 = x(-0.018x + 1.336)$$

$$x = 0$$

$$-0.018x + 1.336 = 0$$

$$-0.018x = -1.336$$

$$x \approx 74.2$$

21.

$$\frac{n(n+1)}{2} = s, \quad s = 91$$

$$\frac{n(n+1)}{2} = 91$$

$$n^2 + n = 182$$

$$n^2 + n - 182 = 0$$

$$(n+14)(x-13) = 0$$

$$n = -14 \qquad n = 13$$

Counting numbers can't be negative.

$$n = 13$$

Cumulative Review

23. $3x + 11 \geq 9x - 4$

$$-6x \geq -15$$

$$x \leq \frac{5}{2}$$

25. $x =$ length of section 1 and of section 2.

$l =$ length of section 3

Volume of $3 = \left(\dfrac{2}{3}\right)$ volume of 1

$$2(2)l = \frac{2}{3}(2)(2)x$$

$$l = \frac{2}{3}x$$

Total length $= x + x + \dfrac{2}{3}x = 3$

$$\frac{8}{3}x = 3$$

$$x = \frac{9}{8}$$

$$l = \frac{2}{3}\left(\frac{9}{8}\right) = \frac{3}{4}$$

Section 3 is 0.75 feet long

Putting Your Skills to Work

In Exercises 1-5 use $h = 16t^2 + 80t + 4$.

1.

t	0	1	2	3	4	5
h	4	68	100	100	68	4

* 2.

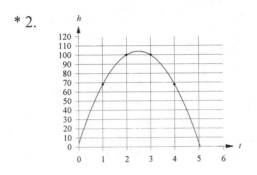

3. $t = 2$

$$h = -16(2)^2 + 80(2) + 4$$
$$h = 100 \text{ feet}$$

4. Maximum height occurs at 2.5 seconds

$$h = -16(2.5)^2 + 80(2.5) + 4$$
$$h = 104 \text{ feet}$$

5. $h = 0$

$$0 = -16t^2 + 80t + 4$$
$$0 = -4t^2 + 20t + 1$$
$$a = -4, \ b = 20, \ c = 1$$
$$t = \frac{-20 \pm \sqrt{(20)^2 - 4(-4)(1)}}{2(-4)}$$
$$t = \frac{-20 \pm \sqrt{416}}{-8}$$
$$t = \frac{-20 + \sqrt{416}}{-8} \approx -0.0495$$

Time cannot be negative.

$$t = \frac{-20 - \sqrt{416}}{-8} \approx 5.05$$

It lands after about 5.05 seconds.

6. $h = -16t^2 + 90t + 5$

$$a = -16, \ b = 90, \ c = 5$$
$$t_{max} = -\frac{b}{2a} = \frac{-90}{2(-16)} = 2.8125 \text{ sec}$$
$$h_{max} = -16(2.8125)^2 + 90(2.8125) + 5$$
$$= 131.6 \text{ feet}$$

344

Chapter 10 Review Problems

1.
$$6x^2 = 5x - 8$$
$$6x^2 - 5x + 8 = 0$$
$$a = 6, \quad b = -5, \quad c = 8$$

2.
$$9x^2 + 3x = -5x^2 + 16$$
$$14x^2 + 3x - 16 = 0$$
$$a = 14, \quad b = 3, \quad c = -16$$

3. $(x - 4)(2x - 1) = x^2 + 7$
$$2x^2 - 9x + 4 = x^2 + 7$$
$$x^2 \quad 9x - 3 - 0$$
$$a = 1, \quad b = -9, \quad c = -3$$

4. $2x(5x - 2) = x(3 - x)$
$$10x^2 - 4x = 3x - x^2$$
$$11x^2 - 7x = 0$$
$$a = 11, \quad b = -7, \quad c = 0$$

5.
$$\frac{3}{x^2} - \frac{6}{x} - 2 = 0$$
$$3 - 6x - 2x^2 = 0$$
$$-2x^2 - 6x + 3 = 0$$
$$a = -2, \quad b = -6, \quad c = 3$$

6.
$$\frac{x}{x + 2} - \frac{3}{x - 2} = 5$$
$$x(x - 2) - 3(x + 2) = 5(x + 2)(x - 2)$$
$$x^2 - 2x - 3x - 6 = 5x^2 - 20$$
$$-4x^2 - 5x + 14 = 0$$
$$4x^2 + 5x - 14 = 0$$
$$a = 4, \quad b = 5, \quad c = -14$$

7. $x^2 + 26x + 25 = 0$
$$(x + 25)(x + 1) = 0$$
$$x + 25 = 0 \qquad x + 1 = 0$$
$$x = -25 \qquad x = -1$$

8. $x^2 + 16x + 64 = 0$
$$(x + 8)(x + 8) = 0$$
$$x + 8 = 0$$
$$x = -8$$

9. $x^2 + 6x - 55 = 0$
$$(x + 11)(x - 5) = 0$$
$$x + 11 = 0 \qquad x - 5 = 0$$
$$x = -11 \qquad x = 5$$

10. $4x^2 - 16x + 15 = 0$
$$(2x - 3)(2x - 5) = 0$$
$$2x - 3 = 0 \qquad 2x - 5 = 0$$
$$2x = 3 \qquad 2x = 5$$
$$x = \frac{3}{2} \qquad x = \frac{5}{2}$$

11. $9x^2 - 24x + 16 = 0$
$$(3x - 4)(3x - 4) = 0$$
$$3x - 4 = 0$$
$$3x = 4$$
$$x = \frac{4}{3}$$

345

12. $15x^2 = 26x - 8$

$15x^2 - 26x + 8 = 0$

$(5x - 2)(3x - 4) = 0$

$5x - 2 = 0$	$3x - 4 = 0$
$5x = 2$	$3x = 4$
$x = \dfrac{2}{5}$	$x = \dfrac{4}{3}$

16. $\dfrac{1}{2}x^2 = \dfrac{3}{4}x - \dfrac{1}{4}$

$2x^2 = 3x - 1$

$2x^2 - 3x + 1 = 0$

$(2x - 1)(x - 1) = 0$

$2x - 1 = 0$	$x - 1 = 0$
$2x = 1$	$x = 1$
$x = \dfrac{1}{2}$	

13. $10x^2 = 19x - 7$

$10x^2 - 19x + 7 = 0$

$(2x - 1)(5x - 7) = 0$

$5x - 2 = 0$	$3x - 4 = 0$
$5x = 2$	$3x = 4$
$x = \dfrac{2}{5}$	$x = \dfrac{4}{3}$

17. $x^2 + \dfrac{2}{15}x = \dfrac{1}{15}$

$15x^2 + 2x = 1$

$15x^2 + 2x - 1 = 0$

$(5x - 1)(3x + 1) = 0$

$5x - 1 = 0$	$3x + 1 = 0$
$5x = 1$	$3x = -1$
$x = \dfrac{1}{5}$	$x = -\dfrac{1}{3}$

14. $3x^2 = -14x - 11$

$3x^2 + 14x + 11 = 0$

$(3x + 11)(x + 1) = 0$

$3x + 11 = 0$	$x + 1 = 0$
$3x = -11$	
$x = -\dfrac{11}{3}$	$x = -1$

18. $1 + \dfrac{13}{12x} - \dfrac{1}{3x^2} = 0$

$12x^2 + 13x - 4 = 0$

$(3x + 4)(4x - 1) = 0$

$3x + 4 = 0$	$4x - 1 = 0$
$3x = -4$	$4x = 1$
$x = -\dfrac{4}{3}$	$x = \dfrac{1}{4}$

15. $x^2 + \dfrac{1}{6}x - 2 = 0$

$6x^2 + x - 12 = 0$

$(2x + 3)(3x - 4) = 0$

$2x + 3 = 0$	$3x - 4 = 0$
$2x = -3$	$3x = 4$
$x = -\dfrac{3}{2}$	$x = \dfrac{4}{3}$

19. $x^2 + 8x - 2 = 3x - 2$

$$x^2 + 5x = 0$$

$$x(x+5) = 0$$

$x + 5 = 0 \qquad x = 0$

$x = -5$

20. $x^2 - 6x + 5 = 2x + 5$

$$x^2 - 8x = 0$$

$$x(x-8) = 0$$

$x - 8 = 0 \qquad x = 0$

$x = 8$

21. $$1 + \frac{2}{3x+4} = \frac{3}{3x+2}$$

$$(3x+4)(3x+2) + 2(3x+2) = 3(3x+4)$$

$$9x^2 + 18x + 8 + 6x + 4 = 9x + 12$$

$$9x^2 + 15x = 0$$

$$3x(3x+5) = 0$$

$3x - 0 \qquad 3x + 5 = 0$

$x = 0 \qquad\qquad 3x = -5$

$$x = -\frac{5}{3}$$

22. $$2 - \frac{5}{x+1} = \frac{3}{x-1}$$

$$2(x+1)(x-1) - 5(x-1) = 3(x+1)$$

$$2x^2 - 2 - 5x + 5 = 3x + 3$$

$$2x^2 - 8x = 0$$

$$2x(x-4) = 0$$

$2x = 0 \qquad x - 4 = 0$

$x = 0 \qquad\quad x = 4$

23. $$5 + \frac{24}{2-x} = \frac{24}{2+x}$$

$$5(2-x)(2+x) + 24(2+x) = 24(2-x)$$

$$20 - 5x^2 + 48 + 24x = 48 - 24x$$

$$-5x^2 + 48x + 20 = 0$$

$$5x^2 - 48x - 20 = 0$$

$$(5x+2)(x-10) = 0$$

$5x + 2 = 0 \qquad x - 10 = 0$

$5x = -2 \qquad\qquad x = 10$

$$x = -\frac{2}{5}$$

24. $$\frac{4}{9} = \frac{5x}{3} - x^2$$

$$4 = 15x - 9x^2$$

$$9x^2 - 15x + 4 = 0$$

$$(3x-1)(3x-4) = 0$$

$3x - 1 = 0 \qquad 3x - 4 = 0$

$3x = 1 \qquad\qquad 3x = 4$

$$x = \frac{1}{3} \qquad\qquad x = \frac{4}{3}$$

25. $x^2 - 8 = 41$

$$x^2 = 49$$

$$x = \pm\sqrt{49}$$

$$x = \pm 7$$

26. $x^2 + 11 = 92$

$$x^2 = 81$$

$$x = \pm\sqrt{81}$$

$$x = \pm 9$$

27. $x^2 - 5 = 17$
$$x^2 = 22$$
$$x = \pm\sqrt{22}$$

28. $x^2 + 11 = 50$
$$x^2 = 39$$
$$x = \pm\sqrt{39}$$

29. $2x^2 - 1 = 15$
$$2x^2 = 16$$
$$x^2 = 8$$
$$x = \pm\sqrt{8}$$
$$x = \pm 2\sqrt{2}$$

30. $3x^2 + 4 = 154$
$$3x^2 = 150$$
$$x^2 = 50$$
$$x = \pm\sqrt{50}$$
$$x = \pm 5\sqrt{2}$$

31. $3x^2 + 6 = 60$
$$3x^2 = 54$$
$$x^2 = 18$$
$$x = \pm\sqrt{18}$$
$$x = \pm 3\sqrt{2}$$

32. $2x^2 - 5 = 43$
$$2x^2 = 48$$
$$x^2 = 24$$
$$x = \pm\sqrt{24}$$
$$x = \pm 2\sqrt{6}$$

33. $(x - 4)^2 = 7$
$$x - 4 = \pm\sqrt{7}$$
$$x = 4 \pm \sqrt{7}$$

34. $(x - 2)^2 = 3$
$$x - 2 = \pm\sqrt{3}$$
$$x = 2 \pm \sqrt{3}$$

35. $(4x + 3)^2 = 24$
$$4x + 3 = \pm\sqrt{24}$$
$$4x = -3 \pm 2\sqrt{6}$$
$$x = \frac{-3 \pm 2\sqrt{6}}{4}$$

36. $(2x + 7)^2 = 45$
$$2x + 7 = \pm\sqrt{45}$$
$$2x = -7 \pm 3\sqrt{5}$$
$$x = \frac{-7 \pm 3\sqrt{5}}{2}$$

37. $x^2 + 10x - 11 = 0$
$$x^2 + 10x = 11, \quad \left[\frac{1}{2}(10)\right]^2 = 5^2 = 25$$
$$x^2 + 10x + 25 = 11 + 25$$
$$(x + 5)^2 = 36$$
$$x + 5 = \pm\sqrt{36}$$
$$x = -5 \pm 6$$
$$x = -5 - 6 \qquad x = -5 + 6$$
$$x = -11 \qquad\quad x = 1$$

348

38. $x^2 + 12x + 11 = 0$

$$x^2 + 12x = -11, \quad \left[\frac{1}{2}(12)\right]^2 = 6^2 = 36$$

$$x^2 + 12x + 36 = -11 + 36$$

$$(x+6)^2 = 25$$

$$x + 6 = \pm\sqrt{25}$$

$$x = -6 \pm 5$$

$$x = -6 - 5 \qquad x = -6 + 5$$

$$x = -11 \qquad\quad x = -1$$

39. $2x^2 - 8x - 90 = 0$

$$2x^2 - 8x = 90$$

$$x^2 - 4x = 45, \quad \left[\frac{1}{2}(-4)\right]^2 = (-2)^2 = 4$$

$$x^2 - 4x + 4 = 45 + 4$$

$$(x-2)^2 = 49$$

$$x - 2 = \pm\sqrt{49}$$

$$x = 2 \pm 7$$

$$x = 2 + 7 \qquad x = 2 - 7$$

$$x = 9 \qquad\quad x = -5$$

40. $-5x^2 + 30x - 35 = 0$

$$x^2 - 6x + 7 = 0$$

$$x^2 - 6x = -7$$

$$x^2 - 6x + 9 = -7 + 9$$

$$(x-3)^2 = 2$$

$$x - 3 = \pm\sqrt{2}$$

$$x = 3 \pm \sqrt{2}$$

41. $3x^2 + 6x - 6 = 0$

$$3x^2 + 6x = 6$$

$$x^2 + 2x = 2, \quad \left[\frac{1}{2}(2)\right]^2 = 1^2 = 1$$

$$x^2 + 2x + 1 = 2 + 1$$

$$(x+1)^2 = 3$$

$$x + 1 = \pm\sqrt{3}$$

$$x = -1 \pm \sqrt{3}$$

42. $2x^2 + 10x - 3 = 0$

$$2x^2 + 10x = 3$$

$$x^2 + 5x = \frac{3}{2}, \quad \left[\frac{1}{2}(5)\right]^2 = \left(\frac{5}{2}\right)^2 = \frac{25}{4}$$

$$x^2 + 5x + \frac{25}{4} = \frac{3}{2} + \frac{25}{4}$$

$$\left(x + \frac{5}{2}\right)^2 = \frac{31}{4}$$

$$x + \frac{5}{2} = \pm\sqrt{\frac{31}{4}}$$

$$x = -\frac{5}{2} \pm \frac{\sqrt{31}}{2}$$

$$x = \frac{-5 \pm \sqrt{31}}{2}$$

Use $x = \dfrac{-b \pm \sqrt{b^2 - 4ac}}{2a}$ in Exercises 43-67.

43. $x^2 + 4x - 6 = 0$

$$a = 1, \quad b = 4, \quad c = -6$$

$$x = \frac{-4 \pm \sqrt{(4)^2 - 4(1)(-6)}}{2(1)}$$

$$= \frac{-4 \pm \sqrt{40}}{2}$$

$$= \frac{-4 \pm 2\sqrt{10}}{2}$$

$$x = -2 \pm \sqrt{10}$$

44. $x^2 + 4x - 8 = 0$

$a = 1, \ b = 4, \ c = -8$

$$x = \frac{-4 \pm \sqrt{(4)^2 - 4(1)(-8)}}{2(1)}$$

$$= \frac{-4 \pm \sqrt{48}}{2}$$

$$= \frac{-4 \pm 4\sqrt{3}}{2}$$

$$x = -2 \pm 2\sqrt{3}$$

45. $2x^2 - 7x + 4 = 0$

$a = 2, \ b = -7, \ c = 4$

$$x = \frac{-(-7) \pm \sqrt{(-7)^2 - 4(2)(4)}}{2(2)}$$

$$x = \frac{7 \pm \sqrt{17}}{4}$$

46. $2x^2 + 5x - 6 = 0$

$a = 2, \ b = 5, \ c = -6$

$$x = \frac{-(5) \pm \sqrt{(5)^2 - 4(2)(-6)}}{2(2)}$$

$$x = \frac{-5 \pm \sqrt{73}}{4}$$

47. $3x^2 - 8x - 4 = 0$

$a = 3, \ b = -8, \ c = -4$

$$x = \frac{-(-8) \pm \sqrt{(-8)^2 - 4(3)(-4)}}{2(3)}$$

$$x = \frac{8 \pm \sqrt{112}}{6}$$

$$x = \frac{8 \pm 4\sqrt{7}}{6}$$

$$x = \frac{4 \pm 2\sqrt{7}}{3}$$

48. $4x^2 - 2x - 11 = 0$

$a = 4, \ b = -2, \ c = -11$

$$x = \frac{-(-2) \pm \sqrt{(-2)^2 - 4(4)(-11)}}{2(4)}$$

$$x = \frac{2 \pm \sqrt{180}}{8}$$

$$x = \frac{2 \pm 6\sqrt{5}}{8}$$

$$x = \frac{1 \pm 3\sqrt{5}}{4}$$

49. $3x^2 - 5x = 4$

        $3x^2 - 5x - 4 = 0$

        $a = 3, \ b = -5, \ c = -4$

$$x = \frac{-(-5) \pm \sqrt{25 - 4(3)(-4)}}{2(3)}$$

$$= \frac{5 \pm \sqrt{73}}{6}$$

50. $4x^2 + 3x = 2$

$4x^2 + 3x - 2 = 0$

$a = 4, \ b = 3, \ c = -2$

$$x = \frac{-(3) \pm \sqrt{(3)^2 - 4(4)(-2)}}{2(4)}$$

$$x = \frac{-3 \pm \sqrt{41}}{8}$$

51. $2x^2 - 9x + 10 = 0$

$(2x - 5)(x - 2) = 0$

$2x - 5 = 0 \qquad x - 2 = 0$

$x = \dfrac{5}{2} \qquad\qquad x = 2$

52. $\qquad 4x^2 - 4x - 3 = 0$

$(2x + 1)(2x - 3) = 0$

$2x + 1 = 0 \qquad 2x - 3 = 0$

$x = \dfrac{1}{2} \qquad\qquad x = \dfrac{3}{2}$

53. $25x^2 + 10x + 1 = 0$

$(5x + 1)^2 = 0$

$5x + 1 = 0$

$x = -\dfrac{1}{5}$

54. $2x^2 - 11x + 12 = 0$

$(x - 4)(2x - 3) = 0$

$x - 4 = 0 \qquad 2x - 3 = 0$

$x = 4 \qquad\qquad x = \dfrac{3}{2}$

55. $3x^2 - 6x + 2 = 0$

$a = 3, \ b = -6, \ c = 2$

$$x = \frac{-(-6) \pm \sqrt{(-6)^2 - 4(3)(2)}}{2(3)}$$

$$= \frac{6 \pm \sqrt{12}}{6}$$

$$= \frac{6 \pm 2\sqrt{3}}{6}$$

$$= \frac{3 \pm \sqrt{3}}{3}$$

56. $\qquad 5x^2 - 7x = 8$

$5x^2 - 7x - 8 = 0$

$a = 5, \ b = -7, \ c = -8$

$$x = \frac{-(-7) \pm \sqrt{(-7)^2 - 4(5)(-8)}}{2(5)}$$

$$= \frac{7 \pm \sqrt{209}}{10}$$

57. $4x^2 + 4x = x^2 + 5$

$3x^2 + 4x - 5 = 0$

$a = 3, \ b = 4, \ c = -5$

$$x = \frac{-4 \pm \sqrt{4^2 - 4(3)(-5)}}{2(3)}$$

$$= \frac{-4 \pm \sqrt{76}}{6}$$

$$= \frac{-4 \pm 2\sqrt{19}}{6}$$

$$= \frac{-2 \pm \sqrt{19}}{3}$$

58. $5x^2 + 7x + 1 = 0$

$a = 5,\ b = 7,\ c = 1$

$$x = \frac{-(7) \pm \sqrt{(7)^2 - 4(5)(1)}}{2(5)}$$

$$= \frac{-7 \pm \sqrt{29}}{10}$$

59. $x^2 = 9x + 3$

$x^2 - 9x - 3 = 0$

$a = 1,\ b = -9,\ c = -3$

$$x = \frac{-(-9) \pm \sqrt{(-9)^2 - 4(1)(3)}}{2(1)}$$

$$x = \frac{9 \pm \sqrt{93}}{2}$$

60. $3x^2 = 6 - 7x$

$3x^2 + 7x - 6 = 0$

$(x + 3)(3x - 2) = 0$

$x + 3 = 0 \qquad 3x - 2 = 0$

$x = -3 \qquad x = \dfrac{2}{3}$

61. $-27x^2 + 3x = -12x^2 - 12$

$-15x^2 + 3x + 12 = 0$

$-3(5x^2 - x - 4) = 0$

$5x^2 - x - 4 = 0$

$(5x + 4)(x - 1) = 0$

$5x + 4 = 0 \qquad x - 1 = 0$

$5x = -4 \qquad x = 1$

$x = -\dfrac{4}{5}$

62. $2x^2 - 1 = 35$

$2x^2 = 36$

$x^2 = 18$

$x = \pm\sqrt{18}$

$= \pm 3\sqrt{2}$

63. $\dfrac{(y-2)^2}{20} + 3 + y = 0$

$(y - 2)^2 + 60 + 20y = 0$

$y^2 - 4y + 4 + 60 + 20y = 0$

$y^2 + 16y + 64 = 0$

$(y + 8)^2 = 0$

$y + 8 = 0$

$y = -8$

64. $\dfrac{(y+2)^2}{5} + 2y = -9$

$(y + 2)^2 + 10y = -45$

$y^2 + 4y + 4 + 10y + 45 = 0$

$y^2 + 14y + 49 = 0$

$(y + 7)^2 = 0$

$y + 7 = 0$

$y = -7$

65. $3x^2 + 1 = 6 - 8x$

$3x^2 + 8x - 5 = 0$

$$x = \frac{-8 \pm \sqrt{8^2 - 4(3)(-5)}}{2(3)}$$

$$= \frac{-8 \pm \sqrt{124}}{6}$$

$$= \frac{-8 \pm 2\sqrt{31}}{6}$$

$$= \frac{-4 \pm \sqrt{31}}{3}$$

66. $2x^2 + 10x = 2x - 7$

$$2x^2 + 8x + 7 = 0$$

$$x = \frac{-8 \pm \sqrt{8^2 - 4(2)(7)}}{2(2)}$$

$$= \frac{-8 \pm \sqrt{8}}{4}$$

$$= \frac{-8 \pm 2\sqrt{2}}{4}$$

$$= \frac{-4 \pm \sqrt{2}}{2}$$

67. $2y - 10 = 10y(y - 2)$

$$2y - 10 = 10y^2 - 20y$$

$$0 = 10y^2 - 22y + 10$$

$$0 = 5y^2 - 11y + 5$$

$$y = \frac{-(-11) \pm \sqrt{(-11)^2 - 4(5)(5)}}{2(5)}$$

$$= \frac{11 \pm \sqrt{21}}{10}$$

68. $\dfrac{3y - 2}{4} = \dfrac{y^2 - 2}{y}$

$$y(3y - 2) = 4(y^2 - 2)$$

$$3y^2 - 2y = 4y^2 - 8$$

$$0 = y^2 + 2y - 8$$

$$0 = (y + 4)(y - 2)$$

$$\begin{array}{ll} y + 4 = 0 & y - 2 = 0 \\ y = -4 & y = 2 \end{array}$$

69. $\dfrac{y^2 + 5}{2y} = \dfrac{2y - 1}{3}$

$$3(y^2 + 5) = 2y(2y - 1)$$

$$3y^2 + 15 = 4y^2 - 2y$$

$$0 = y^2 - 2y - 15$$

$$0 = (y - 5)(y + 3)$$

$$\begin{array}{ll} y - 5 = 0 & y + 3 = 0 \\ y = 5 & y = -3 \end{array}$$

70. $\dfrac{5x^2}{2} = x - \dfrac{7x^2}{2}$

$$5x^2 = 2x - 7x^2$$

$$12x^2 - 2x = 0$$

$$2x(6x - 1) = 0$$

$$\begin{array}{ll} 2x = 0 & 6x - 1 = 0 \\ x = 0 & x = \dfrac{1}{6} \end{array}$$

71. $y = 2x^2$

x	y
-2	8
-1	2
0	0
1	2
2	8

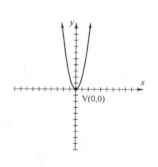

72. $y = x^2 + 4$

x	y
-2	8
-1	5
0	4
1	5
2	8

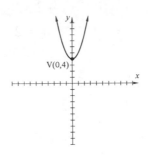

x	y
-1	0
0	-4
1.5	-6.25
3	-4
4	0

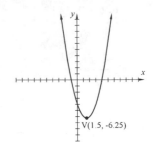

73. $y = x^2 - 3$

x	y
-2	1
-1	-2
0	-3
1	-2
2	1

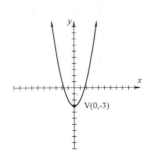

76. $y = \dfrac{1}{2}x^2 - 2$

x	y
-2	0
-1	-1.5
0	-2
1	-1.5
2	0

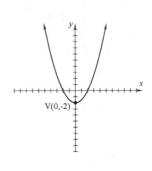

74. $y = -\dfrac{1}{2}x^2$

x	y
-2	-2
-1	$-\frac{1}{2}$
0	0
1	$-\frac{1}{2}$
2	-2

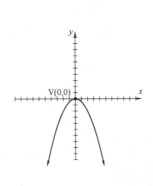

77. $y = -2x^2 + 12x - 17$

Vertex: $x = \dfrac{-12}{2(-2)} = 3$

$$y = -2(3)^2 + 12(3) - 17 = 1$$

$V(3, 1)$

x	y
1	-7
2	-1
3	1
4	-1
5	-7

75. $y = x^2 - 3x - 4$

Vertex: $x = \dfrac{-(-3)}{2(1)} = \dfrac{3}{2}$

$$y = \left(\frac{3}{2}\right)^2 - 3\left(\frac{3}{2}\right) - 4 = -\frac{25}{4}$$

$V\left(\dfrac{3}{2}, -\dfrac{25}{4}\right)$

78. $y = -3x^2 - 2x + 4$

Vertex: $x = -\dfrac{-2}{2(-3)} = -\dfrac{1}{3}$

$$y = -3\left(-\dfrac{1}{3}\right)^2 - 2\left(-\dfrac{1}{3}\right) + 4 = \dfrac{13}{3}$$

$$V\left(-\dfrac{1}{3}, \dfrac{13}{3}\right)$$

x	y
-2	-4
-1	3
0	4
1	-1

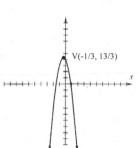

V(-1/3, 13/3)

79. $L =$ length

$w =$ width

length: $L + 2w = 11$ (1)

    area: $Lw = 15$ (2)

Substitute $\dfrac{15}{w}$ for L in (1)

$$\dfrac{15}{w} + 2w = 11$$

$$15 + 2w^2 = 11w$$

$$2w^2 - 11w + 15 = 0$$

$$(2w - 5)(w - 3) = 0$$

$2w - 5 = 0 \qquad w - 3 = 0$

$w = \dfrac{5}{2} \qquad\qquad w = 3$

$L = \dfrac{15}{w} = 6 \qquad L = \dfrac{15}{w} = 5$

The dimensions are 5 feet by 3 feet

or 6 feet by 2.5 feet.

80. $x =$ first leg

         $x - 4 =$ second leg

$$x^2 + (x - 4)^2 = 20^2$$

$$x^2 + x^2 - 8x + 16 = 400$$

$$2x^2 - 8x - 384 = 0$$

$$x^2 - 4x - 192 = 0$$

$$(x - 16)(x + 12) = 0$$

$x - 16 = 0 \qquad x + 12 = 0$

$\quad x = 16 \qquad\qquad x = -12$

Negative length isn't allowed

$x - 4 = 16 - 4 = 12$

The legs are 16 cm and 12 cm

81. $x =$ width

        $x + 6 =$ length

$$x^2 + (x + 6)^2 = 30^2$$

$$x^2 + x^2 + 12x + 36 = 900$$

$$2x^2 + 12x - 864 = 0$$

$$2(x^2 + 6x - 432) = 0$$

$$x^2 + 6x - 432 = 0$$

$$(x + 24)(x - 18) = 0$$

$x + 24 = 0 \qquad x - 18 = 0$

$\quad x = -24 \qquad\qquad x = 18$

Negative length isn't allowed

width $= x = 18$ inches

length $= x + 6 = 18 + 6 = 24$ inches

82. $h = -225t^2 + 291,600, \ h = 0$

$0 = -225t^2 + 291,600$

$225t^2 = 291,600$

$t^2 = 1296$

$t = 36$ seconds

83. $x =$ members last year.

$x - 4 =$ members this year.

$$\frac{720}{x} + 6 = \frac{720}{x-4}$$

$(x-4)720 + 6x(x-4) = 720x$

$720x - 2880 + 6x^2 = 24x = 720x$

$6x^2 - 24x - 2880 = 0$

$6(x^2 - 4x - 480) = 0$

$x^2 - 4x - 480 = 0$

$(x-24)(x+20) = 0$

$x - 24 = 0 \qquad x + 20 = 0$

$x = 24 \qquad\quad x = -20$

Negative number of members isn't allowed.

24 members last year.

84. $r =$ speed on the trip to there

$r + 15 =$ speed on the trip back

$$d = r \cdot t$$

$$\frac{d}{r} = t$$

$$3.5 = \frac{90}{r} + \frac{90}{r+15}$$

$3.5r(r+15) = 90(r+15) + 90r$

$3.5r^2 + 52.5r = 90r + 1350 + 90r$

$3.5r^2 - 127.5r - 1350 = 0$

$7r^2 - 255r - 2700 = 0$

$(7r + 60)(r - 45) = 0$

$7r + 60 = 0 \qquad r - 45 = 0$

$$r = -\frac{60}{7} \qquad\quad r = 45$$

Speed must be positive

$r + 15 = 45 + 15 = 60$

Speed going was 45 mph.

Speed returning was 60 mph.

Use $y = -0.05x^2 + 2.5x + 60$ in Exer. 85-88.

85. $x = 2030 - 1980 = 50$

$y = -0.05(50)^2 + 2.5(50) + 60$

$= 60$ pizza stores

86. $x = 2040 - 1980 = 60$

$y = -0.05(60)^2 + 2.5(60) + 60 = 30$

Difference $= 30 - 60 = -30$

30 fewer pizza stores

87. $-0.05x^2 + 2.5x + 60 = 80$

$-0.05x^2 + 2.5x - 20 = 0$

$x^2 - 50x + 400 = 0$

$(x-10)(x-40) = 0$

$x - 10 = 0 \qquad x - 40 = 0$

$x = 10 \qquad\qquad x = 40$

Years 1990 and 2020.

88. $-0.05x^2 + 2.5x + 60 = 90$

$-0.05x^2 + 2.5x - 30 = 0$

$x^2 - 50x + 600 = 0$

$(x - 20)(x - 30) = 0$

$x - 20 = 0 \qquad x - 30 = 0$

$x = 20 \qquad\quad x = 30$

Years 2000 and 2010.

How Am I Doing? Chapter 10 Test

1. $\quad 5x^2 + 7x = 4$

$5x^2 + 7x - 4 = 0$

$a = 5, \ b = 7, \ c = -4$

$x = \dfrac{-7 \pm \sqrt{7^2 - 4(5)(-4)}}{2(5)}$

$= \dfrac{-7 \pm \sqrt{129}}{10}$

2. $\quad 3x^2 + 13x = 10$

$3x^2 + 13x - 10 = 0$

$(x + 5)(3x - 2) = 0$

$x + 5 = 0 \qquad 3x - 2 = 0$

$x = -5 \qquad\quad x = \dfrac{2}{3}$

3. $\quad 2x^2 = 2x - 5$

$2x^2 - 2x + 5 = 0$

$a = 2, \ b = -2, \ c = 5$

$x = \dfrac{-(-2) \pm \sqrt{(-2)^2 - 4(2)(5)}}{2(2)}$

$= \dfrac{2 \pm \sqrt{-36}}{4}$

There is no real solution.

4. $\quad 4x^2 - 19x = 4x - 15$

$4x^2 - 23x + 15 = 0$

$(4x + -3)(x - 5) = 0$

$4x - 3 = 0 \qquad x - 5 = 0$

$4x = 3 \qquad\quad x = 5$

$x = \dfrac{3}{4}$

5. $\quad 12x^2 + 11x = 5$

$12x^2 + 11x - 5 = 0$

$(4x + 5)(3x - 1) = 0$

$4x + 5 = 0 \qquad 3x - 1 = 0$

$4x = -5 \qquad\quad 3x = 1$

$x = -\dfrac{5}{4} \qquad\quad x = \dfrac{1}{3}$

6. $18x^2 + 32 = 48x$

$18x^2 - 48x + 32 = 0$

$9x^2 - 24x + 16 = 0$

$(3x - 4)^2 = 0$

$3x - 4 = 0$

$3x = 4$

$x = \dfrac{4}{3}$

10. $x^2 - x = \dfrac{3}{4}$

$4x^2 - 4x = 3$

$4x^2 - 4x - 3 = 0$

$(2x + 1)(2x - 3) = 0$

$2x + 1 = 0 \qquad 2x - 3 = 0$

$x = -\dfrac{1}{2} \qquad x = -\dfrac{3}{2}$

7. $2x^2 - 11x + 3 = 5x + 3$

$2x^2 - 16x = 0$

$2x(x - 8) = 0$

$2x = 0 \qquad x - 8 = 0$

$x = 0 \qquad\quad x = 8$

8. $5x^2 + 7 = 52$

$5x^2 = 45$

$x^2 = 9$

$x = \pm\sqrt{9}$

$x = \pm 3$

9. $2x(x - 6) = 6 - x$

$2x^2 - 12x = 6 - x$

$2x^2 - 11x - 6 = 0$

$(2x + 1)(x - 6) = 0$

$2x + 1 = 0 \qquad x - 6 = 0$

$x = -\dfrac{1}{2} \qquad x = 6$

11. $y = 3x^2 - 6x$

Vertex: $x = -\dfrac{-6}{2(3)} = 1$

$y = 3(1)^2 - 6(1) = -3$

$V(1, -3)$

x	y
-1	9
0	0
1	-3
2	0
3	9

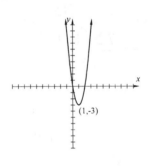

(1,-3)

12. $y = -x^2 + 8x - 12$

Vertex: $x = -\dfrac{8}{2(-1)} = 4$

$y = -(4)^2 + 8(4) - 12 = 4$

$V(4, 4)$

358

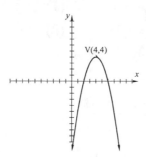

x	y
2	0
3	3
4	4
5	3
6	0

V(4,4)

Cumulative Test for Chapters 0 - 10

1. $3x\{2y - 3[x + 2(x + 2y)]\}$
$= 3x\{2y - 3[x + 2x + 4y]\}$
$= 3x[2y - 3(3x + 4y)]$
$= 3x[2y - 9x - 12y]$
$= 3x(-9x - 10y)$
$= -27x^2 - 30y$

13. $x = $ length of one leg
        $x + 3 = $ length of other leg

$x^2 + (x + 3)^2 = (15)^2$
$x^2 + x^2 + 6x + 9 = 225$
$2x^2 + 6x - 216 = 0$
$x^2 + 3x - 108 = 0$
$(x + 12)(x - 9) = 0$

$x + 12 = 0 \quad\quad x - 9 = 0$
$\quad x = -12 \quad\quad\quad x = 9$

Length can't be negative, so
$x = 9$ and $x + 3 = 12$.
The lengths are 9 m and 12 m.

2. For $x = -1$, $y = 2$
$$\frac{3x - 2xy}{5x} = \frac{3(-1) - 2(-1)(2)}{5(-1)}$$
$$= \frac{-3 + 4}{-5}$$
$$= -\frac{1}{5}$$

3. $\frac{1}{2}(x - 2) = \frac{1}{3}(x + 10) - 2x$
$3(x - 2) = 2(x + 10) - 6(2x)$
$3x - 6 = 2x + 20 - 12x$
$13x = 26$
$\quad x = 2$

14. $S = -5t^2 + vt + h$
$S = -5t^2 + 33t + 14$
$0 = -5t^2 + 33t + 14$
$0 = 5t^2 - 33t - 14$
$0 = (5t + 2)(t - 7)$

$5t - 2 = 0 \quad\quad t - 7 = 0$
$\quad t = -\frac{2}{5} \quad\quad\quad t = 7$

Time must be positive.
It will strike the ground after 7 sec.

4. $16x^4 - 1 = (4x^2 + 1)(4x^2 - 1)$
$\quad\quad\quad\quad = (4x^2 + 1)(2x + 1)(2x - 1)$

5. $(x - 3)(2x + 5)(x + 2)$
$= (x - 3)(2x^2 + 9x + 10)$
$= 2x^3 + 9x^2 + 10x - 6x^2 - 27x - 30$
$= 2x^3 + 3x^2 - 17x - 30$

6.
$$\frac{3x}{x^2-4} = \frac{2}{x+2} + \frac{4}{2-x}$$

$$\frac{3x}{(x+2)(x-2)} = \frac{2}{x+2} - \frac{4}{x-2}$$

$$3x = 2(x-2) - 4(x+2)$$
$$3x = 2x - 4 - 4x - 8$$
$$3x = -2x - 12$$
$$5x = -12$$
$$x = -\frac{12}{5}$$

7. $y = -\frac{3}{4}x + 2$

$\text{slope} = -\frac{3}{4}$

$y - \text{intercept} = 2$

8. $m = \frac{4}{3}, \ (-6, -2)$

$$y = mx + b$$
$$-2 = \frac{4}{3}(-6) + b$$
$$-2 = -8 + b$$
$$6 = b$$
$$y = \frac{4}{3}x + 6$$

9. $3x + 2y = 5$ (1)

    $7x + \ y = 19$ (2)

Multiply (2) by -2

$$3x + 2y = 5$$
$$\underline{-14x - 2y = -38}$$
$$-11x \qquad = -33$$
$$x = 3$$

Substitute 3 for x in (1)

$$3(3) + 2y = 5$$
$$2y = -4$$
$$y = -2$$

$(3, -2)$

10. $\left(-3x^3y^2\right)^4 = (-3)^4\left(x^3\right)^4\left(y^2\right)^4 = 81x^{12}y^8$

11. $\sqrt{18x^5y^6z^3} = \sqrt{9 \cdot 2x^4xy^6z^2z}$

$$= 3x^2y^3z\sqrt{2xz}$$

12. $\left(\sqrt{2} + \sqrt{3}\right)\left(2\sqrt{2} - 4\sqrt{3}\right)$

$$= 2(2) - 4\sqrt{6} + 2\sqrt{6} - 4(3)$$
$$= 4 - 2\sqrt{6} - 12$$
$$= -8 - 2\sqrt{6}$$

13. $\dfrac{\sqrt{5}-3}{\sqrt{5}+2} = \dfrac{\sqrt{5}-3}{\sqrt{5}+2} \cdot \dfrac{\sqrt{5}-2}{\sqrt{5}-2}$

$$= \frac{\sqrt{25} - 2\sqrt{5} - 3\sqrt{5} + 6}{\left(\sqrt{5}\right)^2 - 2^2}$$
$$= \frac{11 - 5\sqrt{5}}{5 - 4}$$
$$= 11 - 5\sqrt{5}$$

360

14. $3(t+b) = 2a - 5t$

$3t + 3b = 2a - 5t$

$8t + 3b = 2a$

$8t = 2a - 3b$

$t = \dfrac{2a - 3b}{8}$

15. $\qquad H = 25b^2 - 6$

$H + 6 = 25b^2$

$\pm\sqrt{H+6} = \sqrt{5^2 b^2}$

$\pm\sqrt{H+6} = 5b$

$\dfrac{\pm\sqrt{H+6}}{5} = b$

16. $\qquad 2x^2 + 3x = 35$

$2x^2 + 3x - 35 = 0$

$(x+5)(2x-7) = 0$

$x + 5 = 0 \qquad\qquad 2x - 7 = 0$

$x = -5 \qquad\qquad x = \dfrac{7}{2}$

17. $(2x+1)^2 = 20$

$2x + 1 = \pm\sqrt{20}$

$2x = -1 \pm 2\sqrt{5}$

$x = \dfrac{-1 \pm 2\sqrt{5}}{2}$

18. $\qquad \dfrac{60}{R} = \dfrac{60}{R+8} + 10$

$60(R+8) = 60R + 10R(R+8)$

$60R + 480 = 60R + 10R^2 + 80R$

$0 = 10R^2 + 80R - 480$

$0 = R^2 + 8R - 48$

$0 = (R+12)(R-4)$

$R + 12 = 0 \qquad\qquad R - 4 = 0$

$R = -12 \qquad\qquad R = 4$

19. $3x^2 + 11x + 2 = 0$

$a = 3, \quad b = 11, \quad c = 2$

$x = \dfrac{-11 \pm \sqrt{11^2 - 4(3)(2)}}{2(3)}$

$= \dfrac{-11 \pm \sqrt{97}}{6}$

20. $\qquad 6x^2 + 11x - 10 = 0$

$(3x-2)(2x+5) = 0$

$3x - 2 = 0 \qquad\qquad 2x + 5 = 0$

$3x = 2 \qquad\qquad 2x = -5$

$x = \dfrac{2}{3} \qquad\qquad x = -\dfrac{5}{2}$

21. $x^2 = 72$

$x = \pm\sqrt{72}$

$x = \pm\sqrt{36 \cdot 2}$

$x = \pm 6\sqrt{2}$

22. $3x^2 + 4 = 79$

$3x^2 = 75$

$x^2 = 25$

$x = \pm\sqrt{25}$

$x = \pm 5$

23. $y = x^2 + 6x + 10$

Vertex: $x = \dfrac{-6}{2(1)} = -3$

$y = (-3)^2 + 6(-3) + 10 = 1$

$V(-3, 1)$

x	y
-5	5
-4	2
-3	1
-2	2
-1	5

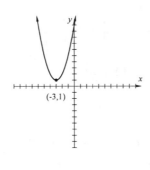
(-3,1)

24. $x = $ width, $3x - 2 = $ length

$x(3x - 2) = 96$

$3x^2 - 2x = 96$

$3x^2 - 2x - 96 = 0$

$(3x + 16)(x - 6) = 0$

$3x + 16 = 0 \qquad x - 6 = 0$

$x = -\dfrac{16}{3} \qquad x = 6$

Length must be positive

$3x - 2 = 3(6) - 2 = 16$

The width is 6 m and the length is 16 m.

Practice Final Examination

1. $-2x + 3y\{7 - 2[x - (4x + y)]\}$

$= -2x + 3y[7 - 2(x - 4x - y)]$

$= -2x + 3y[7 - 2(-3x - y)]$

$= -2x + 3y(7 + 6x + 2y)$

$= -2x + 21y + 18xy + 6y^2$

2. $2x^2 - 3xy - 4y, \ x = -2, \ y = 3$

$2(-2)^2 - 3(-2)(3) - 4(3)$

$= 8 + 18 - 12 = 14$

3. $(-3x^2 y)(-6x^3 y^4) = 18x^5 y^5$

4. $5x^2 y - 6xy + 8xy - 3x^2 y - 10xy$

$= 2x^2 y - 8xy$

5. $\dfrac{1}{2}(x + 4) - \dfrac{2}{3}(x - 7) = 4x$

$3(x + 4) - 4(x - 7) = 6(4x)$

$3x + 12 - 4x + 28 = 24x$

$40 = 25x$

$\dfrac{8}{5} = x$

6. $\qquad p = 2a + 2b$

$p - 2a = 2b$

$\dfrac{p - 2a}{2} = b$

7. $5x + 3 - (4x - 2) \le 6x - 8$

$$5x + 3 - 4x + 2 \le 6x - 8$$
$$-5x \le -13$$
$$x \ge \frac{13}{5} = 2.6$$

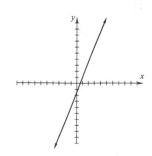

$$\begin{array}{ccc} & 0 & 2.6 \end{array}$$

8. $(2x + y)(x^2 - 3xy + 2y^2)$

$$= 2x^3 - 6x^2y + 4xy^2 + x^2y - 3xy^2 + 2y^3$$
$$= 2x^3 - 5x^2y + xy^2 + 2y^3$$

9. $4x^2 - 18x - 10 = 2(2x^2 - 9x - 5)$

$$= 2(2x + 1)(x - 5)$$

10. $3x^3 - 9x^2 - 30x = 3x(x^2 - 3x - 10)$

$$= 3x(x - 5)(x + 2)$$

11. $\dfrac{2}{x - 3} - \dfrac{3}{x^2 - x - 6} + \dfrac{4}{x + 2}$

$$= \frac{2}{x - 3} \cdot \frac{x + 2}{x + 2} - \frac{3}{(x - 3)(x + 2)} + \frac{4}{x + 2} \cdot \frac{x - 3}{x - 3}$$
$$= \frac{2x + 4 - 3 + 4x - 12}{(x + 2)(x - 3)}$$
$$= \frac{6x - 11}{(x + 2)(x - 3)}$$

12. $\dfrac{\frac{3}{x} + \frac{5}{2x}}{1 + \frac{2}{x + 2}} = \dfrac{\frac{3}{x} + \frac{5}{2x}}{1 + \frac{2}{x + 2}} \cdot \dfrac{2x(x + 2)}{2x(x + 2)}$

$$= \frac{6(x + 2) + 5(x + 2)}{2x(x + 2) + 4x}$$
$$= \frac{11(x + 2)}{2x(x + 2 + 2)}$$
$$= \frac{11(x + 2)}{2x(x + 4)}$$

13. $\dfrac{2}{x + 2} = \dfrac{4}{x - 2} + \dfrac{3x}{x^2 - 4}$

$$(x - 2)(2) = 4(x + 2) + 3x$$
$$2x - 4 = 4x + 8 + 3x$$
$$-12 = 5x$$
$$\frac{12}{5} = x$$

14. $5x - 2y - 3 = 0$

$$-2y = -5x + 3$$
$$y = \frac{-5}{2}x + \frac{3}{-2}$$
$$y = \frac{5}{2}x - \frac{3}{2}$$
$$m = \frac{5}{2}$$

15. $m = -\dfrac{3}{4}, \ (-2, 5)$

    $y = mx + b$

    $5 = -\dfrac{3}{4}(-2) + b \Rightarrow b = \dfrac{7}{2}$

    $y = -\dfrac{3}{4}x + \dfrac{7}{2}$ or $3x + 4y = 14$

16. $A = \dfrac{1}{2}\pi r^2 + wl, \ r = 3, \ w = 3, \ l = 8$

    $A = \dfrac{1}{2}(3.13)(3)^2 + (3)(8)$

     $= 38.13$ sq in.

17. $2x + 7y = 4$ (1)

    $-3x - 5y = 5$ (2)

    Multiply (1) by 3 and (2) by 2

     $6x + 21y = 12$

     $\underline{-6x - 10y = 10}$

          $11y = 22$

           $y = 2$

    Substitute 2 for y in (1)

    $2x + 7(2) = 4$

     $2x + 14 = 4$

       $2x = -10$

         $x = -5$

    $(-5, 2)$

18. $a - \dfrac{3}{4}b = \dfrac{1}{4}$ (1)

    $\dfrac{3}{2}a + \dfrac{1}{2}b = -\dfrac{9}{2}$ (2)

    Multiply (1) by 4 and (2) by 6

    $4a - 3b = 1$

    $\underline{9a + 3b = -27}$

    $13a \quad\quad = -26$

       $a = -2$

    Substitute -2 for a in (1)

    $-2 - \dfrac{3}{4}b = \dfrac{1}{4}$

    $-8 - 3b = 1$

      $-3b = 9$

        $b = -3$

    $(-2, -3)$

19. $\sqrt{45x^3} + 2x\sqrt{20x} - 6\sqrt{5x^3}$

    $= \sqrt{9 \cdot 5x^2 x} + 2x\sqrt{4 \cdot 5x} - 6\sqrt{5x^2 x}$

    $= 3x\sqrt{5x} + 4x\sqrt{5x} - 6x\sqrt{5x}$

    $= x\sqrt{5x}$

20. $\sqrt{6}\left(3\sqrt{2} - 2\sqrt{6} + 4\sqrt{3}\right)$

    $= 3\sqrt{12} - 2\sqrt{36} + 4\sqrt{18}$

    $= 3\sqrt{4(3)} - 2(6) + 4\sqrt{9(2)}$

    $= 6\sqrt{3} - 12 + 12\sqrt{2}$

21. $\dfrac{\sqrt{3}+\sqrt{7}}{\sqrt{5}-\sqrt{7}} = \dfrac{\sqrt{3}+\sqrt{7}}{\sqrt{5}-\sqrt{7}} \cdot \dfrac{\sqrt{5}+\sqrt{7}}{\sqrt{5}+\sqrt{7}}$

$= \dfrac{\sqrt{15}+\sqrt{21}+\sqrt{35}+\sqrt{49}}{\left(\sqrt{5}\right)^2 - \left(\sqrt{7}\right)^2}$

$= -\dfrac{7+\sqrt{15}+\sqrt{21}+\sqrt{35}}{2}$

22. $12x^2 - 5x - 2 = 0$

$(4x+1)(3x-2) = 0$

$\begin{array}{ll} 4x+1=0 & 3x-2=0 \\ 4x=-1 & 3x=2 \\ x=-\dfrac{1}{4} & x=\dfrac{2}{3} \end{array}$

23. $2y^2 = 6y - 1$

$2y^2 - 6y + 1 = 0$

$y = \dfrac{-(-6) \pm \sqrt{(-6)^2 - 4(2)(1)}}{2(2)}$

$= \dfrac{6 \pm \sqrt{28}}{4}$

$= \dfrac{6 \pm 2\sqrt{7}}{4}$

$= \dfrac{3 \pm \sqrt{7}}{2}$

24. $4x^2 + 3 = 19$

$4x^2 = 16$

$x^2 = 4$

$x = \pm\sqrt{4}$

$x = \pm 2$

25. $c^2 = a^2 + b^2$

$8^2 = a^2 + 5^2$

$64 = a^2 + 25$

$39 = a^2$

$\pm\sqrt{39} = a$

The length can't be negative.

$a = \sqrt{39}$

26. $x = $ a number

$3x + 6 = 21$

$3x = 15$

$x = 5$

The number is 5

27. $w = $ width

$2w - 2 = $ length

$p = 2L + 2w$

$38 = 2(2w-2) + 2w$

$38 = 4w - 4 + 2w$

$42 = 6w$

$7 = w, \ 2w - 2 = 12$

The dimensions are 12 meters by 7 meters.

28. x = amount invested at 10%

    y = amount invested at 14%

    $$x + \quad y = 7000 \qquad (1)$$
    $$0.10x + 0.14y = 860 \qquad (2)$$

    Solve (1) for x

    $$x = 7000 - y \qquad (3)$$

    Substitute $7000 - y$ for x in (2)

    $$0.10(7000 - y) + 0.14y = 860$$
    $$700 - 0.10y + 0.14y = 860$$
    $$0.04y = 160$$
    $$y = 4000$$

    Substitute 4000 for y in (3)

    $$x = 7000 - 4000 = 3000$$

    $3000 invested at 10%

    $4000 invested at 14%

29. x = number of general admission tickets

    y = number of reserved seat tickets

    $$x + \quad y = 360 \qquad (1)$$
    $$3x + 5y = 1480 \qquad (2)$$

    Multiply (1) by -3 and add it to (2)

    $$2y = 400$$
    $$y = 200$$

    Substitute 200 for y in (1)

    $$x + 200 = 360$$
    $$x = 160$$

    200 reserved-seat tickets

    160 general admission tickets

30. $A = \dfrac{1}{2}bh,\quad x = \text{base},\ 2x + 1 = \text{altitude}$

    $$68 = \frac{1}{2}x(2x + 1)$$
    $$136 = 2x^2 + x$$
    $$0 = 2x^2 + x - 136$$
    $$0 = (2x + 17)(x - 8)$$

    $2x + 17 = 0 \qquad\qquad\qquad x - 8 = 0$

    $x = -\dfrac{17}{2} \qquad\qquad\qquad\quad x = 8$

    Length must be positive.

    $$2x + 1 = 2(8) + 1 = 17$$

    The base is 8 m and the altitude is 17 m.